Harry Shaw was and is a well known face, in and out of the prison system. He was known as a good earner and could hold his hands up. He didn't mind a roll about on the floor if he had to. Bit of the 'Jack the lad' but everybody loved him. That was before he got on the shit and this book will explain better than I could, the battle he had with it, the opportunities, friends and relationships he lost whilst on it.
And the epic battle, which he finally won, which has earned him the respect that he now gets from everybody.

I for one salute you Mr Shaw.

Dave Courtney OBE.

Harry Shaw has written a book I couldn't put down.
A story of a life addicted to A class drugs. The people he met whilst spending time in prison and the lifting experience of their recovery. It opened my eyes. Read it.

Howard Marks (Mr Nice)

Harry Shaw has spent the vast majority of his life surrounded by criminals. His own father spent most of his upbringing in prison, and subsequently Harry turned to crime as a way of getting on in life. He later became addicted to crack and heroin.

During his time in prison Harry got clean and recovered.

He is now a successful businessman with a family he adores. With friends still in prison, he hopes that one day they will follow in his footsteps. He has made some mistakes in life, but hopes to have learned from them. He regularly visits prisons in order to share his experiences with young offenders, giving an example of how they can also turn their lives around.

CONFRONTING

DEMONS

Dedication

Dedicated to my mum, dad, brother and sister,
who stood by me through
the bad times.

To my Claire, daughter Ella, son Josh,
I love you more than words.

Harry Shaw

CONFRONTING

DEMONS

CAMPAIGN
BOOKS

The CIP catalogue record for this title
is available from The British Library
ISBN 978-1-908244-00-0
Campaign Books is an imprint of
Abbott's Publishers
Compass House, Vision Park, Histon,
CAMBRIDGE   CB24 9AD
Please note that names and dates have been changed
This is in order to protect the innocent and also the guilty

<u>Printed & Bound in Great Britain</u>

Acknowledgements

To all my friends who have stood by me. Roland R., Roy S., Toren A., Dennis, Ron, Bob, Craigy Boy, Danny Chalk, Dave B., Julian and Laura.

There are numerous others whom I haven't mentioned but you know who you are.

Without you all, I doubt I'd still be here!

A big thanks to Keith H for reading the *Confronting Demons* manuscript and telling me it was great, but that Harry Shaw was a right plum and needed taking out. Great help! Many thanks to Chris Cross for reading the manuscript and for his continued support throughout the years. Lots of love. Thanks to Gary for taking time to read the manuscript and giving me the confidence to try and get it published. And thanks to Dom for his help and being a good pal.

Thanks to my editor for her help and professionalism. Thanks to Vanessa for putting my mind at rest and for helping me keep the faith.

Forever grateful to Vivien Hoffman. Without her the book would never have happened. She drived me mad [sorry Viv, I meant 'drove'].

And no words can explain the gratitude I feel towards everyone at RAPT. Keep doing it. You save lives.

Preface

I'd like to say I'm well-travelled, 'cause I've toured the length and breadth of England and discovered many of its treasures and riches. Unfortunately, most of that tour took place behind prison walls, and the Securicor vans that chauffeured me from nick to nick didn't go out of their way to take in Windsor Castle and Stonehenge. As for those treasures and riches, well, that's why I found myself behind bars in the first place.

It was inevitable that I would become a criminal. My dad spent most of my growing-up years in prison and I remember travelling all over the country with my mum to visit him. 'Listen, son,' he told me once when I was very young. 'You know blokes like Burt and Tom and Arnie...'

'Yes, Dad.'

Burt was a bank robber, Tom, a thief-on-demand, and Arnie, a drug smuggler. Before Dad got sent away they were always popping round for tea, sitting me on their laps and making ten pound notes miraculously emerge out of my ears.

'They're the only sorta people you can trust, son. It's the straight, law-abiding people you gotta worry about. They're the ones that can get you into trouble.'

This advice, helpful as it was, didn't save me from eventually falling foul of those law-abiders, and landing up in prison just like my old man, except, unlike him, I had an extra load to bear on my sentence. A smack habit.

With heroin, being in prison was wonderful and cosy and relaxing. Without it, every day stretched into grim infinity, reducing me eventually to some of the lowest depths a man can plummet.

This is the story of me, and the kindred souls I met inside; blokes who demanded more than most people demand out of life, and paid the price. They, like me, fell through the depths of hell, those dark recesses that are only to be found in the chasms of our minds. But, at last, we chanced on a path leading out of those depths, and began to crawl towards our freedom.

HMP BELMARSH

Getting into hot water

Prisons are full of interesting people. Fascinating creatures, criminals are. Especially when you've been down the block for a couple of months, as I just have, with nothing but a flaky ceiling to chat to. Now I'm back on the wing, I'm looking forward to some company. Anyone will do.

I whack my belongings onto the top bunk of my new pad with a cheerful 'all right!' to my new cellmate, who has his nose buried in a book and doesn't so much as grunt. Hmm, maybe I'm wrong about all prisoners being interesting. One look at his gaunt, ashen face and I can tell that this one's only got one subject to yak about.

The door clanks shut and the screw's footsteps recede along the corridor, his boots echoing and keys jangling like a one-man band. I climb on my bunk and resume staring at the cracks in the ceiling, as if I hadn't left off from staring at the cracks in the ceiling in my last cell down the block – this being the days before cons had TVs and mini bed and breakfast-style kettles in every cell. No metal detectors in those days either.

Gradually I notice an unpleasant stink wafting up from the bunk below. After twenty minutes I realise that the fella underneath hasn't turned a single page of his book. I lean over the side to check he's still with us. Two glassy eyes stare up at me.

'Got any gear?' he whispers, feebly lifting his head.

'Nah, mate,' I say, and he slumps listlessly back onto his pillow. 'But I'm waiting on a visit.' It's a rule of mine to always sort out a cellmate if I can for a bit of peace and quiet.

'How long ya in for?' He asks struggling up onto one elbow, his face miraculously regaining signs of vitality.

'Seven, mate.'

He looks at me with respect. I don't tell him I'm in principally for money laundering, because a bit of respect is always a bonus when you're banged up with a scaghead.

'You?'

'Six months,' he says a scowl settling on his mug. 'for a fight I didn't even start. Got my fuckin' 'ead kicked in 'n all. Shouldn't even be in 'ere. What's ya name?'

'Harry,' I tell him. 'With an *aitch*...'

He frowns blankly. 'arry with an aitch...'

'I'm Craig. All I ever did was a bit of light shoplifting,' he continues bitterly, 'bit of till nicking 'n' that. Nothing worth getting banged up for. Fuckin' nob-head magistrates...'

I've stopped listening; my mind's on other things. Will she be on time? Has she been able to get hold of her dealer? Will she make it past the screws without being searched?

Eventually, gates start clanging and screws stride up and down the landings opening cells and yelling out names for visits. Twice, one of them marches up to my cell with a suspenseful jangle of keys and I almost lunge off the bed with anticipation, only to hear boots clump past, to open another door instead.

It's getting late. My cellmate has taken to assuring me every half a minute or so not to worry and that my girlfriend is sure to turn up until I'm an anxious wreck.

'Visit for Shaw!' A screw shouts at last and I hurl myself off my bed and wait for my door to be opened. After a great deal of trudging along corridors and joining

16

up with other prisoners while gates bash against walls then clang shut behind us, we finally get to have something that's taken totally for granted in the outside world; a chance to see someone we actually want to see.

She's looking rough is Dawn. Used to be a gorgeous girl with a curvy arse and fragrant blonde hair. Now she's all pale skin and skinny limbs.

'No problems then?' I grin, grasping her by the arm and pulling her towards me. For a long moment our tongues collide and I notice she's wincing and has her eyes clenched shut as if I'm the last fella on earth she wants to be snogging. I'm starting to wonder what she's playing at until, at last, a hard plastic package is pushed into my mouth. I shift it to my cheek and glare at her suspiciously.

'You been seeing someone?'

She shakes her head quickly. I squeeze her arm harder and she lets out a yelp. Roughly I pull up her sleeve to reveal a row of purplish bruises.

'That hurts, Harry?' She groans, yanking her arm away.

'I warned you not to inject,' I say, sitting down and making her sit too. 'You promised me you'd lay off that fuckin' needle.'

'Yeah, I'll go back to smoking it. It was only 'cause it works out cheaper banging it up,' she mutters. 'Don't matter though, I'm going graftin' this afternoon with Steve. I miss you, babe.' She says hurriedly changing the subject.

Now that I'm not around, she's been doing chequebook fraud with her brother to feed her habit. Doesn't bother with hairdressing no more. She looks at me with a brave smile. My anger abates and just as quickly turns to pity. I cup my hand to her cheek. She nestles against it as she always used to. It's the softest thing I've touched in months.

17

'Sorry, darling. How's Tom?' I ask.

'Your mum says he's doing well,' she manages to say before a tear splashes onto the back of my hand.

I don't want to think about our ten-month-old baby just now and neither does Dawn. I want to take it all away and forget. The brown that is wrapped up in my mouth will help me do that. My stomach does somersaults in anticipation and I can hardly think of anything else as Dawn looks at me knowing what is coming. 'That brother of yours had better be looking after you,' I warn, straightening up, 'otherwise I'll kill 'im when I get out.'

'What d'ya mean?' She raises her voice playing her part. 'Don't you start on my brother again!'

'Keep it up, babe,' I mouth, glancing across at the screws on duty.

'What's your fuckin' problem?' asks Dawn, her voice rising higher. 'You're a right bastard, you are, going on about my brother. I don't know why I bothered coming to see ya!' I see her eyes blazing up close, too late to jerk out of the way as her hand lands me a stinging slap across my face.

The eyes of everyone in the room, screws, cons and visitors alike, are trained on her as she storms towards the exit heels clacking loudly. The dramatic departure of my bird allows me to spit the parcel out of my mouth, shove it down the back of my jeans and bottle it.

Several cons turn to glare at me wondering what my fucking problem is.

I shrug back looking clueless. Then I pushed Dawn's visit to the back of my mind and line up for the strip search. Back in my cell, I go straight to the toilet cubicle and evacuate a tightly-wrapped package.

'Any trouble, mate?' my cellmate asks breathlessly as soon as I emerge. I notice he's got everything ready; the jimmy, the tube, the tapers, the lighter.

'Sorted, Stinky,' I wink at him.

I don't tell him that at least five cons have asked me today if I'm going to be copping. I managed to fob them all off, except for one geezer, a huge muscle-bound fella with skin the colour of cold coffee, meat-for-brains, and the sort of uncompromising expression that comes from doing five million bicep-curls day after day in the gym. 'Sort me out when you get back,' he'd said, throwing me a punch on the shoulder; a light punch but a herald of worse to come if I decide to keep all my smack to myself. Another con, on the way back from his visit told me that Meathead was in here for Grievous Bodily Harm, and that his victim is still unrecognisable.

I don't tell Stinky about the feeling of dread that crawled up my spine and still hasn't gone away.

Ah! Well nothing like a bit of heroin to make your problems disappear. I sprinkle some of the brown powder onto the foil, light one of the tapers that my new pal has made out of toilet paper, melt the powder into a blob and suck up the fumes. A warm glow spreads across my body and life is good again. It's more than good. It's bliss.

Stinky smiles at me, trying to disguise the pleading desperation written all over his face. I smile back and hand the tin foil and tube down to him, thinking what a nice fella I've landed in my cell and how he doesn't smell that much after all.

One by one all my problems float out of my canister and disappear through the already familiar cracks in the ceiling. Now that I've had a bit of gear, prison doesn't seem such a bad place to be… plenty of hot dinners, cups of tea, time to chill; fuckin' 'ell, it's almost like a holiday…

The hatch in my cell door crashes open sending my dreamland thoughts scuttling to oblivion. A huge, cold-coffee-coloured face squashes itself against the glass.

'Where's my gear?'

I sit up with what I hope is an agreeable expression, because although I really want to advise this meathead to fuck off and let me enjoy my little bit of heaven, without his ugly mug ruining it, I don't want to disrespect one of the brothers, particularly one that's by the looks of it, twice as heavy as me.

'Look, mate, I didn't get enough to sort anyone out so you'll have to wait until my next visit,' I say reasonably.

His eyes switch to Stinky who's staring blissfully at the springs above him and then snatch themselves back to me.

'Bullshit, you fucking bloodclart,' he observes.

'Put it under the door.'

I don't appreciate being likened to a used tampon but I let it go for now. 'I'll see what I can do,' I tell him, attempting to buy time. 'Come and see me when we're let out for dinner.'

He gives me a final look, as if sizing me up to ascertain just how much force will be required to yank my head off my neck and kick it over the prison wall, then slams the hatch shut.

Now I know I've got heavy-duty problems. Meathead will be breathing down my neck, ready to snatch my gear, every visiting time from here on after unless I do something about it. Since my gear is the only thing that makes life worth living in here, I seem to have a life and death situation on my hands. I've tried to talk my way out of it. As that plainly didn't work, I have only one option. I'm going to have to do him.

I'm not feeling very hungry and, given the circumstances, the crap that the cons behind the counter smudge onto my tray is even more unappealing than the Marsh's usual bottom-of-the-league cuisine.

I take my tray back to my cell and start spooning the gunk into my mouth, partly to take my mind off the ordeal ahead and partly in a last-ditch attempt to build up some strength for it. As soon as I've shovelled in a second spoonful, I'm watching it spray in an unexpected arc across the wall. Meathead has thundered in and thrown a punch at my jaw that knocks me sideways.

'Where's my gear?' He yells, then hits me a second time.

'Hold on, hold on,' I groan, clutching the side of my face, the same side that had been tingling from Dawn's slap earlier. I hadn't expected him to come in with both guns blazing. 'I haven't got it on me, but... er, if you give me two minutes, I'll go and get it.'

This seems to calm him down because he sits on Stinky's mattress and drums his fingers on his meaty thighs. I hurry outside, wondering what the hell I'm going to do. Maybe now would be the time to use the knife concealed in the heel of my shoe. Unfolded, the blade has a grand length of two inches, but never mind it's a start.

I reach down to retrieve it and hesitate. If I were to stick this chib into any part of Meathead's body other than his eye, he might barely flinch. And then I'd be in a whole lot more trouble. On the other hand, if I were to stun him first, I might be able to injure him seriously enough to change his mind about ever taking me for an idiot again.

A surge of adrenaline flows through me and something else seems to take over leaving me surprisingly calm. I know exactly what I'm doing. I go straight to the shower room, grab a plastic bucket and march along the landing to the tea urn. I nod to the two screws chatting at a

21

nearby table as I fill the bucket with steaming water. They glance up, nod back and carry on talking. I've only been out of the block a while so they're not expecting any problems out of me just yet; probably think I'm cleaning my cell. Carefully I head back along the landing, barely noticing the steam beginning to scold my hand.

A few feet from my cell, I slip the knife out of my shoe and snap it open. It might be small, but the blade gleams nice and sharp. Fortunately, there's no one around. Arteries pumping with exhilaration, I pick the bucket up with both hands and kick the door open. It crashes against the wall. My entire being is concentrated on this single moment in time.

Meathead glances up bewildered. His hands fly to his face, helpless to prevent a scorching torrent of water sluicing over him, searing his hands and head, turning brown skin pink, making him scream like a baby.

Somewhere in the distance I hear the bucket clatter to the floor. I plunge the knife into his head, again and again. His arms lash out blindly getting in the way. Blood mixes with water cascading to the floor. Meathead staggers to his feet, pulling off his shirt, trying to peel away the agony but his skin comes away with it, leaving a raw, red mess.

There's a shrill alarm and the sound of pounding feet. I hurl the knife through the bars at the window. A blur of dark faces converge in my vision, fists, feet, punching and kicking. Meathead's mates are yanking me off trying to hurt me. Screws come rushing and soon they're everywhere as I'm half-carried, half-dragged along the corridor.

'Blimey,' a thought comes from somewhere in all the chaos, 'I've only been out a day and already I'm heading straight back down the chokey!' The last thing I see, as a screaming Meathead is hurried to the hospital, is my cellmate in the middle of the crowd peering worriedly after me. 'Course he's worried. The stinky bastard is wondering where his next bit of scag is coming from.

Now, as I explained, this story ain't just about me and my exploits courtesy of Her Majesty's hospitality – it's about a bunch of other unfortunate sods who eventually end up with me in Pentonville and some of the heroic, nutty and downright misguided things they do to get there. And no two criminals were ever more heroic, nutty and misguided than my mates Roland and Mackey.

Roland and Mackey

Down and dirty

'But Deptford's a piss-hole,' sulks Roland. 'No one's got no money round there.'

'That's the point. It's sweet, mate. Nobody will be expecting no thieves,' Mackey explains as if he were talking to a three-year-old. Sometimes Roland is remarkably stupid.

'That's 'cause there's nothing worth nickin',' says Roland, still not getting it.

'You just follow the pro and keep a look out,' replies Mackey, the chipper black fella with all the answers.

Roland scowls. They're walking from Greenwich towards Deptford. Greenwich is a lot swankier than Deptford, but it's market day in Deptford and Mackey's convinced there'll be cosy pickings. Mackey's bounding along like a rat on speed, as he always does when he's about to nick something.

'Slow down, you cunt, I'm knackered,' says Roland. Roland is pale and gangly with dirty blonde hair spiked up with a bit of gel and jeans that are ripped and faded by accident rather than design.

'Well, you have a kip on that bench and I'll see ya later,' says Mackey. He strides on ahead in the full knowledge that Roland *will* get a move on, because Mackey's a much better thief than Roland, and Roland's desperate for a hit. It's been hours since they shot up. Mackey slows down though, because he likes to talk and he needs someone to listen. Generally, Roland is sufficiently impressed to make a few encouraging noises allowing Mackey to drone on, barely engaging any thinking mechanisms at all.

Even though Mackey's parents are West Indian and he's never been west of Hounslow, he likes to tell people he's kissed the Blarney Stone. He's got the gift of the gab all right. Learnt all the spiel as a toddler grafting biscuits off grandmas on park benches. He's never been good-looking; always had to make more of an effort than other kids and now he's doing a life sentence in instalments. Not quite as often as Roland though. Roland might as well have, '*I'm the one you're after*' tattooed on his forehead.

'Urry up!' Early bird catches the worm,' Mackey grins cheerfully.

They're entering Deptford's long curving high street with its familiar smell of rotting vegetables and leaking bin bags.

'Come getcha tomaaaatoes,' a voice booms beside Roland's ear, making him flinch. 'One paaaaand twenny a paaaand!'

'You stay outta my way, mate, and if I give the signal leg it that way,' says Mackey pointing up the street.

Roland folds his arms, jealous. Mackey's always so fucking hyper when he's on the job, doesn't seem to get any of the unpleasant fluttering sensations that make Roland practically shit himself every time *he* tries to slide something off the back of a lorry. Mackey has patiently taught him all his tricks but Roland's only just come out of a three month sojourn in the clink for a scam of Mackey's in which Roland ignored, or maybe forgot, the most vital instruction.

'And, if you get into hot water, always remember,' Mackey's voice now resounds in his ears like an ill-fated déjà vu, 'drop the booty. Let it go. Drop it like it's burning

25

your fuckin' fingers. There's always plenty more touches to be had.'

Mackey always says the same thing three times if he can get away with it. Most of the time, Roland can barely get a word in edgeways which is rarely a problem because Roland doesn't tend to have very much to chat about. Apart from his next fix.

Ten minutes later they meet up in an alley to compare takings. Mackey's got a handbag that he slipped off some dozy bird's shoulder while she was rummaging through a stall selling lingerie; a wallet that had been winking invitingly from some geezer's back pocket as well as a pot of loose change; a hat that he liked the look of and some earrings for his mum.

Roland's pleased with himself too. He found a stall selling genuine Levi and Wrangler jeans. As soon as the trader was busy bagging up a purchase for a customer, he *swagged* a hefty box off the back of his stall and disappeared into the crowd.

Mackey rummages through the handbag, his lightning fingers tossing out a pair of knickers, a tube of lubricant, two tampons and an assortment of condoms. He delves back into the bag and about fifteen more shiny packets spray onto the tarmac.

Roland bursts into laughter. 'Great touch Mackey, mate. You shouldn't have robbed her. You should have shagged her.'

'No wonder she was so dozy; must be knackered after shafting punters all night. Should be loaded,' says Mackey. His fingers close round a plastic purse and deftly turn it inside-out to expose one five quid note, a few coins, and an assortment of plastic; Blockbuster Video, Matalan, Super-save Discount Bargain Centre... Mackey's face falls and he upturns the bag to give it a final shake. A strawberry flavoured condom falls out.

Obviously doesn't believe in banking,' he frowns.

Obviously doesn't believe in unprotected sex,' laughs Roland. 'What else d'ya get, mate?' He's longing to tell Mackey that he was right about Deptford being a piss-hole. Almost as much as he's longing to see Mackey pull out a wad big enough to finance a month's worth of smack.

Mackey tosses the money into the pot of change and snaps open the wallet. 'If at first you don't succeed,' he sings cheerily.

Things are looking up. About ten cards in this one; one credit card, two debit cards, a library card, a Texaco card, a Boots Loyalty card... In vain he looks for some *bona fide* ID so that he can do some spending. 'Fuck me, they're all useless,' he groans.

'Any cash? Asks Roland, mentally composing a cutting I-told-you-so for later.

'Nah,' says Mackey, spotting a lone twenty-pound note in the fold of the wallet. 'What's this though? He pulls out instead a folded letter and makes a big show of unfolding it to distract Roland while he slips the wallet under his arm. 'Let's see... 'Dear Tom...' Oh, whoopee, it's a love letter?' 'I hate you, you bastard. You will never see your *dorter* again.' D... O... R... What?'

'Daughter,' snorts Roland. 'Div.'

'Oh, daughter, *right.* 'So, screw you, I'm getting a restraynin' order against ya. Don't come near me or the kid or you will get arresttid...'

'Nicked, pillock.'

'Shit, wait a minute, there's a date on this letter,' Mackey frowns, peering at the top of the page. 'Twenty-first Febree. Febree! Fucking 'ell, I thought *my* spelling was shit. What's the day today, Roly?'

'Dunno, mate.' Now that he's out of prison, dates mean nothing to Roland, except for the day his incapacity benefit comes in.

'It was the twenty-first yesterday, me sister's birthday,' says Mackey, shaking his head with regret. 'Fuck me. That means that poor bastard lost his kid one day, and his wallet the day after. I'm the scum of the earth, Roly. Scum of the fuckin' earth. If she'd 'ave put his address on the letter, I'd stick his wallet through the letterbox. I would, Roly, I really would.'

'No, you wouldn't. Anyway, that bloke's probably a violent nutter,' says Roland reaching for his box. Trouble with Mackey, thinks Roland, he's too nice to be a proper thief. Sometimes Mackey feels so bad about the things he's done that he can't nick anything for a couple of days and Roland has to wait until he gets over it. 'Otherwise why would she write a letter like that?'

'Yeah, you're right,' says Mackey perking up a bit. One good thing about Roland is that he doesn't have a conscience. Mackey envies him his total lack of sympathy when relieving other people of their property. Trouble with Roly, though, he thinks slipping the wallet into his back pocket, he's too stupid to make a proper thief. 'What d'ya get then, Roly mate? Open it up; open the box, let's see what ya got then.'

Roland's been itching to trounce Mackey with his booty. Judging by the weight of it, there are probably about thirty pairs of Levis that he might be able to sell on down Greenwich market tomorrow. He could do with a new pair of jeans for himself too.

'Fuck me!' whistles Mackey as soon as Roland's ripped open the box. 'No wonder the geezer was looking the other way. He saw you coming a mile off. You did him a favour, mate, off-loading that stuff for 'im.'

28

Roland glowers at the layers of neatly-folded multi-coloured neon vests that meet his gaze. He pulls one out and lets it fall open making Mackey hoot with derision. 'Some people would like these,' Roland says stubbornly.

'Yeah, maybe a couple of hippies going to a rave in the middle of summer.' Mackey agrees. 'But only if they were colour-blind and the vests were going cheap.' He shakes with laughter, barely able to get the words out: 'Fifty pence a vest! Come get 'em! Three for a paaaaaand!'

Someone walks past and Roland shuts the box in embarrassment.

'Nah, wait a minute. I know who'd buy 'em,' says Mackey, wiping tears of laughter from his eyes. 'Your mum.' Roland's mum will buy anything so long as it's nicked and cheap. She knows a bargain when she sees one and she's got no taste.

Even Mum, Roland thinks, might turn her nose up at this lot. He's pissed off now. He gets to his feet, lugs the box down the alley and chucks it into a dumpster then saunters back with his hands in his pockets.

You and your smart ideas,' he sniffs. 'I told you Deptford was a piss-hole.' Then he throws in his *piéce de resistance*, the insult he's been hatching for the last five minutes. 'Better let me have these, you faggot, since you haven't had a shag in months.' With a smug grin he gathers up all the condoms and stuffs them into his back pockets.

Unfortunately Mackey doesn't take the bait. His conscience is playing up. 'You can't throw perfectly good clothes in the bin, mate. It just ain't right.'

Roland frowns. 'Life is way too fuckin' short to worry about stuff like that. Anyway, you said they was shit. And I need a fuckin' use-up before I go nuts.'

29

'Say no more,' says Mackey and he's up and bounding along the alley. 'I'll find us a better touch. You keep the change. Just you watch me.'

Roland empties the change into his pocket and gives the pot a flying kick along the alley. His nose has started to drip and he's getting a familiar ache deep in his limbs.

'Keep up, mate,' says Mackey, his eyes darting around as they emerge back onto Deptford High Street.

Mackey's the first to spot their next touch. He always is. Roland could walk right past the pot of gold at the end of the rainbow without noticing. A stocky geezer is hauling a large box out of the back of a van marked 'Dawson's Electrics.'

Mackey's beady eyes spot the van driver lean against the doors and notices that they don't close properly. The driver heaves the box into a nearby building.

'Looks like our lucky day, matey,' says Mackey, which is one of his cheery clichés that always makes Roland's eyes roll. Mackey peers through the doorway to see the driver waiting for the lift in the empty lobby of some offices. 'Quick, unload the van,' he tells Roland, 'I'll tell ya when I see the lift coming down.'

Several buildings along, a low-rise wall borders a patch of waste ground. One by one, Roland heaves the hefty boxes along the pavement and over the wall lining them up behind it. It's exhausting work, especially on an empty stomach and with the encroaching hell of smack withdrawal, and by the time he's looted the fifth box he's almost wishing the driver would come down and catch him.

'How come I get the shit end of this?' he gasps on his seventh return to the van.

'You'll be rewarded in heaven my son. Keep it up! Keep it going!' hisses Mackey giving him the thumbs up from the lobby.

Roland trudges on because he understands that Mackey's kissed the Blarney Stone whatever that is, and that when the van driver comes down Mackey will distract him with some cock-and-bull story allowing Roland to get clean away. Whereas, if Roland was on the lookout, the driver would guess immediately by the dodgy look in Roland's eye that something was up and catch Mackey red-handed. Mackey's always trying to tell Roland he's in the wrong business. Roland doesn't listen because he knows a thing or two about thieving that Mackey doesn't. Roland knows it takes all sorts to make the world go round. They've just got different styles, that's all.

'Sweet, mate. Very, very, sweet,' says Mackey, helping Roland offload the last box because the van driver still hasn't returned. 'Must be 'having a cup of tea, the silly wanker.' There's nothing they can do for the moment but sit on the wall and try to look innocent until the van driver comes down and buggers off with his van.

Roland starts singing a football song, a personal favourite of his because of its rousing melody and one easy-to-remember stanza that goes, 'You're gonna get your fuckin' 'ead kicked in.'

Mackey joins in half-heartedly because the remorse is starting to hit him. He hopes the driver will set off to his next delivery without looking in the back of his van, so that Mackey doesn't have to see the driver's look of shock and dismay. That would give Mackey a horrible, sick feeling in the pit of his stomach which would make him want to tell the driver. 'We was only 'aving a laugh, mate. It's all 'ere behind this wall,' and then Roland would try to kill him. Of course, Mackey would never be that daft

31

but it's thoughts like these that help him sleep at night... Here comes the van driver now.

'You're gonna get your fuckin' 'ead kicked in, 'ead kicked in, 'ead kicked in,' sings Roland, waiting for the driver to open the doors and notice all his hard work emptying it. Otherwise where's the fun in nicking it all?'

The driver emerges from the building. Roland and Mackey watch breathlessly as he opens the driver's door, then changes his mind to go round the back and check that the doors are shut. Satisfied that they're locked, he gets in and drives off.

'Bollocks,' says Roland. 'I was gonna give him a nice friendly wave.' Now that he's done the deed, Roland's stomach has stopped churning and he's feeling elated. He and Mackey make a right pair of crooks says his mum, what with Roly being nervous before the event and Mackey guilt-ridden afterwards.

Mackey's feeling sick. He loves going on a nicking spree but it's a bit like crack for him, a thrilling rush followed by a horrendous crash.

Don't worry about it, mate,' shrugs Roland, recognising the self-reproach in his pal's eyes. 'It's a dog-eat-dog world, innit? We gotta make ends meet; that's all there is to it.'

'You're right, Roly,' says Mackey pulling himself together.

That's the thing about Roland; it's why he and Mackey have never fallen out for long. Roland would never let onto anyone about Mackey's pussy guilt trips. Roland even knows the origin of Mackey's inordinate guilt, and he's never brought that up in jest because he knows it's a really sore spot. Roland knows that it all goes back to the time when a seven-year-old Mackey tried to impress an older kid by stealing a little girl's sandwiches. The result was that Mackey had been taken to the front of the class and made to apologise to said little girl, who laughed at him with infantile glee, causing all his other classmates to join in. The high, followed by the shameful low, has been destined to repeat itself ever since.

'How are we s'posed to lug all this stuff back to Catford then, on the bus?' frowns Roland, his mind ninety-nine percent focused on his next hit.

'Leave it to me, matey,' says Mackey pulling his silly hat down over his ears and stalking away. Twenty minutes later, a slightly battered van screeches up to Roland's feet and Mackey jumps out, leaving the engine running. 'Load it up then! Load it up!'

Roland's bored and his fingers have turned blue. 'D'ya get any brown yet?' he asks.

Mackey looks at him incredulously. 'Any *brown*? Not yet! I've been nicking a fuckin' van, mate. First I had to find one, then I had to get in, then I 'ad to fiddle about with all the bloomin' wires…'

'All right, all right,' says Roland, blowing on his fingers and opening the back doors. 'Fuckin' 'ell!'

Roland stares into the back of the van in amazement. It's piled to the roof with brand new cardboard boxes labelled with names like Hitachi, Phillips and Sony.

Mackey breaks into a grin. 'Looks like it's our lucky day, me old china.'

Roland thinks back over the day so far and is about to make a comment when Mackey shoves him to get a move on.

There's only enough room in the back for about half of the boxes they nicked from the other van, so Roland sits in the passenger seat while Mackey piles the others down by his feet and onto his lap until Roland can't see a thing.

'Wait there,' sings Mackey, all cheery grins again. 'Gonna get some fresh works and swabs from the Needle Exchange.'

'Get me a can a coke, will ya?' groans Roland from behind all the boxes as Mackey slams the door, leaving the engine running.

Barely a few seconds pass and there's a rap on the window. 'You'd better move your van,' a voice barks out.

Roland tries to peer through a few boxes but his arms are pinned to his sides. He hopes it ain't the old bill. His heart thuds in his chest and he stops breathing, hoping whatever it is will go away. After what seems an age, he inhales and lets out a long groan. Mackey jumps into the van with a cigarette dangling from his lips, 'Want a fag, mate?'

'Yeah, but I can't fuckin' move,' comes a voice from behind all the boxes. Mackey shifts a couple of them to see his friend, pale-faced and pop-eyed.

'What's the matter, Roly?' You look like you seen a ghost!'

'Old bill,' says Roland, 'knocking on the fucking window!'

'Where?' gasps Mackey, ducking down and stubbing out his cigarette. 'Ow, fuck!'

'Dunno. Couldn't see, could I?' fumes Roland.

'You fuckin' Dolt!' spits Mackey struggling back into his seat on spotting a transparent plastic envelope wedged under the windscreen wiper. 'Dirty slags 'ave given me a ticket!'

'What you worried about?' asks Roland. 'Ain't your van. Did you get me a coke?'

'That ain't the point,' says Mackey glancing round for the offending traffic warden. 'I'd only been gone two minutes. Why don't they go and get proper fucking jobs?'

'That is a proper job,' frowns Roland. 'We're parked on a double yella.'

'They're scum,' says Mackey, still seething. 'Builders, solicitors, dustbin men... those are *proper* jobs. Some people have to work hard for a living.'

'What, like us, you mean?' asks Roland.

'Yeah, like us,' says Mackey self-righteously.

'You mean, nicking boxes and vans when no one's looking?'

Mackey's about to explode. He opens his mouth and when nothing automatically comes out, rams his foot on the accelerator. The van screeches in the direction of Catford with the ticket still stuck to the window.

'You might wanna slow down, mate,' advises Roland. 'There's a job some arse 'oles do round 'ere called giving out speeding fines.'

Mackey purses his lips, glaring at the road ahead.

'Now that's what you call a proper job,' says Roland from behind the boxes. 'They check you've got insurance and a driving licence and a log book, and, in your case, arrest you on the fuckin' spot. I'd change the plates on this van sharpish, if you're planning on keeping it.'

'Right. Get out, you cunt,' says Mackey jamming his foot on the brake and sending several boxes thumping into the windscreen. 'I've had enough of you winding me up!'

'All right, all right. Keep yer hair on,' says Roland, which is not really the thing to say to Mackey, who's showing signs of early balding. 'Cheer up Mackey mate, let's find out what we nabbed.'

'Sweet,' sighs Mackey, starting up the van and driving it into a quiet area of garages. Their nerves had been getting so frayed that they'd forgotten for a moment about all their booty in the back.

They're sitting in the back of the van staring at heaps of opened boxes lying all around.

'I can't believe it,' says Mackey shaking his head. 'I just cannot fuckin' believe it. I do not believe it!'

'Yeah! I've got that bit already,' says Roland

'It doesn't make sense! Why would someone load up a van with brand new empty boxes?' Mackey gets out and gives a Hitachi box a hefty kick, leaving a large dent in the middle of the High Definition Plasma TV label.

'As I keep telling you,' says Roland, inhaling deeply on a cigarette, 'Deptford is a piss-hole.'

'What's that gotta do with it?' I just don't fuckin get it,' says Mackey. 'And as for this other shit…' he kicks another box in the side and recoils, wincing. 'Why would a van that says 'Dawson's fucking Electrics' be stuffed with boxes full of lentils and fuckin' chickpeas?'

'Because,' says Roland, as if he's explaining things to a retard, 'Deptford is… a… piss… hole.'

'That's not the fuckin' answer to my fuckin' question,' says Mackey looking ready to weep.

'I thought those boxes were heavy,' Roland sniffs in disgust. He's never going to let Mackey forget how he made him thieve fourteen boxes of dried pulses out the back of a van. 'Never mind, it's sweet, mate, sweeeeeet. You're the pro, remember? You could always sell this shit to Ali.'

'Ali!' cries Mackey, cheering up. 'That's the best idea you've had all day. I mean, the *only* idea. Come on, load it back up then and we can get some smack *and* a slap-up dinner.'

Roland had been trying to be sarcastic, but in retrospect it was a pretty good idea to think of Ali, who will not only buy anything cheap and nicked like Roland's mum, but who owns one of those shops that sells everything, including lentils and chickpeas. And Roland will be able to get that can of coke at last.

'Nah, load it up yourself,' he says smugly. 'It was your stupid idea to nick it in the first place.'

Ali gave them thirty quid for the boxes of lentils and chickpeas and mung beans and other crap they'd been dumb enough to lift.

'That van driver must be laughing his arse off now,' says Roland, watching out of the corner of his eye for Mackey's reaction. 'He'll think the thieves are gettin' really desperate round Deptford. Ha! Ha! We did 'im a favour, Mackey mate. Saved 'im doing his back in, luggin' all that stuff outta the van. Real cosy pickin's round Deptford. I'll agree with ya there,' he adds, putting the boot in.

They're driving towards Brixton. Mackey's face is getting darker and broodier by the second. He wishes he hadn't let Roland pocket the money, because if he'd put it in his own pocket, he would now make a sudden lurch across the van, open the door, kick him out and drive off again.

Roland smiles to himself. He loves winding Mackey up. Doesn't want to push it too far though, because Mackey's got that dangerous-fucker look on his face.

'How much we got altogether?' growls Mackey. The day has gone to shit and all he can think about is getting some smack and a bit of crack and forgetting all about it.

'Well, with the thirteen quid from the market, we 'ave made a grand, whopping total of forty-free smackers.'

'Enough for a few small stones and a bit of gear,' Mackey scowls.

Roland is about to remind Mackey of the slap-up dinner he promised when his stomach lets out an exasperated rumble, saving him the bother.

Mackey snatches a guilty glance at his starving friend, and almost mentions the extra twenty he's got stashed in the wallet, but bites his tongue so that he can buy an extra bit of gear when Roly's not looking.

They park the van outside a grimly imposing tower of council flats. Two of the lifts aren't working and the other is being temporarily commandeered as a knocking shop, so they begin the long trek up to the sixth floor.

'Give us the dosh then, Roly,' pants Mackey when they reach the battered green door they know so well. Mackey always does the deal because he's got a cheeky grin and he's kissed that stone and he always gets a better deal than Whitey Boy.

Roland stops dead, searching for the money. Mackey's eyes are on him as he goes from pocket to pocket, turning them inside out. 'You've fuckin' got it,' says Roland, looking a bit panicky.

'No I ain't. I gave it to you,' fumes Mackey.

'Oh, hold up, I must have left it in the glove-box,' says Roland, 'wait there and I'll go get it.' He starts running down the stairs.

'Wait a minute,' says Mackey smelling a rat, 'I'm coming with you.'

'Nah, it's a long way down,' says Roland, speeding up.

'Slow down, you slag,' says Mackey, surprised that his friend can move so bloody fast. They're galloping down stairs, hurdling over banisters. At the bottom, Roland shoves past a punter zipping up his flies as he steps out of the lift and legs it towards the van.

He hurls open the doors, leaps into the back and scrabbles around in the dark until his hand closes on the wallet that Mackey lifted in the market. He's about to leap out and make a run for it, 'cause his legs are longer than Mackey's, when he hears a deep rumble and the van starts up with a lurch that sends him crashing into the side.

Mackey grinds the gear stick into reverse and it's all Roland can do to grasp hold of the slats on the side of the van to stop himself flying out the back. The van lurches forwards and Roland grasps on for life as Mackey sets off around the council estate, making sudden swerves while alternately jamming his foot on the brakes and then the accelerator. Roland's lanky body slams against the sides.

'I'll kill you, you fuckin' thief!' Mackey screams from the cabin. He's mad because he's checked his pocket and found the wallet from the market missing. He knows that Roly's lifted it and Roly's a shit robber so Mackey must be losing his touch.

He thrusts the van into reverse and prepares to slam it into a wall, again and again, until Roland is sorry. The sudden lurch sends Roland flying halfway out the back and grabbing onto the door for safety. Glancing into the rear view mirror, Mackey has a better idea. Instead of crashing into the wall, he shoots forward and screeches out of the council estate, skidding in a tight arc that sends the doors flapping about in the wind. Roland's terrified screams reach Mackey's ears making him grin like a maniac.

'That'll teach ya!' he yells, careering into the main road. 'I'll teach ya a lesson you won't forget, Roly you fuck! I'll teach ya a thing or two!'

Somewhere at the back of his mind, Roland registers that Mackey must be cheering up because he's started to repeat himself again but his more pressing concern is that he's about to die. He's got one foot wedged between the wooden slats and both hands clutching the top of the door and he's being alternately stretched then folded in two every time the door swings back and forth, while from time to time the other door casually batters him.

There's a Range Rover driving along behind and every couple of seconds Roland catches a glimpse of astonishment in the eyes of the woman behind the wheel. Suddenly, Mackey rams his foot on the brakes and Roland finds himself lying on the bonnet of the Range Rover gazing pleadingly into those eyes. 'Don't stop!' he wails.

'Take that, you prick!' Mackey yells out the window belting away.

The driver brings her car to a dramatic halt sending Roland sprawling onto the tarmac. She jumps out and runs round to him leaning over his face so that he can see right into her cleavage.

'Oh! Gosh, are you all right? Shall I call you an ambulance? She gasps.

Roland glares at her. She's a good-looking rich bird and normally this would be the stuff of his dreams. But his head is spinning and every cell in his body hurts. Nothing that a bit of smack won't cure, though.

'Nah, but you could give me a lift,' he says, putting on the smile that he reserves for ladies but which appears to terrify the shit out of her. She drives him with grave misgivings judging by her trembling hands, back to the tower block, drops him off and screeches away without a backward glance.

Roland stares after her and wipes his nose with his sleeve. It comes away soaked with blood. No wonder she wasn't impressed. Wincing, he reaches round to his back pocket, takes out the wallet from the market and checks its contents. Sixty-three quid. The entire day's takings.

Could have been a lot fucking worse.

Roland and Mackey

On the Ponce

'Who d'ya fink you're looking at?' Roland growls. 'Huh! Got a problem 'ave ya, you wankaaaahhh?'

He steps back and sniffs with satisfaction, then tries another tack. 'So you think I'm weeeeeird, do ya? Well, you're right. I'm a total fucking freeeeak! Now, give us the money!'

He's practising his insane looks in the mirror. It's been eighteen months since he's last had to do this and he's out of practice. He's looking good though, with his hair teased into a series of angry-looking spikes and a vivid collection of bruises displayed between his cut-off jeans and chunky black bovver boots.

He rummages around in his kitchen until eventually finding the letter from the DSS lying under a pile of cups containing varying levels of mouldering tea. Eleven-fifteen, his appointment is. Good, plenty of time. He goes out through the hall and, happening to glance in the mirror, almost scares the shit out of himself.

Opening the front door, he turns to make sure he hasn't forgotten anything. Since hunting everywhere for his tube of gale-resistant hair gel, it looks as if a posse of burglars has turned his one-bed flat upside down then proceeded to break everything in sight. He shuts the door on the chaos and sets off through the streets of Catford.

It's a sunny day, and he takes deep breaths smiling at everyone he passes. The heroin he took half an hour ago lends everything around him, including the hideous Catford shopping centre, an inviting glow. He's a little surprised to notice the wide berth given to him by passers-

41

by until he remembers the fright he just gave himself in the mirror.

The dole office is half-full with an assortment of life's low-earners slumping in the shiny blue plastic seats and a few dishevelled kids running amok amongst them. Roland does a quick check and counts four definite scagheads, two probable ones, and a black fella with staring eyes grinding his teeth. Guaranteed Crackhead.

Roland hands his letter to the receptionist who asks him to take a seat. He sits down, trying to look as menacing as possible in order to deter the kids from running round him in dizzying circles.

For a mind-numbing forty-five minutes, he watches the fallen-on-hard-timers and ne'er-do-wells entering and exiting trying to guess their stories. There's one who's too stupid to get a job, he decides. There's another who's just bone-idle. That one who's just come in has got a cushy job for sure, but she's scamming the taxpayer for extra, judging by the size of the tits jutting out of her skinny ribcage. And that one he thinks, studying a fella with uncombed hair and unwashed jeans, is simply unfit for work. Like Roland himself.

Over in the corner, a group of Deptford Wives all identical with their bleached blonde hair, scuffed stilettos and puked-on mini-skirts, try half-heartedly to keep their toddlers from beating each other up.

Roland glances at the clock again. He's long suspected the DSS have a policy of lying about their appointment times, thus making everyone wait an extra hour just to make sure they really *really* need the dosh.

His eyes flit wearily between the clock and the door until a familiar face comes in all cheery grins and 'how are ya, mateys?' Mackey takes a number from the ticket machine and walks straight past Roland without recognising him. Roland averts his face feeling a lurch of dread. Trust his luck for Mackey to be signing on today. Roland's name will be called out any minute now and Mackey'll be onto him like a terrier onto a slipper. With any luck though, Roland will be able to make it to the interview room before Mackey has a chance to drop any awkward comments.

'No fuckin' way!' a voice yells out, making Roland's heart sink. 'It's you, ain't it, Roly? Roland the punk! I don't believe it!'

Roland slumps in his seat.

'Trying to look hard, ah ya? Well it ain't working, you wanker! Ha ha ha!' Mackey glances around the room, grinning 'Hey, kids! That's Uncle Roly over there. He's a party clown in his spare time, but don't tell no one, 'cause it's cash-in-hand! Ha ha ha!'

Roland slumps deeper into his seat while Mackey draws all the scroungers and addicts in the room in on his joke. 'Look, kids, he's pretending to be all scaaaaaarrrry.'

'You're a silly punk!' shouts a pig-faced little girl of about five. 'I ain't scared of you!'

'She's onto your game, Roly,' grins Mackey, folding his arms. 'You ain't foolin' no one with that demented disguise.'

Roland glowers out of the window, praying for his name to be called. This sort of humiliation simply isn't worth the sixty-three quid and all the bruises he ended up with after doing the dirty on Mackey last week.

Mackey jumps out of his seat and sits next to him. Everyone's watching. This is the best entertainment there's ever been down at the dole office. Mackey taps the palm of his hand against the tip of one of Roland's spikes and winces as if it's done him an injury.

'I'll give ya the money back,' Roland mumbles, slapping the hand away. 'But I gotta see the doctor about my sick pay or I won't have nothing to give ya.'

'Yeah, yeah.' Mackey grabs a kid's plastic lorry from where it lies discarded on the floor and starts singing into it as if it were a microphone. 'God Save the Queen, she ain't no human beeeeing,' he croons, looking just like Johnny Rotten from the Sex Pistols, and making all the dossers and single mums laugh their fucking heads off.

'Shut up!' pleads Roland.

'Roland Dwight?' a voice rings out and Roland glances up in relief to see a woman scanning faces from a doorway. He's on his feet like a shot and hurrying towards her, but Mackey's diving to his knees and grabbing hold of his ankle and being dragged across the room like Nancy to his Sid Vicious, wailing, 'Don't leave me, Sid! Don't leave me!'

Reaching the door, Roland remembers just in time to put on his limp and his fake twitch. The madman walk is an essential part of his act, and Mackey's ruining it. Roland slips in a swift kick just in time to separate himself from Mackey and make it into the doctor's office alone. The woman shuts the door and Roland can hear her outside asking Mackey to please stand up and be a gentleman.

'Ah! Mr Dwight, take a seat,' says a man of about forty wearing a well-cut suit, a stethoscope and a professional frown.

'Oh! Shit,' thinks Roland, twitching and limping his way towards the empty chair. 'It's going to be difficult to pull one past this geezer.'

The doctor scans several pages of notes from a folder, sniffing several times with what sounds like a mixture of distaste and deep suspicion.

'It says here that you are a drug user. Is that correct?'

Roland doesn't reply, but allows a stream of dribble to emerge from the corner of his mouth, trickle down his chin and land on his Guns 'n' Roses vest.

'Come, now,' sighs the doctor, 'you can answer my questions, I'm sure.'

Roland twitches several times then allows his eyes to roll back into their sockets, showing the whites of his eyeballs. From past experience he knows to avoid all medical questions.

'As you are probably aware,' the doctor tells him, 'I am here to ascertain whether you are fit and able to work.'

Roland feels a lurch of dread at the doctor's last words. He screws up his nose and gazes, wide-eyed, at the window. 'Daleks!' he exclaims. 'Daaarrrrleks!'

The doctor watches impassively while Roland stands up and walks to the window, making several violent jerks with his head. He presses his face to the glass with an enthralled expression, as if he can see an entire scene from his favourite cult TV show behind it. 'Dr Who? Dr Who! Dr Who-ooo-ooo!'

'Sit back down please, Mr Dwight,' says the doctor, striding over to guide Roland back to his seat. 'Just sit down and relax for a moment.'

Roland peers out of the corner of his eye to try to see what the doctor is scribbling. For a moment the doctor glances up as if searching for some sort of inspiration. His eyes lock onto Roland's in a moment of total, shared lucidity. Roland twitches hurriedly, slamming his shoulder right into his ear; but it's too late.

The doctor goes back to writing his report. 'Mmm hmm. Fit and available for work, I should say,' he mutters. 'In my professional opinion, Mr Dwight would make an excellent actor, or possibly an artist of some sort. Ah! Yes. Let me see... Scam... Con... Piss... any one of these categories would be remarkably suited to Mr Dwight's particular set of skills.'

Roland's mind is racing. Surely the doctor can see that Roland is utterly unfit and unable to work! For fuck's sake, who would employ a lying, thieving, drug addict with vicious bruises all over him? Any minute now, Roland will have to join the queue with Mackey for Job Seeker's Allowance and pretend he's applying for phantom jobs every coupla weeks, or worse still, turn up for work and try to get sacked as quickly as possible. The thought of earning his living makes him break out in a sweat. Suddenly he remembers something that a prisoner once did in Belmarsh when he wanted to be left alone for a bit of peace and quiet.

'Daarrrleks,' he says again, more forcefully this time. Staring into space, he unzips his flies and takes his penis out. It dangles limply onto the seat. 'Daaaaaarrrrrrleks,' he says, allowing a grin to spread across his face while his fingers rub furtively at his prick.

The doctor leans back in his chair with a long-suffering frown. He scores a line through the notes he has just made and laces his fingers together.

'Put it away, Mr Dwight, there's a good chap,' he sighs. 'You may go. Shortly you will receive another letter in the post informing you of your entitlement to Incapacity Benefit. That is, of course, if you can read it.'

Roland makes his way of the room, so triumphant he forgets all his bizarre afflictions and only just remembers to feign a minor twitch at the door.

Roland and Mackey

Behaving badly

Mackey hasn't bothered to change the plates on the van or to disguise it in any way. He's been driving it around for so long now that his conscience has given up plaguing him about it. By some miraculous cross-wiring in his brain he thinks it's his and that's with no log book, M.O.T. or even a set of keys. He's been using it to do house clearances and a couple of dodgy removal jobs, but the money's gone straight on the brown and it's all too much like hard work. He's ready for some easy pickings and he's got Roland along as a look-out.

When Roland showed Mackey his bruises the day he came out of the doctor's office, Mackey decided to let bygones be bygones and promised Roland that they'd never fall out again over a poxy sixty-three quid. So now they're on their way to the other side of London to make a proper packet.

It's late Sunday afternoon, just starting to get dark and the pub is packed with punters squeezing a last few hours of leisure out of their weekend. It used to be called 'The Queen's Arms', now it's the 'Mad Hatter Inn'; one of those fashionable gastro pubs that makes the clientele from the old pub think they've gone up in the world and had better swap their pints of Stella for glasses of Pinot Grigio.

The sound of rowdy laughter wafting over the beer garden towards Roland and Mackey in their van gives them away though. Proper East London laughter it is. Ha fuckin' ha ha; not tuh huh huh huh, like it is a few miles away in Islington.

'Can't we 'ave a drink first?' Roland asks Mackey, peering in at the blur of happy faces. They've just jacked up their last bit of brown and are feeling relatively normal, like those laughing punters in the pub.

'You can have all the drinks you like in a bit,' says Mackey, rubbing his hands with anticipation. He's wearing that mad-rat-on-speed look again. 'Only not in this pub, Roly mate. *This* pub is the one we are doing over. Now you stay 'ere and give us a hoot if there's a problem, ok?'

'Yeah, yeah, it's all under control,' Roland nods, gazing thirstily into the pub.

'Keep your eyes peeled and the engine running,' Mackey drums into him. 'And get ready to hit that pedal the second I jump in.'

Mackey's burgled pubs all over London. He screws them on a weekend when they're busy like this. Usually he works on his own but it won't hurt to have a lookout, and Roly has his uses sometimes.

Roland watches his friend climb up the metal rungs of a fire escape. With his dark clothes and skin, he can hardly be seen, not like Roland who would stick out a mile in his white trainers and battered denim jacket. He watches admiringly as Mackey leans over the fire escape, latches onto a drainpipe and starts climbing like a cat towards an open window. Wouldn't catch Roland climbing up no drainpipes. He tried it once. The pipe came away from the wall and landed him smack in the middle of a bunch of stinging nettles, giving him a vicious clout on the head and all. He'd scratched himself like a flea-ridden gorilla until his skin had peeled.

Still, he's feeling thirsty and the punters in the pub seem to be having a whale of a time. Mackey's bound to be gone five minutes, plenty long enough for him to get a pint down his neck and be ready and waiting to make a clean getaway. He ain't stupid though, he'll make it quick. He manoeuvres between crowds of laughing customers in the garden, past all the lucky smiling people in the pub, and straight up to the bar. His last fiver's waving about in his hand, then a brimming pint of Carling's at his lips, and slurp, slurp, slurp, it's all gone down with a nice burp at the end.

Meanwhile he's had about a minute and a half to appreciate all the up-for-it-chicks in the pub, and to admire the cunning tricks with the lighting and the tasty-looking dishes on the chalked-up menu. It's nothing like as satisfying as a dose of H, but still, it's nice to have a taste of what normal people get up to sometimes.

The alcohol's making him feel warm and convivial, so might as well have another, he reasons, digging around in his pockets, yes... just enough for a second pint. Not taking any chances, though, he'll take this one with him. Out through the garden and back to the van, and Mackey still ain't back yet so Roland leans against it, slurp, slurp, slurp, enjoying that wonderful fizzing sensation at the back of his throat.

So far, Mackey's doing unbelievably well. He's found a rolled-up stash of pinks in an underwear drawer in a bedroom, (stupid place to hide your fifties, don't you bloody well know,) as well as a few items of gold jewellery and a swish digital camera with about three hundred family photos on it... Uh! Oh, twinge of guilt coming on... Never mind, maybe he'll get 'em processed and put 'em in the post.

Stuffing the booty into every available pocket, he tip-toes into the living room where the landlord of the pub happens to be fast asleep on the sofa, with the entire takings from the week in the till tray on his lap.

Mackey's always saying it's his lucky day, but even *he* recognises that he's been joking until today. Today is his day. It's the luckiest day of his life. He would have been happy with the fifties and the jewellery and down the drainpipe in a flash, but what burglar worth his cotton socks could pass up an opportunity like this? What with the din from the pub and the landlord's snores drowning out everything including the racket from the TV, he reckons he just needs to be a bit careful not to jog the till and it will be like nicking candy from a baby, a deaf and dumb baby, to boot.

The landlord has a massive beer gut which wobbles obscenely with each deafening snore. He's fallen asleep with his hand on the armrest, clutching a pint of lager, three quarters full. Mackey reaches cautiously for the stack of pinks in the till, keeping his eyes glued to the tilted glass. One wrong move and the lager will be all over fatty's lap, making him wake up with a yell.

The fifties are swiftly in his pocket and Mackey's reaching for the scores when he hears a scrabbling noise and a hushed curse somewhere in the flat. No time to worry what it might be, he cuts his losses and retreats to the bedroom to make a hasty escape. A pair of white knuckles are gripping the window sill.

'Help me, mate!' gasps a familiar voice and Roland's head pops into view.

'What the fuck are *you* doing up here?' Mackey hisses.

Roland starts to wobble on the drainpipe. Mackey grabs him by the scruff of his neck and drags him into the room.

'Have you been drinking?' he fumes. He glances out of the window to see the van in the same spot with its engine running. For a moment he decides to keep what he's got, shimmy down the drainpipe and leave Roland to his fate. But the thought of Roland getting all those scores and tens in the till, after making such a fucking useless stab at being a burglar, pisses him right off.

'Stay the fuck in this room and keep quiet,' he says, hurrying back to the living room. The landlord is still asleep but his lager has started to spill ever so slightly out of his glass. Mackey reaches for the twenties and stuffs them in his pocket. Suddenly he almost jumps out of his skin. From the other side of the room, he can see Roland tip-toeing towards him, lifting one knee up high and then the other, while pushing his arms through the air as if he were swimming underwater.

'What the fuck are you doing?' Mackey mouths incredulously.

'Ssssshhh!' says Roland in a deafening whisper, 'I'm trying to be quiet!'

Mackey freezes to the spot, eyes glued to the landlord, amazed that he hasn't woken up. Surely Roland can't have got pissed in all of five minutes? Either that, or he's treating this burglary like some kind of joke. It's a fuckin' liberty, whichever way you look at it.

'Get out, you cunt!' Mackey whispers frantically. He reaches for the tens. The landlord's hand relaxes a little and the lager trickles out of the glass.

Without thinking, Roland props the glass up, and seeing as it comes away in his hand without any resistance, he decides he might as well drink it. Slurp, slurp, slurp. He's not stupid though; he suppresses the burp.

Jesus Fucking Christ Mackey thinks to himself, stuffing the tens in his pocket and grabbing the fives. It's not worth being in this business. Not with the amount of stress he has to put up with.

Suddenly the landlord stops snoring. For ten... twenty... fuck knows how many seconds... Mackey and Roland stand rooted to the spot, gazing at the landlord with rising apprehension. He's turned slack-jawed and pale, and his enormous stomach, which had been rising and descending by ten inches at a time, has gone still.

Mackey clutches his forehead. Where in the world he got the idea that Roland would make a good look-out he will never know. He makes for the bedroom, ready to shove his mate through the window head-first if needs be. Just then a terrible grating explosion erupts from the landlord's mouth, making all the hairs on Mackey's neck stand on end. Then the landlord resumes snoring as if nothing had happened.

'It's all right, he's got sleep apnoea,' Roland whispers knowingly, 'I read about it once in a maga...'

'Shut up!' winces Mackey, heading swiftly to the bedroom. If Roland makes one more stupid remark, Mackey will make off with all the dosh and leave his mate to face the consequences. He's about to make his escape when he hears a noise that sounds as if Niagara Falls has started up. Glancing round, he sees Roland taking a slash in the toilet as merrily as if he were in his own house.

Mackey can't believe his ears. Nor can he believe the amount of piss that's gushing out of his mate. Suddenly, he gets a familiar panicky feeling in his chest. 'Time to go. Hurry up, Roly!'

'I can't stop!' shouts Roland over his noisy pissing. After that second pint of lager, climbing up a drainpipe had looked like such a good idea, and why should Mackey have all the fun? He hadn't reckoned on needing to take a leak right in the middle of their getaway, though.

Mackey's half way down the drainpipe before Roland gets one leg out the window, still zipping his flies. Amazingly, the landlord's snores are still ringing out from the living room. If he gets away with this, Mackey promises himself while shimmying deftly to the bottom, he'll get a proper job, honest-to-God he will.

'Does this van belong to you, sir?' says a voice in his ear, making him freeze.

'Van? What van?' he says spinning round, too late to prevent a police officer yanking his hands behind his back and another one clicking on the cuffs. It all happens so speedily that one minute, Mackey's a free man, and the next he's looking at one hell of a long stretch *inside,* without so much as a moment in between to contemplate the difference.

He glances up to see Roland clambering gaily down the drainpipe. Mackey is about to yell out in warning when he remembers how Roland broke every rule in the unspoken Burglar's Code of Conduct, so he keeps his mouth shut. At least he'll have a so-called mate in jail.

Glancing down to see the old bill waiting for him in the shadows, Roland desperately tries to work his way back up the pipe. There comes a dreadful wrenching sound as the drainpipe tears away from the wall, and with a sickening déjà vu, Roland flies through the air and lands with a groan at the policemen's feet.

'You're nicked,' says one of them.

Roland keeps his eyes shut, pretending to be dead. Or at the very least, unconscious, because then maybe, just maybe, this will all go away like a bad dream, and he'll wake up in his own bed again and never be so pleased to see his stinking filthy bed sheets.

'Thanks, *mate,*' Mackey spits at him, 'if it wasn't for you taking a piss on the job, we'd 'ave been outta here.'

Roland is too indignant to keep up the pretence of being dead. 'If *you* hadn't taken so fuckin' long I wouldn't have had to come in and get ya!'

'A right pair of useless crooks, you are,' one of the policemen chuckles grimly, making Mackey wonder if he's been talking to his mum. 'You might 'ave got away with it if it wasn't for the stolen van.'

Roland glares at Mackey self-righteously.

'Then again,' the other cozzer laughs at Roland, 'you were spotted by a member of the public shimmyin' up a drainpipe. It was the white trainers that caught her eye.'

Mackey aims a swift kick at Roland's arse, making the old bill laugh as if this were the ending to a classic comedy from the good old days.

It's certainly the end of the good old days for Roland and Mackey.

HMP Belmarsh

Back down the Chokey

Time flies down the Block. The Governor thinks he's punishing me for the Hot Water Job on Meathead. He's trying to pin it on me as Attempted Murder, except there's no evidence, and no witnesses either. I don't care. I gave up caring a long time ago. Down the Block it's lunchtime, then dinner, then phone call and back to bed with a yelled conversation out the windows till you're tired, and zzzzzzz... sleep like a baby.

Yeah, it gets a tad monotonous down the chokey but me, my mind drifts in a pleasant haze, not bothering to contemplate anything much, except when I have a chuckle to myself about how I used to dash round on the outside like everything was so fucking significant. Took a few stretches in here to cure me of that notion. 'Course, I'm not letting on to the screws about this. I put up a good moan whenever I remember.

Yep; all in all my time spent on Good Order and Discipline has been surprisingly bearable, even though I've never been known for either. So, of course, I had to go and fuck it all up, didn't I?

Down the Block, we get closed visits, and with our visitors stuck behind a pane of glass it's impossible to smuggle anything through. On the other hand, we can get clothes brought in, which is one of those insane loopholes that's allowed me to rekindle my heroin habit in virtual solitary confinement. Belmarsh has only been open a while and the Governors haven't learnt from all their mistakes yet.

With all the single-minded attention to detail of an addict with nothing to do but twiddle his fingers all day long, I've been on the phone every night for a week planning my next use-up. The last conversation went like this:

'Now don't forget my jeans, Dawn.'

'Yeah, don't worry Harry. Anything else you want?'

'Er, well okay, a shirt and some socks and those jeans.'

'Yes, all right. Guess what? Tom started walking on Saturday. Your mum said he toddled all the way from the kitchen door to the cooker and that's at least six steps…'

'Really?' That's great. Gotta go in a minute. Don't forget my jeans, babe.'

'*Okay,* I'm bringing the jeans. I just need to ask you something. You know I told you about that div, Gary?'

'Gary?' No… oh yeah. Forget about him, he's a prick. Listen, when you bring the jeans tomorrow make sure you fold them us nice and neat, know what I mean?'

'Fold them up nice and…? Oh, yeah, all right, *all right.* Well, this div Gary, he's only gone and…'

'Tell him I'll fuckin' do him if he lays a finger on you or my kid. Now listen, Dawn…'

'Do him? What are you talking about? He's only gone and won the lottery. Well, five numbers came up. Only fifteen grand, but I thought I'd be nice to him anyway, know what I mean?'

'Oh right, yeah. Well shag him if you must, but only if you can get half the dough… No, wait a minute, don't shag him. Don't shag anyone. Forget I said that, Dawn, you're still my girl. Gotta go babe. Don't forget the jeans. Love ya.'

'*Fuck you and fuck your jeans!*'

'Sorry darling',' I say to the empty dial tone. I know I laid it on a bit thick about the jeans, but it makes me feel better to know that she has them uppermost on her mind. The screws tape our conversations but they've proved themselves on numerous occasions to be completely dense, so I'm kind of relying on them not to have any unexpected brainwaves regarding this.

I've just had breakfast and there's at least six hours to go until visiting time. I'm starting to get a little worried, that is, completely paranoid, that Dawn's going to somehow fail to hide the gear in the seam of my jeans, when I hear the cleaner paying special attention to the particular patch of floor outside my cell. Something's up and sure enough, after a moment or two I notice two small blue pills slide under my door.

'All right, 'arry?' yells Jimmy from the next cell.

'Er... yeah. Thanks, mate!' I yell back.

'Enough to stop you going on about them jeans?' Jimmy chuckles, or maybe I'm imagining it.

I swallow the Valium in the shower and let the water splash over my upturned face until the pills start to work. The thought of jeans slowly evaporates along with the steam rising from my body.

I lie on my bed with my hands folded behind my head and shut my eyes, enjoying the numbing effect of the drug. I'm feeling the same sort of empty-headed serenity that I was feeling naturally a few weeks ago, before I discovered the jeans trick.

'That still coming?' Jimmy yells outside my window, making me frown. Jimmy's a short, stocky fella who's down the chokey for thumping a screw. We try to keep each other happy.

'Yeah, it's all sorted, mate. Now shut up about it, will ya,' I shout warningly.

Eventually, lunchtime rolls round and I swallow a soggy pie in five gulps, trying not to gag. Then I fold my hands behind my head again and study the cracks on the ceiling. They remind me of the track marks I saw on Dawn's arms last time she visited.

Dawn's a junkie and it's my fault. Tom lives with my mum because Dawn can't take care of him and that's my fault too. But all I'm worried about is Dawn running out of smack and ripping my fucking jeans apart to get at the bit she's put by for me.

Fatherhood, they said, would bring out the man in me; make me a responsible member of the community. I went along with it at first. Cleaned up my act, even went shopping with Dawn and her bump for a pram-stroller-car-seat-all-in-fucking-one. Course, Dawn wanted the most expensive one in the shop, so I ended up strolling out the door with it, all casual like, while she went round gathering up cots and rockers and baby monitors and a few thousand quid' worth of unnecessary crap. Finally, the dippy bird realised I'd fucked off with my wallet, and had to dump the lot before they noticed the missing pram.

I had it in my head that I would get clean and go straight the minute the baby was born. I was even planning to be there at the birth. Trouble was, Dawn went into labour a bit early and there'd been boxing on TV in the pub that night and I was already piss-faced, so when the call came from the hospital and I started thinking about all the blood and pain and mess, I realised I needed a drop more Dutch courage and then, of course, one last bit of white before I packed it all in and naturally a little brown to bring me down so I wouldn't be para from the crack, and after that a line of coke to wake me up again... And I don't think I ever got to the hospital. It's all a bit of a blur really. I just remember lying in bed with Dawn, and a tiny scrap of life screamin' his lungs out between us, while I plummeted down on the worst crash of my life.

I'd thought he'd curl up on my chest and go to sleep with his thumb in his mouth, like in one of Dawn's fuckin' lying mother and baby magazines. I'd thought babies cried until you gave them some milk and then they calmed down. Dawn and me kept passing the bottle back and forth, trying to get some into the little bugger's throat, until finally he glugged it down only to puke it back over us all curdled.

I didn't know that babies could scream so loud you'd gradually lose your wits and get no sleep and be a fuckin' zombie the next day. I didn't know they were so delicate that you wouldn't be able to give them a proper hug until they were about six months old, and by then it was too bloody late.

Dawn hadn't been a junkie when she gave birth, but she was one now, and godblesser, she stuck it out for six months. But, in the end, the baby beat us hands down. We were no match for it. I'd seen him open his mouth with his little tonsils vibrating, and to avert a full-blown panic attack I'd be legging it down the nearest pub. My mum came round and calmly picked him up while he screamed in her face and we both thought she was some kind of superhuman. I still don't know how people have kids without ending up in the nut house.

I feel guilty as hell though. Our son took his first steps a few days ago and when I see him again he'll probably be old enough to beat me round a racetrack. I need some heroin to drown out these thoughts. I can't wait for this fuckin' visit.

It's getting late. Visiting time is from two-fifteen till four and it must be gone three by now. I throw myself off the bed and hammer on the door.

'Guvnor!' I yell.

No answer. Never is first time.

'Guvnoorrrr!'

'Yes, Shaw, what do you want?' asks the screw, the one I can't stand. The officious bastard with the black moustache framing a smug sneer. 'Northern Bollocks,' I call him.

'What's the time?' I bellow.

'Ten to four,' comes the answer. Why are you going sooomwhere?' A horrific noise starts up. Glug-glug-glug. It sounds like a blocked drainpipe but actually it's Northern Bollocks laughing. He's laughing because visiting time is nearly over and it doesn't look like I'm going to get my visit.

'Yeah, you fuckin' prick,' I scream. 'Down your shitting throat as soon as I get a chance, you tosser!' The Valium must be wearing off.

The screw laughs again, glug-glug-glug. I'm sure he knows something I don't; otherwise he would have said something sarcastic about my Good Order and Discipline.

'You all right, 'arry?' Jimmy shouts with concern through his window.

'Yeah mate, just them slags getting me at it,' I shout back, pacing up and down my cell. My mind is working overtime and I'm seriously starting to worry. If I don't get some news in a minute, I'm going to pick up my bed and start slamming it against the wall.

Boots come stamping along concrete. I hear keys going in the lock. I'm so stressed I'm practically tearing my hair out. The door swings open and there, framed in the doorway, is the northern screw with the 'tache. He's smiling like he's about to tell the funniest joke he's ever heard.

'Your missus,' he begins, a snort of glee escaping his nose 'has been caught coming into prison...' another irresistible giggle, '... with Class A drugs on her person.

60

She's been arrested. Glug-glug-glug.' Finally he bellows out the punch-line, the one he's evidently been dying to share with the Block for days: 'Looooks like you're going to be wearing your stinky old jeans again this week!' and he practically collapses with unbearable nasal laughter.

The screws on either side of him smile thinly. They don't move a muscle when I grab Northern Bollocks by the throat, squeezing his Adam's apple until it almost bursts between my fingers. From this position, I just about manage to give him a head butt which cracks his nose, before the other two decide they'd better get their sticks out, and suddenly I'm on the floor; nothing much I can do while they go about their practised manoeuvres for putting me out of action.

Through a cloud of pain and fury, I look up to see blood streaming from Northern Bollocks' nose, but already that smug grin is back on his face. Something tells me that I don't have to worry about him pressing charges on me for trying to choke him, or for the head butt, 'cause he's got this sick look in his eyes and his boot is coming up in the air and blocking out my entire view...

'Leave him alone!' Jimmy bellows from the next cell.

It's the last thing I hear before I pass out.

Not all the fellas who ended up with me on the RAPt programme ended up as smack addicts. My mate Terry, for example, went the route of a raving alcoholic and pill-head.

More times than I can remember, when we were going through some heavy shit on the programme, Terry would get us all crackin' up with one of his silly jokes, though he could be a right horrible bastard, when he wasn't being the life and soul of the wing.

Terry

A marriage made in heaven

Terry rolls out of bed, plants his feet on the floor and heaves himself upright. It was a heavy session last night and the rank smell of alcohol pollutes the air, oozing out of his pores and making him recoil with disgust from his own breath. He staggers over to the mirror, frowning at the reflection of his belly and wondering, for a moment, if it's really his. He's sure it wasn't that enormous the last time he looked.

His frown softens. Of course, it's just swollen from booze last night, as well as those doner kebabs he mopped it all up with. Besides, it's not so long since he won the accolade of Best-Looking Fat Bloke after James Gandolfini, the actor who played that big time mobster in 'The Sopranos.'

'Still a good-looking fucker, ain't ya?' he winks at himself. His gaze falls to his prick. It's the only time he can see it, looking in this mirror. He gives the shrunken attachment a rub and watches it swell nicely. Everything's in full working order. Perhaps he'll let Lorraine have a taste of it later. Lucky girl.

'Lorraine!' he shouts. 'Put the kettle on, love.'

Terry's wife is downstairs, clearing up after the kids' breakfasts. She ignores the shout and loads some washing into the machine.

'Lousy bastard,' she thinks. Came home at three o'clock in the morning reeking of brandy, tossed his arm over her shoulder and passed out with his snoring snout pressed lovingly to her ear. It took all her strength to squeeze out from under him, and, by the time she'd crawled to the other side of the bed, she was awake and counting the hours until she'd have to get the kids up for school.

Terry vaguely remembers having a nice cuddle with his wife last night. He tries again: 'Lorraine, I need a cup of coffee. Put the kettle on!'

'Bollocks!' a scream sails up the stairs. 'Put it on your fuckin' self!'

Terry shrugs. This sort of attitude was what attracted him to Lorraine in the first place; she stood up for herself and spoke her mind. That, and her slim but curvy figure, which worked like a magnet, drawing him night after night to the Ship Inn where she was a barmaid. He's not so sure he likes her lip now. Still, he knows she'll come round because there's this handbag she wants and it costs a packet. All he has to do is mention money.

He leans over the banisters. 'Come on babe, be a darlin' and put the kettle on! I've got places to go and people to see. Bills gotta get paid, ain't they?

Lorraine switches the kettle on. She's thinking about the gorgeous new bag she's had her eye on. She knows Terry will give her the money today. Better keep him sweet.

Her mum's always telling her how lucky she is to have him. Never mind that her mum doesn't know all the ins and outs of how Terry pays for the nice house in the well-to-do street and the designer clothes for both of them, as well as luxuries such as the top-of-the-range king-sized bed she insisted on getting a few months ago. He's not like Lorraine's old man, who'd piss his wage packet up the wall every week before her mum could say, 'what about the rent, Frank?'

Lorraine pours hot water over coffee granules in his favourite cup, the one that says, 'Best Dad in the World.' And he *is* a good Dad. All those cuddles he gives the kids, and toys and a good giggle. Yeah, he's great with

Justin and Sophie, particularly considering that Sophie ain't strictly his. Still, if only he wasn't quite so... *unpredictable*... when he's drunk. She shudders, stirs four spoonfuls of sugar into his coffee rather than the five he thinks he's getting, and forces herself to think about that handbag again until she feels better.

Terry is satisfied to hear the sound of his cuppa finally getting made. He heaves size forty Armani jeans over massive boxers and sucks in his breath to do up the top button, which he then has to undo again to put on his Gucci loafers. He squeezes his upper portions of flesh into a new Ralph Lauren shirt, sucks in his breath a second time to do up that button, and smoothes some gel through his full head of wavy brown hair.

Looking good, he thinks, checking himself in the mirror one last time before making his way downstairs.

Lorraine is putting his coffee on the table when Terry grabs her from behind in a hug that lifts her off the floor.

'Morning, gorgeous,' he says, giving her a smacking kiss on the cheek. He sets her down with a slap on her rump but doesn't let her go, gives her a nice hard squeeze first.

Lorraine can't help letting out a gasp. It sends a thrill through her, even now, when he does that; some primitive reflex sparked off from being protected by a big, strong mate.

As Terry caresses her long blonde curls with his fingers, she finds herself remembering how he used to make her laugh when he came down the Ship Inn with his mates. No matter how good-looking his friends were, it was always Terry who got her heat up; he was the only one who knew how to tease her just where it felt good. He'd look at her with that penetrating gaze of his and come out with something right off the cuff, something so personal and observant that the blood would rush to her face.

'Oh look, you dropped something,' he says pointing to the floor, and without thinking she bends over to retrieve it and feels his hand shoot like lightning between her legs to give her a squeeze. She squeals, then laughs at herself for falling for his tricks, as usual.

'Terry,' she says tentatively, forgetting for a moment all the zillion things that seem to have gone wrong with their marriage, 'Terry...? Terry! You disgusting fuckin' pig!'

'Sorry, love.' Terry did his best to squeeze back the silent fart. His stomach makes an unpleasant gurgle. He curses the takeaway he bought last night as Lorraine's feet go pounding up the stairs.

'Remind me to never go back to that filthy kebab shop,' he calls after her, pulling a wad of notes out of his back pocket and counting out a pile of scores. For a moment back then, he reflects, she went all soft and pliable in his hands. He could have bent her over the table and she would have taken it like a good girl, if only it hadn't been for his dodgy arsehole. She might have a mouthy attitude on her, Lorraine, but get her on her own and she just loves to be told what to do and slapped about a bit until she does it.

His stomach vibrates dangerously and he hurries to the downstairs loo, leaving the money on the side. The sound of liquid spurting against the toilet bowl in a 360 degree arc drowns out the sound of the hoover being switched on upstairs.

Terry leans his head in his hands. He used to put on a pretty passable headmaster's voice and have Lorraine on her knees, lapping at his balls like a kitten. Sometimes, he'd be a police officer. *Now then, young lady, you're under arrest...* He could have been an actor, he reminisces, if he hadn't been brought up by the kind of family who would have seen it as their duty to hammer the shit out of a promising thespian practising his lines in their living room.

The last pint of fluid crap squirts out of his arse with one final trumpet-like fanfare. He breathes a sigh of relief and reaches towards the toilet roll holder. It's empty. There aren't any newspapers either; wouldn't you just Adam and Eve it!

Trousers round ankles, he leans forward opens the door and shouts, 'Lorraine, there's no toilet roll. Bring some down will ya, babe?'

No answer but the relentless whine of the hoover upstairs, accompanied by several thumps into the furniture.

Maybe she hasn't heard him. 'Lorraine, I need some toilet paper!' he yells.

Lorraine's busy. She thinks she heard Terry shout, but it can wait, he's always on at her for something.

'Fuckin' bollocks! Shit! Fuck! *I need some toilet bollocking paper!*' Terry bellows, infuriated.

She heard him that time all right. All those nasty horrible swear words. 'Get it your fuckin' self, you lazy bastard!' she yells down the stairs.

Terry rubs his brow with both hands. What has he done to deserve this? All he does is pay the bills, work his bollocks off for her and the kids, and for what? So he can sit on a stinking toilet with nothing to wipe his arse on. Surely he gives her enough money to buy enough fucking toilet paper?

'Still, calm down Tel,' he reminds himself. He might have shit all over his arse for now, but once he's cleaned up he should be able to get Lorraine in the mood again for a bit of loving.

'Come on babe, you know I love ya,' he shouts. 'Bring us some paper so I can wipe me arse.'

'Fuck off!' she screams back. 'Call me all those fuckin' names? You no-good wanker!'

Suddenly Terry's had enough of the fiery temper that he once found so attractive. 'That's it! You'll be fuckin' sorry!' he roars.

An image flashes into his mind of the new barmaid down at the Ship Inn. She wouldn't talk to him like that. Glancing up, he spots Lorraine's new white bathrobe hanging on the back of the door. Its fluffy fibres make a soothing wipe for his suffering bum hole. When finished, he tosses the robe into the toilet without bothering to flush. It sinks slowly into the brown slurry.

Grabbing his Armani jacket from the coat in the hall, Terry slicks back his hair and storms out.

'That'll teach ya!' he yells, slamming the door behind him.

It's three o'clock in the afternoon and Terry's starting to feel pleasantly smashed. He's leaning against the bar and has just ordered a second double brandy to spice up his fourth pint.

The barmaid looks extra horny today in her bum-hugging skirt with her boobs spilling over the top of a tight blouse. She's wearing that particular saucy outfit just for him, Terry notices. Wore it for him yesterday, too.

He could do with a little extra something, though. Booze is all very well, but it makes you so… pissed. Luckily he's found out that no matter how sloshed you get, a snort of coke makes you feel all the benefits of being drunk with none of the downsides. Costs a bit, though.

'Bollocks,' he thinks, reminded of the generous wad he left in the kitchen. Lorraine and her fucking handbags. Got a whole cupboard of them; all the ones she's got tired of.

Sometimes he doesn't give her the money. Sometimes, he just goes into her favourite shops without telling her and nicks them. Easier that way. Shopkeepers never seem to connect their empty shelves to the friendly looking tubby bloke who was in a minute ago telling them a joke or two.

Terry takes a gulp from his brandy, then soothes his throat with one long swallow from his pint. Used to astound people he did, with the length of his swallows. Just like tipping it down a drain it was. The froth starts spraying out of his nose now if he ain't careful.

'Sherry, I've lost my wife,' he beams, sliding his empty glass towards the barmaid for a fresh one. 'Can I talk to you?'

'Why's that then?' she laughs, bending down to fetch a packet of crisps. Her arse was designed for a good slapping he observes.

'Because my wife always appears whenever I talk to a pretty girl,' he says, beaming even wider.

The barmaid giggles. 'Don't know how your wife puts up with you!' and goes to serve two old bags at the end of the bar.

Terry doesn't know how his wife puts up with him either. 'Because,' he sings in his rich baritone, 'I believe I can fly; I believe I can touch the sky...'

She laughs again, but he's not sure whether it's at him or at something one of those old bags has come out with.

'... I think about your lovely titties every night and day. Spread my arms and whisk you away,' he croons.

He's always been able to remember a melody, specially the oldies, and verses trip off his tongue like a fuckin' poet's. Could have been a great singer and songwriter too, if his cousins hadn't kicked the shit out of him when they found his secret stash of Donny Osmond lyrics.

He's bought a gram of coke and he's in the toilet, delivering a generous heap up his nose. Went in with his head reeling and the pub playing funny tricks on his vision; came out two minutes later feeling on top of the world. Pub looks nice, too. A moment ago it was all vicious patterned carpet, cheap bar stools with plastic tops and horrible fake mahogany. Now it's all shiny leather stools, sophisticated walnut panelling and flashy fruit machines... could almost be a fucking casino!

He marches across the pub without staggering down the step and hugging the juke box for balance, and is pleasantly surprised to find that he can now scan the lists of song titles without the aid of his finger pressed into the glass. All it takes is for his old favourite, *Puppy Love* by Donny Osmond, to blast through the sound system, and he's forgotten all about Lorraine and the shitty start to his day.

His mates should be here soon. Then he'll be able to have a good laugh. He's got some great new jokes lined up for them.

Terry

Party Animal

There's a party on round at some bird Sarah's house. It's an engagement celebration and Terry and his mates haven't exactly been invited, but Terry's an old friend of Sarah's and anyway, everyone knows he's the guaranteed life and soul of a party. When Sarah sees Terry and his pals trooping into her house, she puts on a face like a smacked arse and scuttles into the kitchen without saying hello. Terry and his friends have brought plenty of booze, so can't see what her problem is.

Some of his mates Terry doesn't know too well. One or two, he doesn't know from Adam. But heck, it's a party, so the more the merrier. Terry follows Sarah into the kitchen, cracking open a lager. 'All right, Sarah me lovely?' he beams, offering her a can. 'Where's your lucky fella then, girl?'

Sarah ignores his can of brew and takes a vicious gulp from her wineglass. 'I don't like you when you're drunk,' she says. 'You and your mates get right loud when you've 'ad a few.'

Terry sways on his feet a little. Did this bird just say she didn't like him? As it happens, she doesn't look too delighted to see him right now, so maybe she did. Come to think of it, that last time he offered to buy her a drink down the Ship, didn't she tell him to piss off? He was only being friendly, and had assured her that he wouldn't have copped a feel inside her empty wonder bra if you'd paid him... Anyway, what's wrong with his mates? They're a lot more fun than the sober-looking lot that were here when he turned up. Ah well, once everyone gets a bit more tanked up, it'll be a hoot.

There's a skinny bloke with sticking-out ears standing next to Sarah with one arm round her shoulders. Terry only notices this insignificant bloke when he says tightly, 'Actually, mate, you wasn't invited to this party.'

Terry frowns, trying hard to focus, until realisation dawns on him. 'Ah, so you're the lucky fella!' he beams, slapping the fiancé on his back and making him spill his beer over his shoes. 'Lovely girl, your missus-to-be...'

On the other hand, the missus-to-be seems to be glaring at him, and what did her boyfriend just say about Terry not being invited...?

Terry frowns again. That jug-eared twat is welcome to the sulky bitch. It won't last long anyway, she's shagged her way round London, he decides. Still, he's got nothing against making a toast to them getting engaged.

'Congratulations to the both of ya!' he announces. And he's had so much to drink that, for a moment, he really means it, and a nostalgic tear wells in his eye as he remembers his own long-ago engagement booze-up. 'Shame about her tits, though,' he adds sympathetically. 'You could always pay for some proper ones.'

The fiancé says nothing, just looks at Terry like he'd like to sink his fist into his gut.

Terry ambles through to the living room, beaming in the congenial manner that makes him such an essential element to any good party. His mates are chatting up the girls. One by one, the females sidle off in the direction of the kitchen. It doesn't take long for his friends to clear the room.

Terry enjoys a bit of female company, but, never mind, he can always win them over later. He notices his mate, Vince, and some fella called Lark sitting on the floor, one behind the other, apparently rowing a boat. That makes sense, thinks his addled mind putting together the fish tank in the corner, a picture of a ship on the wall, and the fact that the carpet is blue. And, last but not least, Lark's name which would suggest that he's always up for having a lark.

Sarah's boyfriend surveys the scene. Slowly his knuckles turn white. It's his house, after all, and standing right next to him is a skinhead with a scar running in haphazard fashion from one ear to the other, flicking ash from his fag onto the new blue carpet.

'Can you go now, please. You weren't invited,' the boyfriend tells him.

Scars swills a mouthful of lager around his mouth and, like a wine connoisseur who has appreciated all its fine bouquets and subtle nuances, squirts it on the floor. The boyfriend, noticing several recent-looking grazes on Scars' knuckles, swallows his fury and confronts the boat-rowers, 'Will you please vacate the party you weren't invited to.'

'Piss off. Can't you see we're going somewhere?' says Lark, 'row, row, row ya boat, gently down the...' he sings, dragging his imaginary oars through the water. Some bloke called Dig comes over to see what's going on.

Terry doesn't know Dig. Must be a friend of Lark's. He knows that he's been named after his celebrated punch – *only one punch needed to get the job done*, goes the legend. So does the boyfriend. Still, it's *his* engagement party, and he has his fiancée's honour to uphold.

'As I was just saying to your friends, you weren't invited so can you please leave?'

Dig is six foot two and built like a bear. When he breathes in, his chest doubles in size, making the boyfriend step backwards. Without saying a word, Dig picks up the boyfriend, takes him through the kitchen and tosses him out the back door into the garden. He locks the door and pockets the key.

Seeing this, Sarah rushes out of the kitchen, glances around at the hell Terry's mates have made of her party, and bursts into tears. She charges up the stairs making a wailing noise.

'What's she got the 'ump for?' Lark wonders aloud.

Terry massages his brow until he recalls two important facts. 'She's getting married. And she's got no tits.'

Lark frowns. Then his face lights up and he heads for the stairs.

Terry's dancing in the living room. He's found a CD that had been hidden at the back of the shelf, and has turned it up nice and loud. Tripping over an empty bottle, he grabs hold of the fish tank to steady himself. Some of the water sloshes out the sides. Terry peers in, fascinated by the pretty colours of the fish as they dart hectically about their disturbed little world.

Scars takes the lid off the tank. 'Been eating prawn crackers, makes me fingers smell like pussy,' he explains to Terry with a wink. 'Wouldn't want to make the birds jealous.'

After giving his hands a good scrub with some underwater foliage, he's surprised to find a large grey fish wriggling about in his fingers. He beckons to Terry, struck by an idea.

The girls in the kitchen scream out loud when Scars walks in with a fish's tail swishing about between his lips. Scars is a bit of a fright to look at in the first place, and to see his cheeks protruding in sudden, frantic bulges, makes him look even less approachable. The girls watch, appalled, while he take a swig of lager and swallows the fish with a dramatic burp. He pulls his mouth open with his fingers and waggles his tongue to complete the display.

A pretty girl wearing skinny jeans looks at him in disgust. 'You're an animal!'

'Why doesn't someone call the police and get these yobbos out of here? Says some other girl with a face-ache. 'And get your hand off my arse, you fuckin' prick!' she yells, whirling round to snarl at a guffawing Terry.

Lark is in Sarah's bedroom. She's wiping tears from her face and he's assuring her that her boyfriend is a muppet but that it's not too late; she could do a lot better for herself and all manner of sweet talk in the hopes of getting into her knickers. Remembering what Terry said about her having no tits, and being the considerate fella that he is, he reckons she must be gagging for a proper shag.

Lark knows he isn't big, but he's wiry and not bad looking with his dark, brooding eyes and permanent smile. He's always got a girl on his arm at any rate.

'Let me do that for you,' he says, leaning over to wipe Sarah's eyes.

'Go away.' She says, swiping his hand away, but with not enough conviction for him to take it seriously.

The doorbell rings and Terry, thinking it might be another of his pals, answers it only to see Sarah's boyfriend standing on the doorstep with a swollen eye and mud all over his trousers.

'I've phoned the police,' says the fiancé. 'You'd better be going.'

'You had better come in then.' Says Terry.

Lark's got Sarah to relax a bit. She's returning his kisses at any rate. She's quite drunk and maybe she thinks it's her fiancé she's got her arms around. Lark has heard all the stories about Sarah and doesn't care if she fancies

74

him or not. He just wants to get his end away, lying her down on her bed while he gives her the ride of her life. She's a bit fidgety, he thinks, as if she can't make up her mind if she wants to go all the way or not. But Lark will convince her. He's kissing her neck and she's responding with moans as she flops down in surrender. Lark pops open her blouse and slides his fingers under the promising lacy bulges of her bra. She's moaning away like she's about to get her rocks of any minute now...

The door bangs open and Sarah's boyfriend comes in, white-face with fury, clenching a knife. Lark, spotting a couple of his trusted mates who leap onto the boyfriend and tackle him to the floor, looks up and says, 'Fuck off you mug. Can't you see I'm doing you a favour?'

Just then, the sound of a siren approaching from the distance gets Lark and his mates hurling themselves out of the door as fast as you like. Lark takes a flying jump down the stairs on tripping over the trousers tangled round his ankles.

'Who wants to go for a curry?' yells Terry. Luckily, he's not so pissed that he hasn't had the foresight to order a couple of taxis. Lark is the last to dive head-first into a cab with his scrawny arse hanging out of his trousers, which makes everyone laugh insanely. The second taxi skids round the corner and out of sight, just as the old bill turn up, too late as usual, to restore law and order.

All in all, Terry and his mates agree, it was a great party.

Terry

Pissing his night away

Terry's a popular fella. He's in a nightclub with about ten of his pals from the party and a few new ones too. Every once in a while, the blue neon lights that sweep randomly around the dance floor remind him of police cars screeching towards him. Other than that, it's blinding. The music isn't quite his style, but the pills are starting to sort that out. The beat pulsates through his body making his belly jiggle as if it's having a dance all on its own.

He grins over at Scars, who's running from one girl to another to impress them with his crazy dance moves. The girls are on the pills too, so they don't let his grisly scars put them off. Lark's also popped a couple of Es, and is having a fond reminiscence about his evening.

'Sexy little slag, that Sarah,' he shouts to Terry above the din. 'Soon as I started kissing her she was coming all over the place. Begging me for it. Bet she's getting un-engaged now.'

'She won't have nothing to do with you,' Terry yells back. But he's on happy pills too so he adds, 'Lucky girl eh, Larky Boy?'

And Lark thumps him on the back with affection and lurches off to buy him a drink.

Terry experiments with a few crazy dance moves of his own. For a moment he wishes Lorraine was here to watch him, like in the old days before the kiddywinks and feels an unsettling dip in his mood. He dances a bit faster till he goes up again.

A bloke wearing a flouncy white shirt approaches him with a friendly smile. 'Got a fag, mate?'

Terry shakes his head, friendly-like. 'Don't smoke, mate.' Out of the corner of his eye, he sees Lark at the bar, pointing at the flouncy shirt with one hand while flopping his other hand about at the wrist.

Flouncy Shirt didn't hear Terry. 'Just want a fag, mate!' he repeats, pointing at a cigarette-shaped bulge in Terry's shirt pocket.

Scars dances over, yells in Terry's ear, 'He fancies you. Wants to suck your knob, Tel!' Then he starts laughing like a speeded-up hyena.

'Just wondered if you had any cigs,' says Flouncy Shirt, miming putting a cigarette in his mouth and inhaling.

Slowly, Terry puts two and two together. Fag? No, I'm not a fag. And what's with the frilly shirt? And why was that bloke pointing to the box of condoms that he's just found on a table while sucking on his finger…?

Suddenly the flouncy shirt is covered in blood and its owner is clutching his nose, trying to stop the cascade that Terry has set off with a lightning head-butt. Flouncy Shirt sinks to the floor squealing. Terry, not wanting to have to hit him again, pours his pint of lager over the bloke's face in an attempt to shut him up and stop drawing attention.

It's not long before a couple of bouncers are dragging Flouncy Shirt across the floor. The bouncers give Terry the nod. They won't bother him because they've all known one another for years.

Terry takes a grateful gulp from the brandy and coke that Lark has just given him. It goes down the wrong way and showers out of his nose, making Lark and a couple of his other mates hoot with laughter. Terry feels like a comedian.

It's a great night, he reckons, prancing about on the dance floor like a man half his age and a third of his weight. A coupla lines of white have gathered up all the loose stands and leaks in his brain, while the pills have cast their magic glow over everything. At this moment in time, all is very, very all right with his world. He doesn't really need the three toffee vodka shots that he tosses back one after the other. The third shot burns a hole right through the bottom of his belly making all the happy feelings drain out. A dangerous rumble sounds from somewhere deep in his guts.

Oops, he thinks. Better sit down in one of those awful, scary crimson booths. The ones which, only a moment ago, had reminded him of velvet chaise longues in some sumptuous French boudoir.

A girl sits down next to him. Looks all right till she smiles, revealing a full upper set of wonky teeth. Still, Terry's a gentleman, and tries to be nice. 'Not now, love, I've 'ad a bit too much to drink.'

The girl can't hear him. She smiles and says something.

Terry doesn't hear what she says, but one of those blue neon lights has just momentarily spot-lit her face, giving him a dentist's-eye view of two sets of cavity-blighted, crooked, mottled brown teeth. Must be some sort of coffee, sugar and speed addict, he thinks.

'Would you like to dance?' she yells over the music, clutching his hand and trying to drag him to his feet. Terry feels his stomach give a lurch.

'I'd piss off if I was you, darling,' he manages to utter just before his chin lands on his chest. His face turns grey and his stomach starts heaving in a way that makes the girl with the dodgy teeth watch in alarm.

Rocketing up through Terry's body comes a volatile concoction of brandy, Chicken Dhansak, two Bindi Bhajis, a few pints of lager and about five poppadoms with lime pickle. It ejects with such ferocity

78

that neither Terry nor the girl have a chance to move. The girl recoils, aghast, as a torrent of puke lands on the table, splattering her clothes and sluicing over the side of the table and onto the floor. She leaps to her feet with a scream. Soon all the girls are pinching their noses and screaming, while their boyfriends dash round, looking for someone to punch.

This time the bouncers don't turn a blind eye. Clubbers are falling over themselves to escape into the fresh air and worse still, Terry looks like he hasn't finished. By dint of pulling and shoving and a couple of swift kicks, they get him outside just in time for a pool of vile-smelling fluid to swill onto the pavement.

Terry wipes his mouth on his sleeve and steadies himself against a lamp-post. After a few minutes, the moon stops orbiting a church spire and comes to rest in a treetop.

'Gotta be quiet. Mustn't wake anyone up...' Terry whispers, putting his finger to his lips. He doesn't want to wake Lorraine and the kids. He couldn't stand having a row with the missus in this drunken state. It's those songs though, those party tunes that play in his drunken brain, never ending and loud. They bombard him, until he can take no more, 'There she was, justa walking down the street...'

Curtains twitch in a couple of bedroom windows. Nosy parkers, thinks Terry, giving his neighbours a big wave.

'Singing, 'doo wa diddy diddy dum diddy doo!' he croons, giving them the full benefit of his baritone. Perhaps they'd like to join in, come on out, have a little street party in this stuck-up bit of East London. Did he just say 'party'...? He's almost sure he went to a party earlier, yes... seems to remember something about a fish swimming round someone's mouth... Doesn't remember anything after that, though. No recollection whatsoever of any broken noses or projectile vomiting.

'Everything's so quiet. It's all so fuckin' quiet!' he chuckles, as if he's never been out at three o'clock in the morning before. He fumbles about with the catch to his gate for a minute or two, before realising it belongs to someone else's house.

'...She looks good... She looks fine... She looks good, she looks fine, then-im-gonna-make-ermine.' Terry loves this song. He starts to dance, jigging his fat body to the beat in his head, then: 'Loraineee, Loraineee, I can't find ya... Loraineee.'

'Then piss off and look somewhere else,' a man's voice thunders from over the road.

Terry's managed to get through his own gate and the neighbours are definitely up for that party, because half of them have their lights on and one of them's on the phone, inviting some mates round by the looks of it.

The front door is open and Lorraine's standing there in her nightie with a bundle of clothes in her arms.

'You bastard!' she screams, throwing shoes, jackets and trousers into the garden. Terry vaguely recognises his Diesel jeans as they land in a shrub, followed by his favourite Ralph Lauren shirt.

'You don't mean it Lorraine, my love,' he smiles just as a sopping wet towel slaps against his head, making him fall down with a thump. He peels it off his face and realises that it's not a wet towel but his wife's once-fluffy white bathrobe and it's covered in his own stinking shit.

Gasping and retching, he salvages his beautiful Ralph Lauren shirt from the shrub to wipe the crap off his face. He can fully sense the shocked grimaces of his neighbours watching through their windows.

'You keep away from me and the kids, you drunken no-good fuckin' toad!' shouts Lorraine.

Terry doesn't like that word 'toad.' It implies smallness. And sliminess.

'Now, now, Lorraine, we will have none of that,' he admonishes in his headmaster voice, the one that used to make her giggle and occasionally also obey him. It's not working now though; not without a bloody long cane to put her in her place.

'You stay the fuck away from me, you RAT!'

Terry tries to get up but stumbles onto all fours. 'Who are you calling a fuckin' RAT, you PIG.'

'You, you repulsive scumbag,' screeches Lorraine. 'Show us your tail, you big stinkin' RAT!'

Normally, Lorraine puts up a big pretence with the neighbours; makes out her hubby's got a legit job and no drinking problem. Of course they know better. But tonight she's not pretending, and Terry's not so out of it that he doesn't wonder, if only dimly, whether wiping his arse on her dressing gown might just be the cause of all this drama.

In the distance comes the sound of sirens. Trust one of his neighbours to call the police. 'PIG – ha ha,' he laughs. 'Oink oink you fuckin' PIG.'

'Now you're for it, you RAT!' shouts Lorraine.

And Terry knows his ears weren't deceiving him. It's the real pigs. Still on all fours, he watches two cozzers get out of their car and tries to wave at them only to lurch onto one elbow. 'Oh look, it's Bob and fuckin' DOB,' he grunts. A police van screeches up the road, siren blaring.

'Now, now, what's going on here then?' says one of the policemen.

'We're having a party,' explains Terry. 'I see you've brought a fuckin' meat van. Just right for all you pigs, you better take my wife with you, she's a fuckin' pig,' and he laughs so hard that his knees give way and he keels chin-first into the lawn.

'I would advise you not to call us names, sir,' says the policeman, and with the aid of his colleague he heaves Terry into a standing position.

'Jesus, he fuckin; stinks,' says the other cozzer letting go.

Terry's vision see-saws as the blood rushes out of his head. All he can see is a blur of blue coming out of the van and through his garden gate. The policemen swear as he slumps to the ground with a thud.

'Leave him alone, he's only drunk!' yells Lorraine starting to look worried. After all, Terry's a good provider so her mum always says.

'You're coming with us,' says one of the policemen.

Terry gets it into his head that he's not going anywhere. With all the logic of a fella who's been out on the razz all day and all night, as well as the night before, he bites down on the policeman's leg and doesn't let go.

'Ow!' screams the policeman. 'Get this fat bastard off me!'

The other policemen get out their truncheons and mayhem breaks loose as they all try to get the stinking lump off their comrade's leg.

'Leave him alone!' screams Lorraine leaping across the garden to try to protect her man. 'He's only playing about!'

It's too late now. Terry's drawn blood and Lorraine knows he's going to get nicked. The neighbours are glued to their windows but she doesn't care, she loves her man to bits and will yank the old bill off by her teeth if she has to. One of the cozzers restrains her with difficulty while the others drag her husband along the path, boots going in wherever they want, and pummel him into the back of the van.

'I'm sorry, Tel,' Lorraine sobs hysterically. 'I'm really, really sorry, babe!'

Terry's voice sails out from the back of the van. 'I love you, babe, I fuckin' love you!'

He doesn't notice two small faces pressed to the window in one of the upstairs rooms. Just as well.

Because he's the best fuckin' dad in the world.

HMP Belmarsh

Cellmate from hell

I'm out of the Block and back on the wing. Still getting a few headaches now and again, but when Northern Bollocks kicked me in the head with that crazed look in his eye, he didn't reckon on my having a nut like a wreaking ball. He got a big surprise when I bounced back up the very next morning, acting like I'd just had an invigorating Indian head massage. Still, I haven't forgotten, and if he tries it again, he won't be laughing like a blocked drainpipe no more.

I've got a cell to myself, not bunk beds but two singles, which makes a change, and a couple of new books. I've just heard that an old mate is on his way in, so things are looking up. Mad Max is his nickname, nothing like that Mel Gibson tosser, but a proper Yardie from Brixton. Not really a close mate, but I've done him a couple of favours on the outside so I'm expecting a few from him on the in. Nice fella, when he's on his upswing; flippery fucker when he's not. I wonder how he got caught.

'Do us a favour, Shaw,' says a screw, making me jump because I'm stuck into my book. It's about some American fella who seems really straight and mows his lawn as soon as the blades of grass reach a height of thirteen millimetres. He's a pillar of the community, always chairing fund-raising events and sponsoring charities, but in actual fact he's a fuckin' psychopath. Got a granny tied up in his basement, one of several he's been tormenting over the years. I'm surprised this book hasn't been confiscated.

I earmark the page and turn to the screw with an aggrieved look, though of course I'm going to do him the favour.

'Dunno guv, what did you have in mind?' The screw is prematurely balding and has a permanently beleaguered expression, as if it's all getting too much for him in here.

'Keep an eye on a new prisoner for me,' says Slaphead. 'He's a bit lonely, know what I mean? He's been talking about topping himself.'

A lonely first-timer, that's all I need, I think, wondering how I might cash in this favour with the screw. 'All right, as long as he's not a bacon, send 'im in,' I flash the screw a warning look. It's common knowledge round here how I feel about rapists and child molesters. Most cons feel the same way; except I particularly can't stand the bastards.

'Nah, he's not one of them,' the screw assures me, he wouldn't be so stupid as to pack a nonce in with me.

I stick my nose back in my book and add, 'But if he winds up dead in the morning, don't blame me. Ha ha, I'm only joking.'

The screw chuckles mirthlessly. 'He'd better not, Shaw, got enough paperwork to do on this prisoner as it is.'

Twenty minutes later a screw yells, 'Time to getcha water!' and again I jump, because I'm absorbed in the alternative universe of my perfectionist psychopath. The arrival of Mad Max has slipped my mind and I've forgotten completely about the con who's going to be sharing my gaff. As soon as I leave my cell, I spot Mad Max with his blankets under one arm and a bloated, funny-looking expression, as if he's just had his wisdom teeth taken out, his cheeks all bloated and fat.

'All right, mate, good to see ya!' I yell going over to give him a welcoming slap on the back, remembering that first night in prison can make anyone want to top himself. He gives me a funny smile and mumbles something, and I drag him over to a quiet corner and hold out my hand. He spits two foil-wrapped stones into my palm, making me laugh. Just like old times.

'Stick the rest in here,' I say, glancing round and swiping an empty crisp packet off a table. Gratefully, he empties his stash in the packet, rolls it up, and inserts it up his sleeve. No time to have a natter 'cause it's three minutes to bang-up and everyone's running around getting their hot water and stuff for the night.

Racing about like a maniac, I manage to get the bits we need: a Bic pen, a plastic bottle, a coke can, some blue tack and a scrap of foil, and Max is grateful enough to offer to sort me out again tomorrow.

The adventures of my lawn-manicuring, granny-raping psychopath have flown clean out of my head. I'm so keen to get going on my rocks that, on returning to my cell, I'm startled to see a bloke with doleful eyes and a stubbly chin sitting on my bed. He shudders when I slam the door.

'That's my bed, mate. Yours is over there,' I say, pointing to the bare mattress a few feet away. I stash my crack under my pillow to use once the screws have done their headcount. 'Should have thought that was obvious,' I add, under my breath as he gathers up his bed pack and shuffles over to sit on the other bed.

'This place is a dump,' he says, glancing around the cell.

'Yeah, well don't worry; the screws will be round later to tidy up,' I lie. I sit down and pick up my book. 'You ok, mate?'

'No, not really.'

'Well, go to sleep and forget about it,' I shrug, opening my book and blocking out his miserable face. When I'm feeling low, I appreciate it if everyone around me keeps quiet and respectful. No emotional stuff. Just let me come round in my own time.

Not this bollocks, though. 'Me missus sent me a 'Dear John' letter,' he mumbles.

'What's that?' I wasn't expecting to hear from him again so soon. 'Your name's John?'

'No, it's Don,' he says. 'What's yours?'

After a long pause, while I re-read my last paragraph, I growl, 'Harry... With an aitch.'

'Oh, yeah, 'arry. They said you was really friendly, the screws. Said you was the one to talk to, not like the rest of them bastards.'

My eyes widen but I say nothing, gazing intently at my book.

'I just spoke to her on the phone,' he continues in his gloomy voice. 'She wants to end it with me. Says she's not going to wait for me to do my sentence, she's got her own life to lead and I shouldn't 'a been so stupid trying to make money the easy way, when other people have proper jobs earning thirty, forty grand a year, and take their kids on 'oliday...'

'Oh yeah, got kids have ya?' I curse myself for opening my mouth; just that I've had kids on my mind lately, wondering how Tom's coming along and whether he can say 'Daddy' yet. Not that he'll need to use that word for a while.

'Nah,' sighs Don. 'We tried for years but Susie can't get preggers, says I must have a low sperm count or something.'

I wish the fucking screws would hurry up with their checks.

'I think that's why she's dumping me. She always wanted to have kids. Just before I got nicked, I saw her leafing through a baby magazine,' groans Don. 'Seven years we was together, like in that film with Marilyn Monroe, 'The Seven Year Itch.' She got itchy, I s'pose, got bored looking after the house and that.'

'Yeah?' I mutter, not really listening. I'm itching to get my crack out.

'Oh God I miss her. I miss her so much.'

I read the same paragraph all over again.

'What would you do, 'arry, if you was me?'

I can see the pleading look in his eyes out of the corner of mine. I don't want him committing suicide in my cell.

'She ain't fuckin' worth it, mate,' I sigh, trying to offer a bit of friendly advice. 'How long did you say you was in for?'

'Three months.' A tear splashes out of his eye. 'I can't live without her.'

'Three months and she can't wait?' I say, feeling suddenly angry. This div's only got a poxy three month sentence, a shit and a shave! So what the fuck's he crying for? 'You're better off without her,' I tell him, cursing the spam-headed screw who banged me up with this prick. I'm not a Samaritan and I can't get my mind off the crack under my pillow.

'I can't live without her,' he groans, again.

'You'd better get used to it.'

There's something about this bloke that's starting to really piss me off. I've come across it before. It's something about the way I'm getting tired just listening to him, as if he's lying over there with a long syringe and is slowly sucking the life-force out of me.

Eventually, after Don has bored me half to death with his tale of woe, the screws do their round and I reach under my pillow in relief. Don watches morosely, while I half fill the bottle with water, insert the Bic case into the side of it and plug it up with the blue tack.

'Want some?' I ask, hoping that he doesn't. For one insane moment I thought it might cheer him up.

'Yes please, mate,' he says straightening up. I put some foil on the mouth of the bottle, poke holes into it and sprinkle ash on top, cursing that shiny-headed screw even more.

'Well, go easy on it,' I grunt, setting light to half of the first stone. I suck deeply, bringing the bitter smoke deep into my lungs, before releasing it, along with all my problems, into the air.

My cellmate's banging on in the background but I don't hear. I've gone to Nowhere Land. It's funny how it's nothing at all really but seems like heaven. No golden gates, no angels, no big-breasted blondes giving away twenty-four-hour-blowjobs. No problems, no pain, no worries, no needs. It catches me with a delightful surprise every time as if I've never been here before. It's never enough though, and as soon as I come down, I want more. Then I'm chasing the first one, trying achieve oblivion but never being able to get there again. It smiles at me just out of reach.

I come down with a crash. All my nerve endings are tingling. I'm intensely aware of every sight, smell, sensation.

'So when are the screws coming round to clean this cell?' my cellmate is asking.

I let out a strangled curse.

'Well, anyway,' he sniffs, continuing his monologue, 'about six months ago, it was, the wife started buying all these new shoes... pink stilettos, shiny black boots with silver heels... open-toed silky red things with ribbons that wound round and round her ankles... She never wore them with me.

Used to get all dolled up to go out with her girlfriends, but when I took her out for a curry she wore her trainers.'

I'm so pranged out that I can hear every nuance of his nasal, whinging voice. I can almost see the wisps of energy leaving my body against their will and being sucked into the vacuum of his miserable aura. I knew it wasn't a good idea to smoke crack without anything to bring me down, but this is horrendous. I lie back on my bed with my eyes squeezed shut, trying to relax.

'Have some,' I croak, longing for him to shut up.

For several minutes every creak of the bed, every self-pitying sniff, and all his cack-handed fumbling about with the pipe and lighter make me want to scream.

At last everything goes blessedly silent.

Then he starts up again.

'Christ, I miss her, 'arry. You don't know what you've got till you come in 'ere, do ya?' I should'a treated her better while I 'ad the chance.'

I stare at him, gob-smacked. Did he just smoke half a stone?' He should be coming down right about now! I peer at the table and see the half rock still sitting there. So he hasn't smoked it... Then what was all that faffing about for...? Gradually it dawns on me that Don didn't smoke the half rock because he went instead for the whole rock, that I'd stupidly left lying on the table. Now I want to kill him.

First, however, this comedown is so awful I need another go. I know I'll just come plummeting down again but maybe, just maybe, it won't be quite this bad.

'You fuckin' cunt,' I say, grabbing the pipe. 'I told you to go easy on it.'

He stares at me innocently.

'This bit was for you,' I say, holding up the tiny bit of crack, which had been the smaller of the two rocks to begin with.

His face crumples, like a kid that's about to start crying. 'Oh Christ, I'm sorry, mate,' he gasps, 'I didn't realise. I thought you was offering me the other one and I would never 'ave...'

'Just shut up,' I groan, inhaling on the fumes and soaring away from him and Belmarsh and this whole poxy world for a few magical moments. Then I'm soaring all the way back again. A miserable bearded bloke with scraggy hair swims into focus. Oh fuck, it's him again. The crash is upon me. Empty thoughts are clashing around my head and I just have to grit my teeth and keep still for a while.

Then, from somewhere outside all this madness comes a sane, logical thought. I clutch my head to try to stop it whirling.

'You said your wife started buying sexy shoes about six months ago?'

Don nods, 'yeah, spent a small fortune on all sorts. Pink stilettos...'

'And did you always know where she was when she went out with her mates?'

'Yeah, they always went down the Crown and Anchor or the Jolly Roger. But, come to think of it, if I went to the Anchor, then she's 'ave been down the Crown all night. And if I went to the Crown, she'd 'ave been down the...'

'Did you never ask the landlords if they'd seen her?'

'No.'

'All right then, brain-ache,' I sigh, shutting my eyes to stop the harsh angles of our cell hurting my throbbing brain.

'Did you ever come home early when you were supposed to be out for the night and find anyone there?'

'Well, only me mate, Tony. But he'd be there waiting for me.'

Fuckin' hell, this moron should have been thrown in jail for sheer stupidity. 'How many times did you catch this Tony round yours?'

'He came round quite a lot,' frowns Don. 'What d'ya mean, catch 'im? He used to fix the boiler 'cause it kept breaking down.'

'Boiler kept breaking down, eh?' No wonder she dumped him. 'Is he a plumber then?'

'No, he's foreman at a ball-bearing factory, earns thirty to forty grand a year.'

'Thirty to forty grand, hmm. And does he take his kids on holiday every year?'

'Er, yeah, think so. How did you know that?'

'Listen, brain-dead,' I say, changing tack, 'did you notice anything different about your wife before you got nicked? She had any strange pains or weird food cravings or anything? Let me think… How about her tits?'

'Oh, 'arry, you've never seen such a lovely pair! Susie always said they was her best feature. Come to think of it, she did mention that they hurt a couple of times. Complained they was swollen. I told her she had nothing to complain about, ha ha.'

I sit up, holding my head till it stops orbiting. For a moment I feel so triumphant that the pranging completely stops. 'Your wife's up the duff and Tony's the father!'

Don stares at me, dumbfounded. Gradually his face clouds over. He's going through his memory, recalling details, checking facts, until he's wearing a deep, brooding scowl. He knows I'm right. Burying his head in his hands, he lets out a deep sigh from some very dark place inside him.

'Told you she wasn't worth it,' I say cheerfully. 'Now just forget about her and get on with your life.' I pick up my book and try to read from where I left off, but, another side-effect of my come-down, the words seem to trickle off the page and wander along the walls. Don makes a trembling lump under his blanket. He's trying to keep it down, but I can hear every sniffle and sob as if he's doing it deliberately right into my ear.

'Don, for fuck sake, will you be quiet?'

The sniffling stops but the sobbing and shuddering continue. After wife-beaters and kiddie molesters, there's no one I hate more than a fella who can't keep a fuckin' lid on it. After five minutes, I'm about to blow a fuse. On and on he goes. Every so often he moans, 'I have no life without her!'

'Shut the fuck up!' I shout.

'I want to die,' he cries, and now I'm so fuckin' mad I grab my yellow Bic razor and throw it at him. It bounces off his back and clatters to the floor.

'Here you are, you fuckin' prick, do it then!' I growl. 'Just give me some fuckin' peace or I'll 'ave a go at it myself.

At last the shaking subsides and silence ensues.

I lie in my bed, staring at the shadows on the ceiling for two, maybe three hours, until at some blessed moment I'm released into unconsciousness.

Suddenly, I'm wide-awake and my chest is pounding.

There's a sound of footsteps hurrying towards my cell. The door bangs open and a shaft of light spills across the walls. The first thing I notice is that the yellow Bic razor is no longer on the floor. The next thing I see is a puddle of blood seeping out from the toilet cubicle.

Oh great! I sigh to myself watching Don being carried out on a stretcher. Well, at least I'll get some peace and fuckin' quiet.

Next day I'm back down the Block, getting a whole lot more peace and quiet than I bargained for. Turns out, Misery Guts made a complete hash of topping himself and blamed me for making him do it. Now the hairless screw-fuck that I was doing the favour for has got a shit-load of paperwork on his hands and no sense of humour, and when he remembered that quip I made about not blaming me if the prisoner wound up dead in the morning, he put two and two together and made me the bloody scapegoat.

Being in prison for years, and caring about no one and nothing except your next hit of smack, you tend to grow a bit emotionally distant. Over time, my heart fossilized into something about as warm and genuine as one of them tacky red symbols on a Valentine card. On the RAPt programme, we had to learn to reverse all that and start feeling again. The first time I realised that I still had a heart that actually gave a fuck about somebody other than me, was when I met Freddie.

Freddie

Searching for peace

Matted, curly hair rolls down past Freddie's shoulders, almost hiding the yellow-tinged face hovering over his smouldering rock. He sucks the acrid fumes through the pipe, holds them in until he starts to splutter, then lets them go. Greyish-blue plumes spiral upwards, obliterating the nicotine-stained ceiling along with the rest of the dilapidated flat. Freddie's no longer in it. He's somewhere high above the clouds with their grey rain that seem to piss deliberately on this East End council estate.

This is a well-run crack house. Apart from the dealer, who's a shifty-eyed black geezer with shoulders three times thicker than Freddie's, there's two muscle-heads guarding the door day and night, and, outside, a kid on a bicycle on the look-out for unwanted visitors.

Neither the dealer nor the heavies on the door have any idea of the real size of the operation. The fella in charge has a dozen dens in blocks of flats all over East London. He spends nothing on décor, ambience, furniture, cleaning… and since he's known in local parlance as 'the Killer,' he gets no shit from his workers and makes a killing in profit.

Freddie's got his eyes fixed on the ceiling, allowing nothing to come between him and his little bit of heaven. He'll have to leave the golden gates behind in a moment and go tumbling through the layers of fog back to reality, but it's worth it. Just to experience that moment of exhilarating, almost unbearable beauty – who could turn that down, when you know damn well that's how reality is *supposed* to be? As if all the pain and fear and disaster that ever happened to you could fall away in an instant, and what's left is how your life would have been if none of that had every happened.

All of a sudden, his eyes are like saucers. Every nerve ending has become unbearably sensitive. He can hear every breath, sigh and fidget of everyone in the vicinity. An obsessive idea that he might have dropped a bit of rock begins to gnaw at his mind and he finds himself hunched over his seat, raking his fingers over the ripped velour.

Fortunately, he's got a buffer between heaven and hell ready to go in a syringe, although he could only afford a bit and it won't last long. Eventually he finds a vein that still works and the heroin seeps soothingly into his bloodstream.

In a pleasant state of semi-delirium, Freddie hears a knock at the door. He glances along the hallway to see one of the shaved-headed doorkeepers peer through the spy-hole and draw back the bolt. A blonde girl comes in and the doorkeeper gives her a slap on the arse, making her swerve on her spiky heels.

'Leave it out. It's me tea break,' she snaps.

Through glazed eyes, Freddie notices that her face is bruised in several places and there's no earring in one ear, only a bloodied slit. Underneath her trashy outfit she's got a good figure and could be a looker. Not that he's interested.

The blonde girl nods at him with recognition, no point in either of them saying hello. She scores a stone for twenty quid and sits down, huddling over the rubbish-strewn coffee table to break her rock in two. She places half on top of the gauze-covered mouth of a bottle and lights a match. The stone melts to a clear liquid and evaporates into smoke, which she inhales from a straw inserted into the centre of the bottle. Seconds later she's gone to some enchanted land where everything seems to have been conjured specially for her.

Freddie stares at her without seeing, the needle still dangling from his thigh. The dealer turns up his pod and taps his feet, his glassy eyes seeing nothing, roaming the walls as if he were anywhere but in this dump.

Another knock at the door. One of the doorkeepers peers through the spy-hole and says, 'Black fella. Don't know 'im.'

The other doorkeeper takes a look. 'He's called Fire, evil piece of shit, so I've heard.'

He draws back the bolt. Rapists, murderers, scum of the earth... so long as they can pay for the goods, this is the most welcoming place in all London.

Fire strolls in, half swagger, half casual limp, and a leer that says he's afraid of no one, certainly not the pussies on the door. He glances around with black eyes dead as coal, then approaches the dealer and mutters a few words in his ear. Glancing up at the evil-looking incomer, the dealer pulls a bag out of his pocket and hands over a stone.

Fire strolls over to Blondie and swipes the pipe out of her hand. She barely registers him as he sits opposite her and sets about his business.

Freddie's glad his family can't see him. Anyone who knows Freddie's vast clan of violent-nutter relatives, and everyone around here does, would never dream of so much as hooting at Freddie to get out of their way.

His two older brothers have tried getting him back on the straight and narrow, or rather the crooked and narrow, but Freddie doesn't want to know about normal life. For him, everyday reality is for people who might as well be an alien race, who have two-point-four kids and get up at the same time each day.

The most Freddie hopes for is to be able to escape out of this world from time to time, with its puke-stained armchairs and the ripped poster of tupac that makes no attempt to cover a disturbing gash on the wall. It's what makes him drag his skinny frame up the piss-soaked stairs day after day, and what will make him trudge down them in an hour or so, while he can still use his wits to make enough readies for his next ticket back to heaven.

Matt and Ritchie are driving around the streets of Bethnal Green in their white van. Unless they're together, it's difficult to distinguish which is Matt and which Ritchie. They're both six foot and muscular with close-cropped hair, just good-looking enough to have the birds fighting over them. They're pretty straightforward: into football, sex and violence, in that order, so when there's no footy and their girls are on the rag, they can amuse themselves by watching a bit of bare-knuckle fighting down at the old industrial site.

Their mum's out of her wits. Last time she saw Freddie, his lovely chestnut curls were all matted, and he'd flinched as if she'd crushed his ribs when she'd tried to give him a cuddle. Freddie's always been her favourite, even though he's an oddball. People always thought he was shifty, the way he would never look them in the eye properly. As a kid, he was always rescuing abandoned cats and dogs and showing them an affection that made his mum jealous.

One day his mum read an article in a magazine, realised he'd got some syndrome called 'Asperger's', and it all made sense after that. It was such a relief, being able to put together all those baffling clues, such as his lack of social skills and unexpected strokes of genius. Like, when he was six years old and his dad was 'Away,' and his older brothers had nicked a van to take them all to Margate for the day, but didn't know the fuck how to get out of London. Three times they took the wrong turning and got stuck in the same alley, until Freddie piped up, 'You should have turned left at Park Street, then gone straight ahead at the lights and under the flyover.' Turned out he's memorised the whole 'A to Z' and hadn't bothered to tell anyone. From then on, as long as Freddie was with them, the family could go anywhere in Greater London without getting lost, apart from Westminster and Bow, 'cause those pages had been ripped out.

Anyway, mum wants him back and since dad's away again, it's mum's word that's law.

Matt and Ritchie have been tipped off where to go, but for twenty minutes they've been driving round in circles. Where's Freddie when they need him? Exasperated, Ritchie winds down his window and waves to a black teenager shuffling casually down the road.

'Any idea where Burgess Heights is, mate?' he yells.

The teenager strolls on not taking any notice, lost in music coming from his pod.

Ritchie winds up his window, fuming. 'Stupid wanker!'

'You're the stupid wanker,' snaps his brother, recognising the same burned-out chip shop for the third time in ten minutes.

'Wasn't talking to you, wank-stain,' says Ritchie.

Matt slows down at the lights. 'Oh? Thought you was calling me stupid,' he frowns.

Ritchie breaks into a grin. 'Come to think of it, you are stupid. You'd get lost in a fucking car park.'

'Who are you calling stupid, you wanker?' says Matt. 'You couldn't follow directions up your own arsehole.' He breaks into a grin. 'There it is, you moron, I said I knew where we was going.'

Ritchie peers incredulously through the window to see a sign reading 'BUG SHITS.' 'Fuck me,' he says, mentally filling in the missing letters that some smart-arse has whitened-out, 'we must have driven past that sign ten times.'

'Three, you fucker,' says Matt feeling pleased with himself. He only spotted the 'Burgess Heights' sign because he happened to toss his fag out the window at the right moment.

Fire is coming down from his rock and needs to take his mind off the pranging. He's not stupid enough to get addicted to the brown stuff like the curly-headed white boy with the poisoned yellow eyes in the armchair.

He watches Blondie place the remainder of her stone on the gauze and light a match. He notices that, when she inhales, her cheeks cave in just as if she's sucking dick. He thinks about inserting his penis in her mouth, way down, further than she can take it. He thinks about sticking it in a bit further. And further still. His cock stiffens. He loves it when they start choking. Ships it out quick though before they puke. He watches her lean back with a euphoric smile, far away in her own world.

She's only seventeen or eighteen, looks so innocent with her head lolling on the back of the couch and her knees splayed open. He can see the bulge of her breast beneath her sparkly top as well as a series of purple finger marks, which turns him on even more.

He waits for her high to wear off before making his move. Sitting next to her, he plants one hand on her leg. Wouldn't want to distract her from her ten quid's' worth of paradise.

'Come in de bedroom wid me.'

Blondie swivels her head towards him and with a well-practised eye, assesses the size of the prick clearly visible under his jeans. 'It'll cost ya. Twenty.'

Normally, it's ten for a blowjob, twenty for a shag and forty for the works, but she's always underselling herself. Every time she gets one of those huge cocks in her mouth her jaw starts to ache, and after a while it goes into spasm, and trust her luck to get some bastard who thinks it's cool to hold back his spunk. She looks at his face, recognises something in his eyes, and shudders.

'I heard you was called Fire,' she says warily. 'Why's that, then?'

'Just you wait and see, baby,' he says, squeezing her thigh, 'I got me a real fiery reputation.'

Blondie wishes she hadn't asked. 'Get me a stone and I'll give you a blowjob,' she says, a little uneasily. To be honest, she'd rather go for the shag because her cunt is immune to cock, no matter how big nor hard nor how long they go at it, just so long as the punter doesn't fold her in two and jab it in right to the hilt. She's only seventeen but her fanny feels nothing, stopped feeling years ago when it was still tight and dry and surprised to have anything pushed in it.

'Come wid me,' says Fire, tightening his grip on her leg.

'Money first,' says Blondie glancing anxiously to the dealer and then to Freddie slumped in his armchair. No help from either direction. She leaps up and makes a dash for the door only to feel a stinging slap across her face that knocks her against the wall.

Her cheek swells up nice and red, Fire notices.

'See that, baby, I move like greased lightning,' he says, grabbing her by the arm and dragging her across the room. He kicks open a door leading into a filth-ridden kitchen, then tries another door. A grey-faced junkie with a

101

large festering sore on his arm has passed out on a piss-stained mattress.

Blondie makes one last-ditch effort to escape by grabbing the doorframe with both hands and crying out to the dealer, who shakes his head; nothing to do with him. Freddie rocks back and forth on his chair, eyes squeezed shut.

Fire gives Blondie's hair a yank till she trots after him with a squeal. He's going to have his way with her now; never mind the comatose junkie or the less than romantic surroundings or even the diseases sure to be lurking in Blondie's juicy little cunt. He needs to take his mind of his descent.

'Burgess *Heights?* Fuck me, no wonder they call it the shits,' says Matt driving into a decaying labyrinth of concrete and graffiti.

'Whooaa, slow down,' says Ritchie, spotting a kid of about fourteen patrolling the courtyard on a brand new bicycle. Matt pulls into the kerb and they go to the back of the van and take out a ladder and several tins of paint. They're both wearing paint-splattered T-shirts and jeans, so when the kid takes no particular interest, they return to the back of the van for their baseball bats.

Seconds fly as they wait for him to pedal by. They make a lunge for him, Ritchie grabbing the kid in a headlock with a hand clamped over his mouth and Matt jamming his bat under his chin.

'One squeak and your tongue will be tasting your own brains,' he warns.

The bike crashes to the ground, wheels spinning. Matt hurls the kid into the back of the van and locks it. An old woman walks past. Ritchie beams, stepping out of her path like a gentleman.

'I didn't see nuffing,' she mutters, shaking her head. 'Nuffing, nuffing, nuffing.'

'That's right, you 'ave a nice day, darling,' says Matt.

Now their adrenaline is pumping. They run past the fallen bike, into the lobby of the block of flats behind it and charge up the steps two, sometimes three at a time. Reaching the third floor, they get their breath back to scan the door numbers. A dirty-looking fella in white Reeboks is walking away from them in the direction of the door that they want.

Ritchie holds Matt back with a discreet nod. They wait until the crackhead has knocked on the door, then raising their bats, speed silently after him.

Blondie is on the bare mattress next to the grey-faced junkie. Her sparkly top has been ripped down the middle to expose her bruised breasts and her face aches from the extra couple of smacks Fire's given her to keep quiet. She's not expecting any sudden heroics from the junkie; he hasn't so much as twitched in the last five minutes.

Fire is leering at her, teeth white against black lips. He's taking out the massive prick she's been dreading. Slowly he runs one finger along its length then all the way back again, as if he's waiting for her to start clapping. Disgusted, she reaches down to remove her g-string. Doesn't want him destroying that too. She glares at him, silently pleading: *Come on you bastard, get it over with!*

Fire breaks into a broad grin. He lowers his jeans and kneels on the mattress next to the living corpse; no point shoving him off the bed and waking him up. With one hand he grabs Blondie's ankles and hoists them over her head. She's impressed by the size of his tool, he can tell. He prods it several times against her fanny till it slides in, nice and tight.

'Oh no, you bastard, not like that!' sobs Blondie, her knees thumping against her shoulders while his penis stabs repeatedly against her cervix. 'Please, not like that!'

'You want me, baby,' croons Fire. 'Oh yeah, baby you want me.'

She can't move in this position; could scratch him with her fingernails, but what would be the fucking use? Nothing she can do but experience that searing pain, over and over again.

Freddie's rocking in his chair, faster and faster, holding back tears, trying to block out the sounds coming from behind the door.

His eyes glow a sickly shade of yellow. He can almost feel the poison in them. Hep B. He's had it for a while, but he's heard that if it doesn't kill you in the first month, you're safe. He reckons he's survived, though he feels like the living dead. Maybe he really *is* dead and this is all some kind of purgatory, or an ongoing nightmare, that one day he might wake up from.

White Reeboks hears footsteps, glances round. Too late, Matt's bat smashes down on his head and white Reeboks turn red as blood splatters down from the wound.

The doormen try to slam the door but they're not fast enough. Matt hurls himself against it, stamping on Reeboks' body as it slumps to the floor. All his senses are alert, and he's getting the incomparable thrill that comes from spilling blood. He rams his weight against the door, squashing one of the doorkeepers between it and the wall. Ritchie hits the other doorkeeper so hard over the head that the clunk reverberates along the corridor. Walls are decorated crimson as the doorkeeper slumps to the floor with a groan.

Matt yanks the door towards him, then slams it once more into the body behind it. Matt reaches round and grabs him by the collar. The doorkeeper's nose is broken but he's a fighter, starts swinging at Matt with both fists. Fair game, thinks Matt, drawing back his bat and smashing it at full tilt into the man's shoulder. At the same time, one of the doorkeeper's punches connects with Matt's chin, incensing him all the more.

Suddenly Matt can feel nothing but rage. As if all life's problems can be blamed on this one doorkeeper, he pounds him again and again with his bat, swinging it back and forth, up and down, enjoying the noise it makes as it connects with flesh and bone. The doorkeeper goes down on top of his mate. 'Calm down, Matt,' urges Ritchie, spotting a yellow-faced figure rocking back and forth in an armchair. 'It's all right Freddie, we've come to get ya!'

'Fuck off!' Freddie screams at them. 'Leave me alone and fuck off!'

'There's appreciation for you,' says Matt, slamming his bat into a wall and glancing around for another victim.

'You might wanna look in there,' Freddie mumbles, pointing to the bedroom.

Fire is listening anxiously behind the door. It might be the Filth out there and he can't afford to get sent down the shovel again. Sooner or later some con finds out you enjoy a nice rape and then you're prime target for any grudge going. He looks at Blondie and runs a finger across his throat. She nods, holding back tears.

On a count of three, Matt and Ritchie rush at the door, hitting it so hard that it comes off its hinges. The force sends Fire sprawling across the floor with the door thudding down on top of him. The junkie on the mattress comes to, wonders what the fuck is going on and hurriedly passes out again.

105

Matt and Ritchie notice the girl on the bed. She's hugging her knees, shaking and hiccupping with fear, her clothes in tatters and her skinny thighs covered in fresh bruises. The sight awakens in them some noble urge, like shining knights of old, giving them free reign to wreak vengeance.

'It's your time to get fucked now, you dirty cunt!' says Matt, heaving the door off the black fella.

'Do you wanna try a blowjob first, or take it straight up your hole?' asks Ritchie giving the fake Yardie a kick in the crotch before he can make any moves.

'What? You're not putting my bat anywhere near his stinking arse,' frowns Matt.

'Blowjob it is then,' Ritchie decides, placing the stubby end of his bat over Fire's tightly-clenched mouth. 'Open wide and it won't hurt.'

'Much,' chuckles Matt.

The black fella ain't opening up, even though his balls have been crushed and he's dying to let out a howl. With a bit of persuasion from Ritchie, smashing his kneecap, his mouth flies open. Ritchie tries to fit his bat in but it's too big, and time's running out. No matter; Matt hammers his bat against Ritchie's handle, smashing Fire's teeth till it slides in, nice and tight. Ritchie's bat is embedded deep in Fire's throat, rendering him unconscious.

The old bill are bound to be here any minute, what with all the yelling and thumping going on, but the brothers can't go without grabbing hold of the dealer, who's shitting himself in the kitchen. They empty his pockets and make him swallow a handful of crack, then drag the choking bastard out onto the balcony, where they hang him upside down by his knees from the railings. They leave him dangling like that, squealing for help.

'Where's Freddie?' Ritchie asks suddenly.

'He's done a runner, the slippery little bugger!' says Matt and they're off, hurdling over the groaning bodies at the door and tearing along passageways and down stairs.

Poor Freddie with his Hep B and useless muscles has almost made it to freedom when he finds himself being picked up and slung into the back of a van, along with a couple of bloodied baseball bats and a pissed-off looking black kid. The kid dives out of the van running, only to trail to a halt when he sees that his brand new bike has vanished.

'Can't trust anyone these days, can ya?' Matt laughs at him.

'Hang on there, mate!' Ritchie shouts with a wave to the dealer dangling from a balcony three floors up. The van screeches away in the opposite direction to the route taken by the police fifteen seconds later.

Freddie

Funky chicken

The van pulls up in another run-down council estate between a beaten-up banger and a flash BMW. Same decaying concrete, slightly better graffiti. Matt pulls his bloodied T-shirt over his head and digs out two clean ones from the glove compartment, tossing one to his brother.

'We did a good thing back there, giving the girl that money,' says Matt, getting a lump in his throat.

'Yeah. P'raps she'll use the money wisely.' Says Ritchie, changing shirts. 'Put a deposit on a flat, get clean... buy a few decent meals and some clothes...'

Blondie's eyes had lit up when they gave her the dosh they collected from the dealer. Watching her rapist get a blowjob must have been the most gratifying experience of her life, and that pile of crumpled notes would have been the icing on the cake. It wouldn't have taken her long to calculate how many rocks she would be able to buy.

'Yeah, *right,*' laughs Matt, seeing the reality of the situation. 'Still, it was a nice thought whilst it lasted.'

Ritchie carries Freddie in a fireman's lift up four flights of stairs. He and Matt decided against the one functioning lift because it had a dead dog in it and they didn't want to upset Freddie any more than he was already.

'Tenth floor, did you say?' Ritchie asks, gasping for breath.

'Nah, this is the right floor, weedy,' says Matt, pulling a bunch of keys out of his pocket. Ritchie sets his brother down to catch his breath. Freddie staggers into a wall and slides against it until he's sitting on the floor with foam coming out of his mouth.

Matt leans down to peel open one of Freddie's eyelids. 'You all right, bruv? You look like shit.'

Freddie scowls at him.

'Don't worry, kid, we've got you now.'

'That's exactly what I'm fucking worried about,' Freddie mutters.

His brothers hoist him to his feet and they half-shove, half-drag him along the corridor until reaching a door painted bright yellow.

'Fuckin' 'ell,' laughs Ritchie, 'the door's almost as yellow as Freddie.'

Matt sets about opening the locks. 'Must have that junkie's disease, Hippotitus,' he says

'What, the door?'

'No, Freddie, you div.'

'I'm dying here. I need a hit,' wails Freddie slumping between them.

'You dirty little bastard, that's how you caught it in the first place, ain't it?' shouts Matt, finally getting the door open.

'Caught what?' Freddie sobs.

'Hippotitus, you dirty slag.'

'I think you mean hepatitis, you dyslexic twat,' corrects Ritchie.

'I'm not joking. I'll die if I don't get a hit,' Freddie chokes.

'Hippotitus, hepatits, bollockatitus... it's all the same,' mutters Matt shoving his brother through the door. 'You're a filthy junky, letting our family name down.'

Matt borrowed the flat from a mate and his brother hasn't seen it until now. Ritchie checks it out while Freddie collapses on the floor, holding his knees and rocking. There's no furniture, just a breakfast bar with three stools screwed to the floor, as well as a rug and four pictures with smashed glass hanging at wonky angles on the wall. They look like they've been used for target practice.

Ritchie peers out the window into the gathering darkness to see a rubbish-strewn courtyard dangerously far below. 'Perfect. There's no way you can get out!'

'And don't bother screaming,' advises Matt. 'Hardly anyone lives in these flats so no one will hear ya.'

He takes a pair of handcuffs from his pocket, clamps one cuff tight around Freddie's wrist, then drags him over to the breakfast bar and clamps the other half round the leg of a stool. 'Hope you don't mind, sicko. I borrowed these from your girlfriend,' he laughs at Ritchie.

Freddie's in too much pain to protest. He's got the shivers and he's started to sneeze. He only did a tiny bit of brown in the crack house, and it's already wearing off. Not totally unsympathetic, his brothers haul a rug across the floor for him to lie on. It smells so strongly of decomposing takeaways that Freddie wishes they hadn't.

Matt and Ritchie stand at the door, surveying the scene with satisfaction. 'This time it'll work,' says Matt.

'Last time we was too nice,' says Ritchie.

'Gave you a nice comfy bed and a bottle of water and even some porn to take your mind off things.' None of that this time, though, because Freddie legged it at the first opportunity.

'Be good and I'll bring you back some metronome,' says Matt.

'Metro-what?' asks Ritchie, suspicious of his brother's diagnosis.

'Stops 'em from clucking,' Matt says authoritatively. 'The Germans invented it.'

'Clucking? Is he a fucking chicken?' Frowns Ritchie.

'Metronome helps with withdrawals,' explains Matt.

'You mean Methadone,' Freddie screams. 'A metronome is a ticking pendulum.'

'Yeah, whatever,' shrugs Matt. 'I'll bring you some later. If you behave yourself, that is.'

'Ha ha. Not much else he can do, is there?'

'Fuck off. You'll find me dead in the morning,' Freddie whispers, exhausted from his outburst.

'Maybe we should send in your girlfriend,' Matt grins at Ritchie, 'seeing as she likes handcuffs and that. She'll show him a good time.'

'She wouldn't spit on a scrawny little fucker like Freddie,' says Ritchie. 'Why don't you send in your bird? She's always upstairs humping her vibrator every time your back's turned.' Ritchie once found a Pussy Treat Deluxe in Matt's bedroom and Matt's never heard the end of it.

Freddie would laugh if he could, but a combination of crack and heroin withdrawal, hepatitis and paranoia have robbed him of his humour. He listens to keys clunking in locks and his brothers' footsteps receding.

It isn't long before the cold sweats are on him and then the aches set in. It's worse than the flu; much worse, because there's a cure for it. Heroin. And he can't think about anything else.

He yanks on the stool but it doesn't give a millimetre. Reaching over with his free arm, he heaves against it with both hands, again and again, until his hair dangles wetly in his eyes. The stool doesn't budge.

'Wankers!' he screams at the top of his lungs. He lies back down, chest heaving, despair flooding his mind.

Back when this all started, he would never have dreamed it would come to this. Not when he was nineteen and popping the little white pills that made him dance and be happy and actually enjoy being around other human

111

beings. People had always found him weird, couldn't put their finger on why, exactly, but Freddie had always known he was different. He'd had better conversations with crippled dogs than with his so-called friends.

Ecstasy changed everything. For the first time in his life he understood why his mum was always trying to put her arms round him, and why girls wanted to stare into his eyes. Now he was no longer pushing his mum away and avoiding eye contact with pretty girls. Next he discovered coke, and his social life got even better. He became confident and talkative, and all the clever things he's had stuck in his head for years were able to tumble out at last, and girls were tripping over themselves to be with him.

When someone offered him a crack pipe for the first time, he wondered if that, too, would help him be more like other people. And it did. It made him feel fuckin' amazing. He didn't get addicted like the media was always warning about. The comedown wasn't much of a laugh though, until someone gave him some brown stuff to ease the fall, and *that* he did become addicted to, within a week. He barely noticed; too busy travelling back and forth to the Land Where Nothing Matters. But the white... the white just took his soul, sucked out his personality, and rendered him about as vital and interesting as watching paint dry.

His sweat seeps into the stinking rug. An intense ache inhabits every part of his body at once; penetrating so deep it feels as if his marrow is being sucked slowly out of his bones.

His eyes are bulging out of their sockets, super-sensitive, taking in way too much information and sending it whizzing around his brain... Three aluminium bar stools with nasty, red, cracked plastic seats... four broken, askew pictures framing landscapes so bland they seem to drain the life out of him... a tiny crack in the wall in the shape of a caterpillar eating a spider... or maybe it's a spider putting up a fight with a caterpillar, which come to think of it looks more like a giant bedbug... Whatever, it's fucking unbearable; all of it. It's becoming so unbearable that if he had an axe he'd chop off his own hand to escape.

Anger swells amidst the throbs and aches, and with a desperate yell he swivels round and shoves his feet with full force up into the seat of the stool. It definitely moved that time, the fucker!

He kicks at it again, pushing it back and forth, round and round. The screws in the floor are coming loose. He's going to get free! The thought keeps him heaving against the stool like a madman until there's a sound of straining metal and ripping linoleum, and at last it tears away from the floor.

He's got a bar stool handcuffed to his wrist but nothing's going to stop him, certainly not the yellow door with its collection of burglary-proof locks. He makes straight for the window and rams the stool against it, smashing the glass and sending a cascade of glittering shards onto the courtyard below.

Sticking his head through, a refreshing blast of wind hits his face, replaced by a stab of vertigo. But what the fuck, rather be down there smashed to pieces than up here in hell.

He scrapes the stool against the window frame to remove the glass splinters lining the edge, then hoists the stool through and climbs onto the ledge. First, with his free hand, and then the other, he reaches to the drainpipe lying three feet from the window. Luckily he's had a bit of practice at this sort of thing – speedy getaways along unlikely escape routes, though never from a fourth floor window with a bloody great handicap hanging from his arm.

Fuck his lousy fuckin' brothers! Freddie always had the thinking brain, even though he couldn't communicate those thoughts most of the time. He would be helping his academically-challenged brothers do their homework and, later, tot up their dodgy takings and winnings, even though they were years older than him. They shouldn't have underestimated him.

It's not long before he's found a likely touch; a quiet house on a smart street. He's rung the bell a couple of times and got no answer. There's no car in the drive and only a hall light on, and more importantly no burglar alarm.

Sweat's pouring down his neck and slime is seeping out of his nose. He doesn't have the patience to fuck about jemmying doors like a professional, so he smashes the stool through a side window and hauls himself after it.

Within seconds he's in the master bedroom, tipping the contents of a jewellery box into his pocket. As luck would have it, the owner has stashed her cash in the same place as her jewellery. Only seventy in notes but it'll do and he's out of here. If he hadn't got a stool attached to his arm he would have been out of here already.

He runs down the stairs, and is about to climb back out the window when he spots a brand new camcorder lying on a side table. 'Leave it!' his senses scream. He's got one ankle over the sill when a dog barks, making him jump back in, then footsteps come stampeding towards the house. An Alsatian leaps up at the window, fangs bared. A torch shines into the room and suddenly

Freddie's spotlighted like an actor in his own true crime reconstruction.

'Come out with your hands up!'

Freddie's just done a runner from the dreaded Harris brothers. Ain't no way he's not gonna give the old bill the slip if he can help it. He races back through the house, unlocks the French doors to the garden, and tears outside with rings spilling out of his pockets.

He comes to a stunned halt. Three cozzers are standing in the garden as if they've been waiting for him to join them for a fucking barbeque. The house must be wired up to the local station, he realises with dismay.

No time to worry about that. He charges at full pelt towards the fence and is about to throw himself over it, stool and all, when sharp teeth sink into his leg and he keels to the ground with the Alsatian slathering all over him.

'Looks like we've got an escapee,' quips one of the cozzers and the three of them fall about laughing, as if Freddie's bar stool is an essential part of his act as a comedian.

Freddie's always been good with dogs, he remembers, struggling up onto one elbow, and this one will be licking his face in a minute... A big flat boot is planted on his chest, knocking the last bit of hope out of him.

This is not purgatory, Freddie realises, and it's not a nightmare either. Finally, he admits defeat as two dreaded words resound in his ears, dragging him back to reality.

'You're nicked.'

HMP Belmarsh

Holiday from hellmarsh

'Give us a bit a gear, Jel.'

'Ain't got enough, 'arry,' mumbles the blessed-out druggie in the cell at the other end of the landing from mine. He's gouching out on his bed with his eyes half closed and a dreamy smile. I feel a stab of anger because I sorted him out last week.

'Don't make me say it again,' I say lowering my voice. 'Just sort us out a bit, will ya?' It's not a question and he knows it.

With a sigh he shifts onto his side and pulls down his jeans and boxers. Holding the door shut, I avert my gaze while he retrieves a parcel out of his arse. It strikes me that if ever I need a reminder that being a drug addict is shit, this has to be one of them. He wraps a small amount of powder in a piece of paper and reluctantly hands it over.

'Cheers, mate,' I say sticking it up my nose to return to my cell.

Luckily I'm banged up on my own, so I don't have to worry about desperate cellmates like Stinky watching my every move with envious eyes. As soon as the screws have done their head-count, I smooth out the wrinkles in a bit of silver foil by rubbing it on the table with toilet paper. Listening to the shouts coming from the other cells, I can tell that everyone's at it right now.

'Pass us that works, mate!' I hear Bernie's voice.

'One minute, mate, I'm just doing the line... Ow! Fuck! There you are. You might wanna sharpen it first!'

'Nah, be all right.'

'Urry up mate! You owe me one.'

I frown at the tiny amount of brown powder revealed in Jel's wrap and think about getting hold of a needle. Not to shoot up, because then I'd be in an even worse mess than I am already, but because needles work like currency round here. Doesn't matter how blunt they get, most cons just stab them in, regardless of the resulting patchwork of livid bruises.

Once I've smoked my gear, I lie on my bed and try to enjoy its paltry glow. Unfortunately, it's not enough to drown out all the horrible new worries I got going on round my head.

First of all, I got a phone call from Dawn saying that she's never going to risk her livelihood again to sort me out in here. Then she mentioned that div Gary she was on about before, in a way that makes me certain she's been milking his dick so she can help him spend his money. But worse than all that, I'm worrying about Meathead. The cold coffee-coloured slabhead is out of hospital and on another wing, to protect us from each other, but his mates are still here and word's out they want to put it on me.

I spent half of last night scraping my toothbrush against the wall. When I'd whittled it down to a lethally sharp point, I went to sleep with it under my pillow, and one foot hanging out the side of the bed so I'd be the first out when the doors are unlocked. First thing in the morning is the most likely time for exacting revenge in here. At any rate, that's the time when one of Meathead's previous adversaries had his knuckles crushed to bits when he didn't get out of bed quickly enough.

When the gates clang open, I have no desire to leap out of bed brandishing my toothbrush. I've been having one of those dreams where I'm shaggin' some gorgeous bird, and it's ten times better than it ever is in real life. On the outside, I'd wake up and feel a bit disappointed, but if there was a girl lying next to me, I'd

117

wake her up for a shag and try to keep the dream going for a bit. In here, however, I wake up, undergo a devastating anti-climax, and try to escape back into my dream. Not a chance in hell of that though, with all the clanging gates and screws shouting, 'Come and get your breakfasts, gents!'

Suddenly I remember the way that one of Meathead's lackeys glared at me yesterday while loudly describing the permanent scars caused by scalding water.

I yank on my clothes and join the breakfast queue with my chib in my pocket. What's left of my hard-on wilts as an aroma of porridge and soggy toast assails my nostrils. A wave of nausea washes over me and I'm relieved I'm not queuing up for dinner.

We can tell what day of the week it is by the stinking food we get. Today, for example, it'll be Moody Shepherd's Pie, which means that it's Tuesday, because they're using up Monday's Mince Stew. Tomorrow it will be sausages, which means that Thursday, of course, will be Moody Toad in the Hole. Fridays are the worst, even though they're not using up anything from the day before: fish and sodden chips. The fish is a bit bigger than a fish finger but not so tasty.

I take my tray of porridge and toast back to my cell, feeling an unusual watering in my mouth because today they've surprised me with an egg. I don't get to titillate my taste buds just yet though, because Jel pokes his head out of his cell and shouts, 'come 'ere quick 'arry. I've got something for ya.'

I put the tray on my table and hurry to Jel's cell, remembering how stingily he sorted me out last night and thinking he must be making up for it today, and fucking hell! That's two surprises in one day; first the egg and now an extra bit of brown, and things are really starting to look up.

118

The blow to my back is my third surprise. It sends me sprawling to the floor and knocking my head against a bedpost. It's dark in the cell and I'm disoriented. I can just make out Jel sitting at the table. Glancing round, I notice a blanket strung over the window. Then suddenly from out of the shadows comes a fast-moving lump of wood and on the end of it some huge black geezer yelling, 'You know what this is for, you bloodclart!'

The lump of wood is swinging at my head, my arm is flying up to block it and all at once it's exploding with pain. Again and again, the shadow pulls back its arm and the cosh smashes into my body.

I'm scrabbling about on the floor, trying to get my chib out of my pocket where it's stabbing my thigh, and cursing myself for letting drugs get the better of my instincts. But the bastard keeps swinging his bat, giving me no chance to defend myself.

All of a sudden he's gone and I'm left lying on the floor with warm liquid seeping out of my head and an excruciating pain all over my body. I drag myself upright and stumble to the door, hanging onto it with my good arm, while the other one dangles uselessly.

'You know it's fucking over for you, don't you?' I spit at the shadow sitting at the table with his head in his hands.

He groans, 'They would have killed me if I didn't do it.'

'You better bring me some gear, you treacherous slag!'

I lurch down the landing to my cell. On the table, a gruesome-looking egg stares up at me, making me want to heave. I lower my head under the tap and give myself yet another fucking shock, this time watching a river of red rush down the plughole. Eventually red turns to pink, then pink turns to pale pink and I collapse gingerly onto my bed, suppressing a scream when my battered arm rolls off the edge. I pick it up with my good arm and wait with gritted teeth for Jel to bring my medication.

'I'm really sorry, Harry,' he says, handing me a wrap and even remembering to pronounce the 'H'.

'It ain't over, Jel. It ain't fuckin' over,' I glare at him as he backs out of my cell mumbling apologies and closing the door quietly behind him. I know he's thinking warily about the hot water job I did on Meathead.

I lie on my bed sweating with pain, waiting for the screws to close down and cons to get behind doors so I can administer my pain relief.

I stay in my cell all day so that the screws don't ask awkward questions. Time passes quickly because Jel gave me four times what he gave me last night. Even with a fucked-up arm and a bashed-in body and nothing to look at but the cracks in the ceiling, heroin is a bird-killer. I could do my sentence out in the freezing yard as long as I had gear. I wouldn't even *mind* being in jail. Fuck, I suspect heroin would make even *hell* bearable.

Some time after bang-up I drift into a sort of nightmarish fever with huge wooden batons swinging at me out of the shadows and agonising pains shooting up and down my arm and the gorgeous bird from my dream flashing her alluring fanny at me, always a few exasperating inches out of my reach.

I come round to the sounds of the servery opening up and a screw yelling, 'Come and get your breakfasts, gents!' I'm surprised to see a bulge under the blanket. Right next to my hard-on lies an arm the width of a road hump. I try to lift it, making my erection shrivel away in alarm as a thousand red-hot nerve endings spring to life. My arm flops back onto the bed, making me yell out in agony.

'Oh shit,' I groan to myself. 'I'm going to have to go and see that bloody Indian doctor.'

'Bloody-Nora, Shaw,' exclaims the doctor, 'what the bloody hell has happened to you?'

'I fell over,' I tell him. My arm is lying on the table between us like some false appendage left over from The Elephant Man.

The doctor's eyebrows shoot up to his hairline. 'Well Shaw, you must have fell over bloody hard because you are going out to the hospital.'

'Ordinary hospital? On the *outside?*' I gasp. Fuck me, I think to myself, Blimey! That's almost like going on holiday!

He must be taking this seriously, because everybody knows that coming to see Dr Gangali is a total waste of time. Dr Gangali takes one unconcerned look at your bleeding nose' your swollen tonsils/your bashed-in ankle and says, 'just a little blood/swelling/bruise. Not to worry, it will heal up in no time at all. Here's some nice Ibuprofen to help it along.'

'Can I have some painkillers, doctor? I ask, pushing my luck.

'What sort of painkillers are you after?' he says, which shocks the hell out of me because, as the legend goes, whenever anyone's asked him for pills he's never said 'OK' or 'maybe', he's always said 'no.'

'Could I have some DF1 18s or Codeine, Dr No?' I ask so eagerly that I accidentally let slip his nickname. Hurriedly, I put on an expression as if I'm dying and groan, 'Even better, you could give me some Oramorph.'

Dr No breaks into a broad smile and I curse myself for my slip-up. 'No, no, no,' he says, obviously remembering his professional edict, which probably goes something like: Heal Thyself... With as Little Expense to the Taxpayer as Possible. 'Not to worry, Shaw, I've got some nice Ibuprofen for you.'

My arm is hurting so bad I'm about ready to have it chopped off. Nevertheless, feeling like a prize mug, I accept a bottle with three pills rattling about in it.

'Perhaps in hospital I'll be able to get some *proper* medication,' I say pointedly. 'Am I going out to hospital right away, Dr No?' I ask, not bothering to keep the stingy bastard's nickname to myself any more.

'Yes,' he nods, stunning the hell out of me. 'Just as soon as we can arrange your transportation.' I stare at the worst case of what looks like elephantiasis that either of us has ever seen and slump in my seat. 'Arranging transportation' might as well be a euphemism for 'in a few hours, if you're lucky.'

Even when Dr No says 'yes', he really means 'no'.

I'm chained to a fresh-faced, skinny Asian screw. A bouncy-walking doctor is leading the way and a sour-faced back-up screw is bringing up the rear.

We make a strange procession in this mixed hospital ward, and even though my arm seems to have swollen to the size of a punch-bag and the relentless agony of my wound is etched deep into my bruised face, patients are cowering in their beds as if my primary desire is to break free and attack them. They're praying that I'm just passing through their ward.

'I'm afraid we don't have any private wards available, Mr Shaw,' the doctor says cheerfully, arriving at an empty bed between two old fellas wearing flannel pyjamas, one of whom conceals his head in his newspaper. 'But I'm sure you'll settle in absolutely fine.'

'Afternoon, mate,' I beam at the old codger in the next bed, who hurriedly shuts his eyes and pretends to be asleep.

'I'm sure I'll settle in absolooooootely fine, doctor,' I beam, noisily rattling my chains. 'Once I've got some painkillers into me.'

'Ah yes, of course. Of course,' mutters the doctor, observing the patients shuddering in their beds up and down the ward. 'We'll provide you with something to make you comfortable. Very comfortable indeed, I should think.'

The bloke that's pretending to be asleep loses a few wrinkles in his forehead. The sour-faced screw draws the curtains around us and hands me some prison issue pyjamas. They will mark me out as a criminal as surely as if they had downward pointing arrows printed all over them.

'D'ya mind unchaining me while I get undressed?' I ask the Asian screw, who looks like a younger version of Dr Gangali.

'No, no, no. We are to remain chained together at all times.' He says, making me check the resemblance to Dr Gangali more closely. He'd already said 'no' about five times before I'd even asked him for anything. 'No, don't even think about it,' he said wagging his finger at a drinks machine in the entrance hall. 'And don't even think about that either,' when we passed a snack machine a bit further on.

He eventually comes round to my way of thinking, however, when I try to undo my flies and his hand brushes against my crotch, making him jerk back, terrified. Somebody must have been winding him up, telling him how convicts turn into bum-bandits at a moment's provocation.

'Don't you even think about it,' he says warningly whilst unlocking the chain.

'Why don't you just cuff me to the bed and go get yourself a cuppa?' I suggest. With one arm out of action, I can't even pick my nose without causing our chain to clank, making all the patients think I'm trying to escape.

'It's not worth my bloody job, Shaw,' he says chaining us up again.

I'm sure Doctor No uses that exact same expression. I'm thinking how I could really end up hating this earnest little fucker when a nurse comes round with my meds. She's nothing like the fantasy nurse I'd conjured up on the way here. She's squat-bodied with a face disturbingly similar to an orang-utan's and for some reason, the shape of her bosom makes me think of a bulldozer.

Swiftly and gently, the nurse administers a shot of morphine into my arm. Before my gaze, she transforms into Florence Nightingale. Better still, Dr No's brother seems to miraculously disappear into nothingness.

From now on, I'm on Cloud Nine. Nevertheless, every time the nurse does her rounds and asks if I need any more pain relief I manage to unpeel one eye and groan, 'Yes, please, I'm in agony.'

'No, no, no. Don't listen to him,' a voice always pipes up in the background. 'Dr Gangali said not to give him too much painkiller, whatever he tells you.' Luckily my beautiful Florence ignores him.

During the night, another screw takes over, leaving me to my drugged-up dreams, but bright and early the next morning Dr No's Brother is back, keen to get on with his all-important task of keeping him and I connected by an all-too-short chain. At some point in the day, I'm shipped out on a sea of bliss to the operating theatre, where my arm is cut open to evacuate poison from the infection that has caused it to quadruple in size.

Every hour or so, Miss Nightingale inserts a seemingly never-ending strip of gauze into the hole to soak up the vivid yellow pus, making Dr No's Brother squirm on the end of our chain. I let out an agonised groan from time to time, partly to keep up my morphine intake but mostly for the satisfaction of causing Dr No's Brother such distress.

'Please be gentle, nurse,' he pleads with Miss Nightingale, who never appears to notice him. I'd like to think she's in on my game, but she just likes to put people out of their misery, sweet soul, and can't tell when they're having her on. Her bosom is starting to remind me less of a bulldozer and more of the lovely soft goose-feather down pillow that I once laid my head on, out of curiosity during a burglary.

The Oramorph is wonderful. As soon as I'm allowed to make a phone call, however, I'm onto my younger brother, Dave, for some Kentucky Fried Chicken with sauce. Not the red or the white sauce, the *brown* sauce. Dr No's Brother, being such a mug, hasn't a clue what I'm organising. Nor does he notice anything untoward when my good old brother turns up with his pupils like piss-holes in the snow, as well as the Colonel's Meal that I so desperately wanted, but don't seem all that eager to eat now that I've got it.

Dave and me attempt to have a conversation, but the disapproving looks coming from Dr No's Brother make it awkward to talk about our usual topics of drugs, crime, and sexy birds. Dr No's Brother is such a prude that whenever I say the word 'cunt' he gets all upset and glances around cringing. 'No, no, no! That word is bloody disrespectful to wimmin-kind!'

Eventually I'm so irritated that I take to slipping the offending word into every sentence. My brother swiftly catches on, until we're having a conversation that goes like this.

'No, really? What a cunt! Did he really say that?'
'Yeah, he called her a cunt, the cunt.'

'What, that cunt called our Mum a cunt? She ain't a cunt.'

'That's what I told the cunt: 'She's not a cunt, so fuck off, you cunt.'

About time some cunt told that cunt he's a cunt.'

'Eh? Who are you calling a cunt?

From the corner of my eye I notice Dr No's Brother growing increasingly flustered. By now, it's all that my brother and me can do to stop ourselves cracking up. But since I'm impatient to get to the real purpose of his visit, I say:

'You forgot my brown sauce, you cunt.' Turning to Dr No's Brother, who's seething with indignation, I ask, 'Didn't you hear me asking this cunt for some brown sauce?'

'It's in the bottom of the fuckin' box, you silly cunt,' says my brother. 'I'm off.'

'Stop it, stop it! Stop saying that dreadful word!' cries Dr No's Brother, glancing around and feeling a bit foolish to see my brother already strolling halfway down the hospital ward with a merry wave.

'What word is that then?' I feign surprise as I dig around in the bottom of the takeaway box. Dr No's Brother says nothing and I can almost see steam rising from his perplexed brain.

Unfortunately, I've upset him so much that when I tell him I need to take a shit he's doubly determined to do his job properly and not let me off the chain. He's a meticulous bastard. Won't even do a crossword puzzle in case I miraculously produce a key to the padlock, take him hostage and hold all the patients to ransom, making him lose his precious job.

'It's going to be a really stinky one,' I warn, straining in my bed. 'It's been at least forty eight hours since the last... one...' A nice big fart erupts, giving him a warning of things to come. I lift the bed sheets and waft the putrid fumes in his direction. He gets the message and leaps to his feet, yanking on my chain.

'We are going to the bloody toilet now, Shaw,' he gasps.

'OK, suit yourself,' I say, thinking he'll come round to my way of thinking like he did last time, especially if I ask him to help me pull down my pyjamas.

Dr No's Brother leads me to the loo by pulling on my chain as if he's walking his dog. Ignoring my pleas, he keeps us chained together and stalwartly looks the other way while I pull down my own pyjamas. The door is half shut between us and he can't see what I'm doing as I sit on the bog and sprinkle some brown powder onto a piece of silver foil. Letting out lots of grunting noises and a few more fortuitous farts, I melt the powder with the lighter that my good old brother smuggled in with my takeaway and suck the fumes through a straw as fast as possible.

Suddenly, my arm is in the air like a fish on a hook and I'm being yanked off the toilet. Dr No's Brother peeks round the side of the door and his eyebrows shoot up to his hairline in an amazing repeat performance of his brother's yesterday. 'He's chasing the bloody dragon!' he shouts, dragging me out of the cubicle and into the ward where the patients are all peering out from behind their blankets and Saga magazines as if they're expecting to see me running around after some fire-snorting scaly creature.

'He was chasing the bloody dragon in the toilet!' Dr No's Brother informs the sour-faced screw who's reading the paper beside my bed, waiting to take over the shift. The sour-faced screw shuffles his paper in front of his face, doesn't want to be associated with Dr No's Brother. The expression 'Chasing the dragon' went out with the dinosaurs, and if word got out round the Marsh, he wouldn't want to get lynched alongside Dr No's Brother.

'Shut up, Gangali,' he mutters.

Gangali! I knew they were brothers!

The screw glances over the top of his paper, notices that I'm high as a kite and says, 'Lie the fuck down, Shaw. You'll be outta here in a few hours.'

Oh shit, back to the hell-hole.

'How's about a nice cuppa tea?' I grin at the refreshments' lady, who grimaces and sets about making my tea with trembling fingers, even though she must be used to me by now.

I lie down with my hands behind my head and a huge beam on my face, determined to wring out every last dreg of happiness from my holiday in St Mary's Hospital.

Some of the fellas I met up with on the RAPt programme became loyal mates for life. We were telling each other secrets we'd kept buried for decades, so we had to learn to trust in each other and it wasn't easy. But there was one fella who I knew, right away, I would be able to trust with my life. Winston was in my corner from the start, and I've been able to count on him ever since.

Winston

Daylight robbery

Winston's admiring his car. It's a brand new Mercedes SLK in dark metallic blue.

Until recently, whenever Winston fancied himself a new set of wheels, he's picked out several nearly-new models in the paper, called up the owners until he found a gullible one, usually a woman, and buttered her up with his posh-sounding voice and phoney background. Then he's turned up, impressed the shit out of her with his sincere smile, his excellently-cut suit and pristine shoes, and while she was admiring all that and blushing at his flattering quips, he's slid into the driver's seat and then taken her car for a trial spin. Simple.

But yesterday he's had a better idea. He'd been checking out the newest arrival in a Mercedes showroom, imagining what it would be like to have fifty grand to drop on such a beauty, when some rich-looking toff had returned a Mercedes SLK that he's just taken for a spin and tossed the keys to the salesman. Winston happened to notice the salesman slip the keys into a drawer, and it took only a moment to persuade the salesman to trot away on some worthless errand, allowing Winston to lift the keys and drive off for his own test drive, never to be seen again.

He strides round to the boot slipping on his gloves; soft kid leather, Austin Reed, last season. It's still chilly and he's wearing a dark grey lamb's wool and cashmere suit, Valentino; striped Jermyn Street shirt and burgundy Patrick Cox shoes, nothing too flash. Always helps to look elegant, especially when you're black and from the East End and the tools of your trade are two small, lovingly polished Beretta handguns.

Winston's always been stylish. As a four-year-old, he impressed the shit out of his old man by borrowing his one and only funeral tie and learning to tie a perfect knot in it. And when, a few years later, Winston was caught with a bunch of other kids on CCTV stealing porn mags from a corner shop, and was hauled up on front of the headmaster, the head had noticed his polished shoes, Winston had admitted that he's polished them himself, and the head had decided there was hope for him yet. All the other culprits had been suspended.

Winston was never one to follow the herd. Whatever the fashion happened to be, he stuck to his buttoned down shirts and crisp pressed trousers. Other kids used to laugh at him for not wearing trainers with no laces, or trousers halfway down his arse, or whatever the fashion happened to be. The other boys stopped laughing when they noticed all the attention Winston was getting from girls, who began competing amongst themselves to impress him with their own fancy clothes. Winston went from nicking porn to stealing upmarket menswear and never looked back.

His style's been slipping a bit lately, though. Today, for example, if someone were to peer under his trouser cuffs they would discover that he was wearing odd socks. A year ago, Winston wouldn't have so much as popped out to buy the paper in mismatching socks. What if he were to meet an attractive girl, and they were to go for a coffee, and he were to recline on some squishy leather armchair and she were to notice the odd socks…? He'd feel so uncomfortable that his chat-up offensive would go to shit.

That's just the way he is. Very particular about certain things. Like coffee, for example. He'd rather vomit than drink a cup of instant coffee. Winston knows how to make a perfect cappuccino and he can't understand why barely a handful of coffee bars in all London share his expertise. One of his girlfriends blamed it on him being born a Virgo. She ditched him, couldn't stand the way that during sex he'd sneakily examine her underarms for stray hairs that she'd missed with the razor.

Glancing around to make sure no one has clocked him, Winston places a small Louis Vuitton bag in the boot of the Mercedes, swings his agile frame into the plush leather driver's seat and enjoys the expensive purr of the engine for a few moments before setting off.

The sun is shining, lending the sprawling council estates along the Hackney Road a summery sparkle. Winston taps his fingers on the steering wheel to the chilled rhythms of Smooth F.M. He's feeling a stirring in his belly, a familiar mixture of excitement and dread. Everything's going according to plan, except the one thing niggling him at the back of his mind, the thing that's behind his wearing odd socks today. He shoves this thing further to the back of his mind as he pulls up outside John's flat.

The once-grand Georgian terrace is now blighted by peeling plaster and stained blankets slung over the windows. A nondescript man wearing a denim jacket, jeans and trainers jogs down the steps, gets into a Ford Focus and drives away.

Winston pulls out from the kerb and follows. At times he follows so attentively that he almost mounts John's bumper. At others he falls behind and finds himself having to ram his foot on the accelerator to stop some other car nipping in front.

John's an excellent driver. He knows all the back roads and the quickest way to get from somewhere to anywhere, so if Winston doesn't keep his mind fixed one hundred percent on the job, his partner will veer off down some invisible side-turning, leaving Winston stuck at a zebra crossing watching some little old granny trying to find her handkerchief in the middle of the road.

Winston doesn't understand why John drives such a shit car. Or why he dresses so badly and lives in a dump. He knows John ain't stupid. John explained to him once how he's got it all mapped out; how he's going to move to Florida and retire. Been saving up, made some clever investments. Only another three years till he's forty and wumph! He'll be gone with that amazing knack he has for vanishing right in front of your eyes.

But what about now? Winston wonders. What about living for the present? Looking good? How about a little romance?

They're entering the area round Victoria Park, a small island of affluence in a sea of residential mediocrity. John parks on a serene avenue of large, well-maintained houses. Leaving the doors unlocked, he walks over to the Mercedes and takes the Louis Vuitton bag out of the boot. Winston climbs into the passenger seat as John gets in.

'Bit flash for the job,' observes John, taking a gun from the bag and slipping it inside his jacket.

Winston frowns. He tucks the second gun into the waistband of his trousers while John slides the clutch into gear, shaking his head as the engine purrs expensively. 'You been on that shit again?'

'All right, Winston? How are ya, mate?' Winston says sarcastically. 'I'm fine thanks. All right yourself, John?'

'Looks like you 'ave,' says John ignoring the dig. 'Your skin's all crusty and you look like you need some more sleep.'

'You ain't looking so dapper yourself, mate,' Winston says prickly. For a long while they ignore one another, staring intently out of the windscreen. They drive past the Old Ford Post Office Depot, glancing in to see several post office vans being loaded up. Not quite ready yet. They drive on.

Winston wants to tell John to mind his own fucking business. He holds his tongue though because he knows that it really *is* John's business and that Winston's increasing fondness for crack is starting to jeopardise their partnership.

Like today. It wasn't just that he couldn't find two clean matching socks. He'd overdone it a bit last night and would have overslept if his downstairs neighbour hadn't banged on his door beggin' for a teabag. He was so relieved that he almost gave the dumpy-kneed bitch a hug, but he had enough problems on his plate without giving her the come-on. If he'd been even ten minutes late, John would never have worked with him again. John doesn't need to be getting wound up before a job wondering where the hell his partner is. Not in this line of work.

'You used to be one cool customer with the ladies,' says John. 'Now look at ya.'

Winston bristles. As far as he could tell when he looked in the mirror before he came out, he looked pretty damn cool, and he doubts that John has noticed his odd socks. 'I'd just keep your mind on the road, mate,' he mutters. 'Keep your fuckin' style advice to yourself.'

'No need to get narky,' John frowns at the road ahead. 'Shit!' He's missed a turning and now they're running into traffic. If he hadn't been worrying about Winston's crack habit there's no way he would have made such a dumb move. It's not like him to make a wrong turn in the middle of a job. The traffic's bumper to bumper and he's stuck behind a van with painted-out windows, can't see a fucking thing up ahead, doesn't know whether there are road-works or an accident or just a busy stretch.

Winston's grinding his teeth. They used to get along fine, he and John, crack a few jokes to ease the tension and sit in companionable silence thinking about business. But now they're barely moving and by the time they circle back to the depot the vans might have all gone on their merry way. There's a bloody great chicane along the middle of the road so they can't do a U-turn. Winston's feeling trapped and agitated and all of a sudden, extremely tired.

'Why don't you pull into the bus lane?' he yawns.

John glowers at the van blocking his view. 'You've definitely been at it again. You know why we can't do that, you fool.'

Winston clenches his fists, using all his willpower to hold himself back from... From he doesn't know what. It's that dig about his drug habit again. It's not a habit, it's a pleasurable fucking pastime. He feels the reassuring weight of the gun pressing against his thigh and just to calm himself down, fantasises about blowing John's head off. It doesn't really help, he knows he'd be fucked without John.

Just then he spots a police car in the side view mirror. He watches incredulously as it cruises grandly along the bus lane.

'Do you see that?' he yells at John, letting off steam in one furious blast. He winds down the window and leans out bellowing, 'Who do you think you are, you dogs? Think you own the fuckin' road, do you? Join the queue like everybody else!'

John grips the steering wheel, eyes wide with disbelief. It's not like Winston to completely lose his rag. Passers-by are staring at the crazy black guy in the flash car with exactly the same expression as John's. John is about to tell Winston to shut the fuck up, when the traffic moves on just far enough for him to cut behind the police car, exit down a narrow side turning and aim back towards the Old Ford headquarters.

It's a Thursday, best day of the week for robbing. The post offices fill up with money so that pensioners can get their readies for the week and people on the dole can learn how to create a brand new look in sixty minutes courtesy of daytime TV, or whatever the fuck they do all day. The more run-down the area, the more money gets loaded up in the posties.

At last a blur of red shoots past the Mercedes at a T-junction. The lights turn green quickly enough for John to follow.

The chase is on. Winston glances at John; he can almost see his mind working through all the variables. John follows the van for a couple of minutes before overtaking and making a couple of swift turns. 'I know where he's going,' he mutters and Winston doesn't doubt him. John's always right, never ends up hanging around the wrong post office like a spare tool.

Winston feels a surge of adrenaline. In a few minutes his pockets will be bulging with notes, he'll have a pipe in his hand and life will be sweet. He wishes he didn't need the pipe in the equation for life to be sweet, but never mind that for now.

John pulls into the kerb outside a post office on the high street. He watches Winston get out of the car and peer into the window of a newsagent. It looks like he's scanning the index cards advertising satisfaction-guaranteed massages, but John knows he's got his eye on the reflections in the glass. John admires Winston's guts. It's a shame that Winston is turning into an unreliable crack-head because he's the best partner John's ever used. He'd had big plans for him. But Winston could have got them both arrested back there for screaming obscenities at the old bill.

Then there's the odd socks. John's not a snappy dresser; he wouldn't think twice about leaving the house with his T-shirt on inside out. But he's a born observer. And those odd socks are an ill omen.

Winston's reflection smiles back at him as a red van pulls up to the kerb. He watches the security man put on his helmet and walk round to the back of the van. A chute snaps open and delivers a case. Winston keeps still while the security man makes a quick scan of his surroundings, paying no particular attention to Winston in his smart suit.

He takes his time, doesn't want the man to panic. Strolls casually away from the window at exactly the right moment to intercept the man at the post office door. The gun slides nicely from his waistband to glide into the vulnerable spot just behind the security man's chin strap.

Winston replaces his cockney accent with the posh one he's diligently copied from newsreaders on BBC Radio 4, 'Don't do anything stupid, sir. NOW DROP THE FUCKING CASE!'

He relishes this moment. It's almost as good as a crack high. Everything slows down and it seems that he is not only in control of this stranger's life, but of every single thing happening at this exact moment in time. It's all been so beautifully orchestrated that no one on the street notices anything out of the ordinary. The security man puts the case on the ground backs into the post office, staring at Winston with terrified eyes.

'Thank you,' says Winston, picking up the case and marching back to the car. It always pays to be polite. John swings open the passenger door and hits the accelerator before Winston has fully sat down. A powerful vroom! Causes heads to turn right along the street as the Mercedes zooms out of sight of the post office and skids around a corner.

Winston smiles to himself. *That's* why he picked this model to be the getaway. Shame they'll have to dump it in ten minutes.

'You prat,' laughs John, his face relaxing into a grin. Winston laughs too.

'What's that line you use on the birds again?' John asks. He's heard it before but it always tickles him.

'Oh, yeah,' says Winston with a big grin. 'When they go: 'What do you do for a living?' I tell 'em, 'I'm an armed robber.' Works every time.'

John shakes his head laughing. He's still chuckling when they get back to his car.

Winston

On the slippery slope

Long, wavy, blonde hair smelling of fresh shampoo transfixes his gaze. It seems to be moving. There's no breeze in this post office. In fact it's stiflingly hot, so it must be moving of its own accord. Perhaps it's growing.

Well, of course, it's growing, Winston thinks, frowning. But hair shouldn't grow so fast that you can actually *watch* it, not like in those natural world documentaries where everything's speeded up and you can see a whole day flash by in a matter of seconds.

This reminds him of a programme he saw about microbes setting up habitat on human skin. All sorts of hideous little critters live there, different sorts for different parts of the body. But the ugliest ones, Winston decided, were the ones that resided amongst the hair follicles. The camera was so powerful you could see right into their gruesome little faces, with their portly bodies full of your blood. Winston's sure he can see one of them living in this woman's hair, and the harder he stares, the more certain he grows that there's a whole family of the microscopic buggers going about their business in there.

Too bad he's stuck in this queue with supersensitive vision. Should at least have brought himself down from his last freebase with a can of special Brew. Could have bought one in the Office two doors down. Doesn't want to be drunk on the job though, and what would people have thought if they saw him in his up-to-the minute pinstripe drinking tramps' brew? This suit's an Yves Saint Laurent, bit too slick for the job really, but his usual one's not back from the dry cleaners.

He makes a quick count of the queue. Five people in front, including the woman with the living hairdo, and only one cashier out of three on the job. Bloody typical. He glances round to check the queue to the rear. Directly behind him is a stocky granny with a mouth pulled tight like puckered elastic; behind her, a middle-aged bloke in a suit, Burton or some crap, looking impatient; and behind him, two birds past their prime who have spontaneously struck up conversation. Shouldn't be any problems there.

Eight grand, he got from the last job, and it lasted three and a half weeks. That's the trouble with crack. When you're up above the clouds nothing seems an obstacle to getting up there again. Then you come down and start thinking about making your next bit of dosh, and it all gets very stressful. Like it did this morning. Why he had to leave this hold-up to the last fucking minute, he doesn't know. Well, he does know, he's just deluding himself that he had a choice in the matter.

So here he is, in a run-down East London post office, on his own with a package under his arm and a gun tucked into the waistband of his trousers.

John's got a new partner. That's all well and good, because Winston can make almost as much money this way and not have to share it. He's got a getaway parked round the corner and he can do this on his own. One day he'll turn up at John's condo in Florida with a posh tart on his arm, a Rolex on his wrist and a fucking great yacht clearly visible in the background, as well as the bigger, better condo right next door to John's. John will be sorry he traded Winston in.

The queue shortens by one more customer. Still only one cashier on the job, a nerd with such thick National Health spectacles he can probably detect the dramas going on in the blonde woman's hair too. Trust Winston's luck that the female cashier must be on her tea break. When he checked this place out yesterday to see where the cameras were, it struck him as an efficiently-run place. Mind you, he wasn't coming down off a high just then; he was about to go up on one.

He shifts from one foot to the other, trying to look normal, but his brow has broken out in a sweat and he keeps having to dab it with his cuff because the handkerchief, which should be neatly folded in his breast pocket, is lying on the table at home. All of a sudden, he feels a painful clunk against his foot.

'Fuck!' he gasps, glancing down accusingly to see his own silver Beretta poking out from beneath his trouser turn-up. Quickly he bends down as if to tie his laces, (Paul Smith shoes, very sleek) retrieves the gun and slips it into his inside pocket where it should have been, except it would have spoiled the line of his jacket. He's pretty sure he heard a disapproving 'Tch!' behind him, probably the old biddy with the sucked-in lips, and wishes he hadn't cursed.

He stands up, straightens his tie, and glances round with an apologetic smile, but there's only the bloke in the cheap Burton, glancing at his watch and the two passed-it birds moaning to each other about all the stuff they could be doing if they weren't standing in this queue, like fluffing up pillows or planting out geraniums or whatever the fuck keeps them happy.

Winston shifts the package to his other arm to conceal the gun under his jacket. He's lost a bit of weight lately and should have realised his trousers were too loose. He glances down to check the package. Just a couple of bricks covered in brown paper with a made-up address. He didn't have any sellotape but he's wound so much string around it that it's just about holding together.

The queue goes down and now he's only two away from the counter. A complicated aroma of shampoo,

140

conditioner, hair spray and something else is assailing his nostrils… sweat, spunk, unwashed bedclothes…

That's it, filthy sheets! No wonder there's something moving about in her hair. She's probably got head lice. Even as he looks, he thinks he sees a tiny egg, and in the egg he thinks he sees cracks open, and a baby louse is born, and look at that… if it ain't mummy-louse clambering over a few follicles to see if it's a boy or a girl…

'Snap out of it!'

Winston glances round guiltily. Did he just say that? The bloke in the cut-price suit is looking at his watch again and the middle-aged birds are moaning about the heat in here, and someone with about ten packages has joined the queue, must be selling stuff on E-bay. Winston shuffles forward two steps; tells himself to get a grip.

It's only the woman with the head-lice in front of him now. She places a package on the scales and takes out her purse. She's already annoyed that she's been waiting so long, and she's furious when her package weighs in at half a gram above the lower price category, and while she's busy belly-aching about her two-pounds-thirty-five-pence charge, the cashier with the magnifying spectacles is getting more and more stressed out, and Winston wishes the lady in front of him would shut up because the last thing he needs is a post office cashier saying to him, 'Just go ahead and shoot me.' And even while he's thinking this, he notices the lady's hair descend several inches, making his stomach lurch, until she reaches behind and yanks it back up again and he realises it's actually a wig which has been slipping down ever so slowly all this time, and he'd really just like to wrench it off her head for playing silly tricks on him, because it's bad enough pranging from the crack without someone totally throwing you off your stride by shampooing and conditioning a fucking wig… And then, by the time she pays her fee and turns round and he notices that underneath that luxuriant hair she's just an old hag, like that arsehole-mouthed granny who was behind him a moment ago, he's a nervous wreck and the last thing he feels like doing is a fucking hold-up.

But what can he do? He needs the money and lots of it, and he's never had a proper job in his life; half a day's work, three weeks' leisure, that's how it's always been with him. He enjoys reading the Independent in the chic cafés and romancing the ladies, proper romancing with sandalwood massage oils and three course meals that include things like *roast fillet of sea bass with a herb crust served on a bed of steamed asparagus,* because he might talk like a Cockney wide-boy but he's got class and aspirations and appreciates the finer things in life, and if he went to prison he would die a miserable death having to eat bangers and that evil-looking gloop called mash.

Anyway, there's no time for thinking. Thinking would say, 'Maybe now is not the best time to rob this post office. Come back when you're feeling a bit sharper.'

He places his parcel on the scales. £24.65 it'll cost to send first-class. He just manages to avoid swearing in amazement, remembers it's not going anywhere and waits for the cashier to slide open the glass window to pick it up and almost collapse under the load.

'Move back or you're dead,' he hears himself demand, in his best Radio 4 accent. His gun is jabbed so close to the cashier's nose that the fella's gone double-eyed. The female cashier, back from her tea break at long bloody last, paralysed with fear. Winston trains the gun on her.

'Don't even think about pressing that button,' he warns, watching her eyes dart several times towards a spot under the counter. Without taking his gaze off either of them, he pulls a neatly folded canvas bag out of his pocket and tosses it to the bug-eyed bloke staring at him in alarm.

'Fill it up, quickly!'

'Yes, yes, right away, sir,' gabbles the cashier, thankfully not ready to take Winston up on his offer of a free suicide. He starts stuffing the money from the till into the bag then glares at his assistant until she hurriedly opens her till and follows suit.

Winston snatches a glance over his shoulder. The bloke in the Burton suit has scarpered, and the two gossiping crones are so busy complaining about the price of celery that they haven't noticed there's an armed robbery in progress. The young man is juggling his armful of packages to answer his mobile and another customer has entered, too late to overhear Winston's threats.

'I haven't got all day,' Winston growls, clicking the barrel of his gun to show he means business. He watches with satisfaction as the cashiers frantically speed up. A couple of fifty quid notes fall but Winston knows it's time to go. He reaches forward and grabs the bag with a polite 'thank you.' Then he marches swiftly to the door, slipping the gun into the bag with the money.

'Put the bag down on the ground!' roars a voice as soon as he emerges into the sunlight.

Winston blinks several times. He can't believe it. Not only are there three old bill screaming at him from behind a police car, as well as another couple of police cars screeching to a halt on either side, but there's a fuckin' camera crew set up on the pavement! Suddenly, Winston finds a boom mike thrust over his head and a Channel 4 camera shoved in his face. Instantly his thoughts fly to his appearance. Thank goodness he wore matching socks, is his first thought, not to mention his favourite Kenzo tie.

Then a feeling of massive, crushing disappointment assails him. He puts the bag down and his hands up, only to shoulder level so that at least he'll look cool on TV. He recognises the man in the crappy suit giving a statement to the police. Then he notices the granny with the mouth like a constipated arsehold glaring at him with condemnation. She's already given her statement to the police, he can tell.

Winston rebukes himself. If it hadn't been for his crack habit, he wouldn't have got all skinny; the gun wouldn't have dropped on his foot; he wouldn't have cursed; the granny wouldn't have noticed the gun... and he wouldn't be in this mess. Always pays not to offend old ladies, he remembers, kicking himself.

Down at the police station he finds out that the camera crew was filming a feature just around the corner on police working to beat crime in the community. When the call came in about the robbery, the documentary makers could hardly believe their luck and were there in seconds.

The good news is that Winston's a TV star. The not so good news is that he gets thirteen years to work on the script.

HMP Belmarsh

Escape Artist

I'm out of the block and back on the spur. I'm watching my mate, Danny, on the opposite landing. His eyes are wide as saucers and his skin a pallid grey. Every couple of seconds he glances at his watch then rubs his limbs, trying to soothe the unreachable aches that dwell deep in his bones. On and on it goes, glancing at his watch, rubbing his arms; glancing at his watch, rubbing his legs… breaking the monotony only to swipe his soaking cuff across his face, and once in a while, to snort a stream of vile snot into a sodden rag.

Poor bastard. He's a good-looking fella, once had a promising career as a footballer. Cheeky grin, easy to get along with, got two kids and a lovely wife, and look at him now. Trainwreck.

His mum's never usually this late. She's been bringing hard drugs into prisons for years – Belmarsh, Wandsworth, Parkhurst, Highpoint, – no matter where Danny's sent down she'll be boarding buses and trains and coaches to make her dearest son's life that little bit more bearable. But not today. Today, security has been stepped up, the dogs have smelt her out, and her unblemished smuggling record has come to an end.

Danny doesn't know this, but his body suspects it. He's gone into full clucking overdrive.

He glances my way, shows me his watch.

I give him a sympathetic nod.

I watch his withdrawals from a safe distance. Can't help feeling pleased that I haven't got a habit like his. Not that it wouldn't be nice to do my stretch shielded in an almost continuous warm blanket of heroin but at least I don't break into agonising sweats the minute the good times run out. That's why I stay off the needle.

Like a lot of heroin addicts I know, I got into the brown stuff by accident. How can I explain it? It would be a bit like crossing the road and trying so hard not to fall down a large hole in the middle, that you go and get hit by a bus instead.

Back when I was nineteen or twenty, I got into selling coke. I had my eye on a new Mercedes and my girlfriend was into the high life and the coke was a nice little business. I had a fella come round regularly to test its purity. Before long I was selling too much coke for him to handle so he showed me how to wash it up with ammonia and weigh the resulting solid rock of crack.

'Point eight grams, for example, means it's eighty percent pure,' he explained, shaking his test tube. While we waited for the contents to settle, he told me how he'd gone through two houses financing his partiality for these little white rocks. And me, instead of thinking, 'Two houses down the drain... I'd better stay away from this shit.' I'd felt kind of curious. To spend that amount of dosh on freebase, it must be pretty good stuff. And it was!

Until you come down. And that's where the heroin came in; by the back door. Just to ease your discomfort between crack hits. Until you run out, and then you're fucked. Like Danny, for instance.

On the ground floor, convicts are rushing about, scoring, begging, cajoling and down-right threatening one another, and, all the while, doors are slamming and metal resounding against metal like a mental asylum. Can't relax for a minute in here. If it's not the racket, it's the constant threat that some loony'll have a homemade spike in my neck the moment I stop glancing over my shoulder.

It was different in the days before piss-testing. Used to be just puff; now half of us are into smack 'cause it's easier to get away with it. The hard stuff is out of your system in three days, while puff hangs about for nearly a month. So, whereas before we were all stoned and bone idle, now we're all jumpy and unpredictable. The prison governors have only themselves to blame.

I glance across at the visitor board. Danny's name is still not on it. A horrible sinking feeling churns through my stomach. Without Danny's mum's visit, another day in the slammer is looking horribly bleak.

I remember the bleak, hopeless look on Don's face when the bald-headed screw shacked him up with me for his first night in prison, poor bastard. He probably still doesn't realise how neatly his wife and her lover set him up and shunted him safely out the way so they could have their baby without his miserable face hanging round to ruin their special moment. He's on the numbers on another wing, banged up with all the nonces. I'm not surprised. He was so slow-witted he was bound to say the wrong thing to the wrong con sooner or later, so put the thicko in the sickos and good luck to him.

'Get your water!' yells a screw and swipes the board clean, signalling the end of visiting time. A racket erupts as prisoners rush about like animals in a zoo at feeding time, collecting teabags, burn and other things they need before lockdown.

For a moment, I wish I was in the Double A-Cat block. There's a high security prison inside this one that houses the well-connected cons, the Mafia and IRA and top bods with thirty-year sentences and nothing to lose. The screws have to walk about on eggshells calling the cons 'Sir' and serving them cups of tea like fuckin' waiters. Then again, I'd be even more likely to get a chib in my neck over there.

I glance over at Danny; can't help flinching. He looks devastated. Anyone would think he'd just found out

147

his mum had died, if they didn't know better. He's still rubbing his arms and swiping his face and blowing his nose, but he's not bothering to look at his watch any more. He's due in court tomorrow and a night from hell is on its way.

In the steely light of the following morning, a prison officer opens his cell and surveys the chaos inside; bedclothes, cups, clothes, books, ripped and torn, all over the floor.

'What have we here?' he quips, 'a fuckin' crime scene?'

Danny's thrashing about on his soaking mattress. He's been withdrawing all night and wants nothing more than to die.

'Come on, come on, get your lazy arse outta bed. This ain't no health spa,' the screw says cheerfully.

Danny lunges off his squelching mattress, grabs his transparent plastic bag of clothes and follows the screw, wiping reams of snot away with his arm. The screw leads him along landings and through barred gates. Danny trudges behind, head down and arms dangling uselessly like a primate with bad breath and B.O.

A second officer unlocks the door to the holding cell where about fifteen cons are waiting to be taken to court. 'You look like shit on toast with lumps on,' he observes, not totally without sympathy.

Danny slumps on a bench, kicking at two other cons so that he can put his legs up. Noting the rabid look in Danny's eye, the cons sit elsewhere.

One by one, names are called and the holding cell empties. Danny rubs his aching shoulders, mops his pasty face and thinks, over and over, 'Just a bit of gear to ease the pain... Please, God, a bit of gear...'

If only he could escape! He'd break someone's leg for a bit of crack... slit a throat for some smack... Hell, he'd do whatever it took to be over in Peckham, booting up gear and smoking the cherry.

It's not going to happen, though. Tooth fairies don't exist, and Santa Clause is nothing but an evil myth.

A screw unlocks the door. 'You're going to court by cab, my son, because no one's going your way. Be on your best fucking behaviour 'cause Mr Bennet don't need no hassle today.' He nods to a younger screw, who approaches Danny with a pair of handcuffs. Danny's eyes narrow. For a moment he stops sweating, stops aching and even stops thinking about gear. Maybe, just maybe, tooth fairies do exist.

'Ouch,' he says as the cuffs clamp down on his wrists. 'They're much too tight, guv.'

The screw's still wet behind the ears. He's so busy slackening the cuffs that he doesn't notice Danny swipe the biro protruding from his pocket. Danny smirks as the screw scurries about, putting paperwork in a plastic bag, thinking he knows what he's doing. Tosser.

Minutes later, Danny's being led into wide-open space. A refreshing breeze caresses his face, giving him his first proper smile in months. There, in front of him, is a slightly battered-looking taxi with the door wide open. If this ain't his ticket to freedom, he'll kick himself for the rest of his life.

The screws squeeze into the back of the cab, one on either side of him. If either of them knew what it was like to be going through enforced cold turkey, or more to the point, for *Danny* to be going through enforced cold turkey, they would never have got in. The taxi sets off through the prison gates and across the car park.

Danny notices the cab driver check him out in his rear view mirror. The driver seems relaxed enough. Danny can't think why. He should be shitting himself.

The screw on Danny's left gazes out the window while the one on his right leafs through his paperwork. Danny shuts his eyes, concentrating. The intolerable aches and sweats have mercifully subsided. His brain is working smooth as clockwork. Mustn't act suspicious.

The taxi drives down Shooters Hill and into Blackheath towards the Magistrates' Court where his pleas and d's await. Guilty; not guilty... who cares any more? He's gonna be guilty as hell in a minute.

He eyes the taxi driver in the mirror, thinks he recognises him from somewhere. Maybe he and the cabbie shared a laugh once in better days, in the back of this very taxi. The car slows down and comes to a halt at the lights.

Now!

Its as if the go-ahead has come from somewhere else, some outside force that has Danny's best interests at heart, because Danny knows without doubt that this is the perfect moment to lunge forward, throw his shackled arms over the cab driver's head and jab the screw's ballpoint pen just hard enough into the cabbie's eye socket to make him yelp.

'Undo these fuckin' cuffs or he'll lose his fuckin' sight!' Danny screams.

The scream and the sudden movement blast through the confined space of the taxi, taking the screws by surprise.

'Fuckin' ell, he means it,' squeals the younger screw staring into the rear-view mirror in alarm to see one vulnerable eyeball bulging obscenely out of its socket. The other screw's in shock, his reams of paperwork scattering useless into the seat well.

Danny settles the matter for them. 'Undo me and get the fuck out of the car or I'm popping this fucking eye!' The taxi driver helps out by making a desperate squeal.

150

The screws have no choice. It's all happened so quickly that, by the time the lights turn green, they're standing outside the cab looking shame-faced and helpless.

'Drive, you cunt!' Danny roars into the driver's ear and hangs onto the seat as the cab lurches into gear and speeds away.

As soon as the screws are out of sight, Danny gives the cab driver's shoulder a reassuring pat. 'Sorry about that. Nothing personal. 'Aven't got a fag, 'ave ya, mate?'

Once the cabbie has recovered his wits and found his voice, and they're both puffing away in relief on the cabbie's cigs, it transpires that the cabbie's an old mate of Danny's dad. And wouldn't you know? He remembers driving Danny home from a couple of junior football matches when he was a kid. It's not long before the cabbie's forgotten how close he came to losing his eye and the two of them are laughing away like old pals. Well, almost. The cabbie's wet himself and his heart's still up in his throat.

'You can drop me off here, Bertie,' Danny grins as the taxi passes Lewisham Station, from where it's only a minute's walk to his mate's crack-house. 'Sorry I can't give you a tip, ha ha.' He leans in and adds sincerely, 'but you know where to go for a favour if ever you need one.'

The taxi driver nods. He's going to have a mighty big favour to call in one day.

Someone else who's become one of my closest mates since we met on the RAPt wing is a slick, stylish fella, a bit like that actor out of a James Bond movie, Daniel Craig. Like Winston, the finicky armed robber, Tams enjoys the finer things in life. He loves his top night clubs, his toned physique and his clobber and, as a mate, he's one hundred percent reliable.

151

Tams

On the pull

There's a good-looking fella drinking a Harvey Wall-banger on the other side of the bar. Tams raises his glass and smiles at him. The man raises his glass and smiles back.

He's slim with fine, light brown hair, expensively styled, and even from this distance Tams can see that he's wearing a white Raf Simons shirt and tan Moschino jacket, slim-cut Stone Island jeans and shoes by Kurt Geiger. He's by far the most attractive guy in this packed Soho bar with its deep purple banquettes, crimson carpet and matching cushions. The lighting is designed to graduate from golden yellow to romantic pink and moody green so gracefully that only your subconscious notices, as it wafts almost imperceptibly between feeling sexy, moody and serene. Or, in Tam's case, simply moody.

Tams wishes the guy would come over and introduce himself. But it doesn't look like that's going to happen, because every time Tams runs his fingers through his silky hair the fella copies him, and every time Tams glances over with one suggestively raised eyebrow, the guy follows suit.

Tams tears his gaze away from his reflection in the mirror on the far side of the bar, and tries to pick up the threads of his friends' conversation. There are two girls and three guys, all talking animatedly, desperate to air their next comment, never mind what the last person has just said. Their eyes gleam with pupils dilated. One of the girls is flicking her hair in the direction of the guy she fancies, while the guy she fancies has his feet pointed towards the other girl, which Tams, who's studied a bit of popular psychology, knows doesn't bode well for the hair-flicking girl. Meanwhile, one of the guys has got the others mesmerised for a moment and he's talking about…

Tams struggles to make sense of the words coming out of his friend's fast-wagging mouth, but, try as he might, he can't make out what the guy is wanking on about.

Tams up-ends his glass and drains it. It's his sixth already but he's feeling about as twatted as a man during Holy Communion, and having about the same amount of fun. He's trying to have fun; he's been trying for the past hour and a half, but somehow the subtle gradation of the lighting, the company of his 'magazine-perfect-looking' friends and the expertly-selected music are bypassing him as if he were some invisible bastard that doesn't belong here.

He gets abruptly to his feet and heads between the tables for the super trendy toilets, apparently designed by some impossible-to-get-hold-of architect flown specially in from Japan. His pal, Simon, gets up too, and that good-looking fella in the trendy clothes on the other side of the bar tags along with them.

Tams enters one of the futuristic cubicles with their super-duper arse-washing, fanny-drying shiny chrome bogs. He's only got a bit of coke, barely enough for a proper snort. Simon slithers in with him and Tams locks the door, waiting for Simon to pull out his supply because Simon is loaded, and because Simon fancies him, and because Simon is keeping a concerned eye on him.

Simon smiles at Tams with that gummy smile of his that other people seem to warm to but which makes Tams feel queasy, and kneels elegantly over the mirrored toilet seat. He's six foot two and wearing a specially tailored Icho suit with a collarless Dunhill shirt in deep fuschia.

Tams, who's five-eight, five-seven in his socks, admires the long, clean lines of Simon's body as he expertly cuts, sweeps and divides the coke into four lines. Tams knows that he will have to kneel down next to him and insert Simon's rolled-up fifty in his nostril, (Simon's a flash bastard) then watch Simon stick the slightly moist wrap almost reverently up his own nostril afterwards. What Tams would really like to do is scoop the coke into a bag, shove Simon's head down the toilet, slam the lid against it a couple of times till he stops smiling that gummy smile, then wash up the coke with a little bicarbonate of soda and have a proper fucking crack hit.

Instead, he sniffs up his double line, roughly inserts the fifty into Simon's nose, giving the smarmy poof a painful thrill, and goes out to take a leak before Simon has time to snort up and snatch a look at his dick.

Simon comes out of the cubicle rubbing his nose as Tams zips his flies. In the mirror Tams catches the disappointed look in his eyes. Fuck him. Simon caught a nice long glimpse of Tam's ample cock once, when Tams didn't get out of the cubicle quick enough.

Tams makes his way back through the svelte clientele sipping on their Flirtinis and their Quick Fucks and their Mind Erasers and other cocktails of the moment. Someone's bought him another Harvey Wallbanger. It waits uninvitingly by his seat.

He sits down, waiting to feel a rush off the coke. He knows it's not going to happen when one of his friends gives him a lovely sympathetic smile and he feels an insane urge to give her a kick up the arse. She's a gorgeous creature with luxuriant chestnut hair cascading in voluptuous ringlets down her bronzed shoulders and brushing against a pair of perfectly sculpted breasts filling out a Christian Lacroix strappy black and gold top. Tams had a feel of her tits a couple of weeks ago. It was a bit

154

like sourcing top quality goods in Harrods for some rich client and being satisfied that they fit all the requirements, without having any desire to nab them for himself.

They worship him, his friends. Think he's lovable Cockney, even though he modifies his accent to fit in with theirs. Usually his quick, casual wit has them cracking up, 'te heh heh heh,' not 'ha ha fuckin' ha ha' round there. But lately, since he's been getting more heavily into the free-base, even when he thinks he's at his funniest, they don't always get the joke. Like earlier tonight, when he told the attractive woman in her early forties at the next table that she looked like a million dollars. It was the "in loose change" aside that didn't go down so well.

Still, he's got a better joke lined up for them now.

'There's this geezer in a pub,' he begins, interrupting a conversation between Simon and Luxuriant Ringlets, 'he says to his mate: "I could have any bird in here."'

The girls titter and Tams takes this as encouragement to continue:

'How's that, then?' asks his mate, looking around at all the good-looking slap.'

The girls don't titter at this and one of the guys looks positively offended.

'Cause I'm a rapist.'

Tams breaks into a grin, waiting for his friends to see the humour and join in. Simon tries to laugh, 'tee huh huh huh,' only to start blushing when no one else does.

The woman at the next table, the one who looks like a million dollars in loose coins, says in a snooty voice, 'Not very much of a comedian, are you?'

The girl with the luxuriant ringlets starts giggling and Tams glares at her, having a sudden vision of smashing her head against the table. The girl catches the look in his eye, flinches, and stops laughing.

'Oh yeah? Well how's this one then?' says Tams, leaning back in his seat with a wide grin. 'Fact: nine out of ten people enjoy gangbangs.' The woman at the next table and Tam's friends stare at him, waiting for the punch-line. They don't realise that there isn't one.

'You don't get it do you, you pretentious twats? Says Tams rising to his feet. He doesn't know what's got into him, telling sick jokes and insulting this decent bunch of people. He can't seem to help himself. Fuck this trendy bar, fuck all its trendy martinis with names he's never heard of, fuck all the great-looking birds with their posh accents and homo-fucks like Simon; he needs some fucking crack.

'I'm sorry. I'll see ya later,' he mumbles, heading for the door. Along the way, he stumbles over a handbag, making some dolled-up little slut squeal with outrage.

At the same moment, Million Dollar Woman figures out his joke and shouts over the noise of the bar, 'You are a sick piece of shit, do you know that?'

Both events coincide with a dip in the general noise level, and Tams' face burns as everyone turns to stare at his departing figure.

Still smarting, he strides along Wardour Street and into Shaftesbury Avenue. He's only got a tenner in his pocket, not enough for a pipe. But he knows how to make money quickly, even though it makes him cringe to think how far he's descended.

The thought of his father flashes through his mind accompanied by a surge of guilt tinged with hatred. His dad's a big name in the London crime world, dealing in large shipments of coke, mostly from Holland and Spain. His dad hadn't minded him snorting the stuff, even a decade ago when he found his teenage son sticking his nose in a kilo of coke hidden temporarily in the loft. But mix the coke with ammonia or bicarb, Tams thinks

156

bitterly, and all of a sudden you're a worthless piece of shit with your entire trust fund cut off.

It's Friday night and it seems as if everyone is determined to bump shoulders with him, as if all the stressed-out angry people in London are making a beeline for each other. There are a few muted curses and infuriated grimaces, and it's a wonder he doesn't break into a fight before joining the queue outside a gay nightclub, keeping his face down in case anyone should recognise him.

It's still early in the club and for once he can see all the lights twinkling behind the modern stained glass artwork. The bar looks like some incredible shining mirage arising out of the darkness with its countless varieties of alcohol in a multitude of different bottles glistening in the silvery light.

There was a time when Tams would have appreciated all this shit. He used to design interiors, mostly offices for artsy companies and bijoux hotel rooms, which made his dad laugh and tell him that was a job for queers. That niggled Tams like nothing else because his dad employs plenty of interior designers to work on his pads and his yacht, and even sketches some of the designs himself, but nobody ever calls Bob Tamsworth queer. They'd have their teeth caved in.

Tams tried advertising after that, and with his spry wit was quite successful, but his dad said that advertising was a poofy industry too and encouraged him to follow in his own footsteps, even though he'd always said that Tams was useless at it. On a family holiday when Tams was a nipper, his mum had hidden a bit of extra Charlie in his nappy and he'd kicked up such a fuss going through customs that his dad had suspected him ever since of trying to get them all arrested.

Tams orders a bottle of San Miguel, cheapest thing in here, and tries not to wince when he gets the change from his tenner. He glances around the club. It must be nearly twelve; it's starting to fill up with homos. One of them will have to buy him his next drink.

His practised eye passes over their clothes. Cheap dressers, most of them, except a couple trying to look the part in their Dolce & Gabbana suits... but what's this? A fella stepping onto the dance floor, jiggling as he walks, must have popped a pill in the bogs. He's wearing the bottom half of a well-cut suit and a striped pink and white shirt, gotta be Lanvin, (though possibly Hermes) unbuttoned at the collar where his tie would have been an hour or two ago.

He's the one. Probably had a few drinks after work, intending to go home, but one thing led to another... and lucky woofter, he's in the right place at the right time to meet Tams.

'Great pills, aren't they?' Tams yells, dancing up to him as if he's popped a few himself.

'Fantastic!' the guy yells back with an appreciative smile. He's tall and gangly with a slightly goofy upper lip, but he's got a bit of style on the dance floor. Tams is the one with the moves though. In addition to his skills in interior design and advertising, he's a bit of a mover in the clubs. His dad used to show him off whenever he threw a party, until Tams reached twelve or thirteen and started making his old man uncomfortable. Tams uses his skills to their best advantage now, throwing out a few casual sashays and knee bends that have the guy in the pink shirt clapping in admiration.

Tams remembers when he used to do pills and be so easily impressed. 'Fancy a drink? He yells.

'Yes, sure!' the man yells back. 'Let me get you one!'

That was a test and he passed it. 'What's your name?' asks Tams at the bar, where it's a bit quieter.

'Grant, and yours?'

'Dean,' says Tams whose real name is George, which he can't stand, so he just shortened his surname to Tams.

'You've got some pretty neat dance moves,' beams Grant. 'Gosh, in this light you actually look the spitting image of James Dean.'

'No, d'you really think so?' asks Tams, one eyebrow arched. People are always pointing out the resemblance.

Grant spares no expense on two cocktails, specials of the club that aren't on the menu.

'How old are you, Dean?'

'Twenty-two,' lies Tams, savouring the subtle flavours of the drink. No cheap vodka or concentrated fruit juices in this one.

'You?'

'Thirty-five. Investment banker. Single. Hampstead. Porsche.' He starts to giggle. 'Now you know everything, we can talk about something more interesting.'

Tams likes his style. Except for that giggle. 'Builder. Single. Brixton. Skint,' he says.

Grant runs one finger along Tams' biceps and Tams flexes his arm for him. He might be short but he keeps himself fit at the gym, and if his James Dean scowl should ever fail, his six-pack always does the trick.

'Builder, Brixton.' Grant murmurs, 'you must be hard, my friend.'

Tams smiles. Or rather he sneers. 'Oh yeah, I'm hard baby. Just you wait and see.' He drains his drink, pops the strawberry between his teeth and smiles, 'Let's go.'

This is going to be even easier than he thought.

Tams

Cracking it

Tam suppresses a whistle as the taxi drives through the automatic gates of Grant's Hampstead abode. A magnificently up-lit Georgian wisteria-clad villa meets his gaze. Parked in the sweeping drive is a gleaming red Porsche, no more than a year old. Tams can't believe he's got so lucky. Grant shoots him a sideways glance and Tams realises that his date is entertaining similar thoughts about him.

Grant pays the cabbie and takes out the keys to his imposing front door. Tams looks at him, a question forming on his lips.

Grant shakes his head. 'Inheritance. Dad died unexpectedly young,' he explains. 'Come in, Dean. Make yourself at home.'

Tams kicks off his shoes and his feet seem to sink several inches into the luxuriant cream carpet. He's touched by Grant's generosity, although the eager, expectant look on Grant's face makes him despise him. Still, he'll try to be nice.

'Go and make yourself comfortable,' he says, giving Grant a shove towards a sumptuous-looking reception room stuffed with old oil paintings, chaise longues and hand-woven Persian rugs. 'I've gotta take a piss.'

On the way from the club, Tams made Grant stop at a cash machine and memorised the silly fool's pin number, then dropped by a dealer en route to Hampstead. Grant wanted some coke but Tams has got something much better than that.

Tams skips up the grand curving stair case and takes a nice long slash in a bathroom that's almost as big as his flat in Peckham. He's tempted to wander about the lavish bedrooms and admire the décor, but first things first. He strides into the first bedroom and whips the sheet off a king-sized sleigh bed. Soft-as-silk Egyptian cotton; never mind.

Grant has put on some funky music, poured them both some excellent Port by the looks of it, and reclined on a maroon chaise-longue. Tams walks up to him, tearing the sheet into strips.

'Gosh, that's er... rather kinky, isn't it?' says Grant taking a nervous gulp from his glass. 'How do I know I can trust you?'

'That is a very good question,' says Tams, walking behind the ridiculous purple sofa to roughly seize Grant's scrawny arms. He deftly ties the wrists together and clambers back over the sofa to incapacitate Grant's legs. Grant kicks out at him in a manner half-playful, half-afraid, so Tams gives him one no-nonsense squeeze in the crotch and the pillock surrenders at once. A final strip secured round Grant's mouth renders him mute.

Tams takes a miniature Martell bottle from his pocket, gets out the crack and a lighter and sets about making a pipe. He's almost done when he notices Grant's eyes watching him intently above his gag. Tams turns away, sucks on the pipe and goes up, up and away into the land of eternal utopia that has been calling to him all this time, yearning for his return. All his problems have evaporated. Even the thing he did yesterday doesn't seem nearly as dreadful as it did then. In fact, the whole event flashes through his mind like some silly, inconsequential television drama.

'*No, no, I no want to get the sack. You 'vill have to shoot me,*' said the Indian fella in the petrol station when

Tams hit on the idea of robbing it. He's never done a hold-up before, didn't even have a gun, but thrusting two fingers in his jacket pocket towards the Indian bloke should have been enough.

'*Give me the money or I'll fucking kill you?*' he's growled with all the aggression he could muster.

'*No, no, no,*' said the Indian, disconcertingly shaking his head and nodding it at the same time. '*Kill me. Go ahead and kill me! But you no take my bloody money. I am calling police now.*'

'*What's your problem? It ain't your fucking money!*' Tams had yelled, beginning to kick himself. He almost wished he *did* have a gun, because then he could have blown the fucking hero's head off.

But he'd had to concede defeat. Even though the robbery had been a complete failure, and he's had his hat pulled low over his eyes and kept his face down, he's been paranoid ever since that he might have been caught on camera. There are better ways of making money, like picking up Grants in gay nightclubs, and he can't believe how the lure of crack could have made him do something so dicey.

He lights another stone, and when he comes back down to earth, notices a decent-looking fella watching him helplessly from the other side of the coffee table. He picks up the Martell bottle, climbs over the table and yanks down Grant's gag to put the pipe in his mouth. Grant sucks dutifully until he's soaring away into heaven. Tams can see it in his eyes. It's such a blissful surprise, going off on a crack holiday for the first time. Briefly jealous, Tams whips out the pipe, tightens the gag and shoves Grant down on the chaise-longue with his foot.

He jogs upstairs to check out the master bedroom. He can tell right away which room Grant has made his boudoir, because it's all opulent Baroque wall-hangings, lush pink setting and a ludicrous four-poster bed that might have come from Liberace himself. Tams potters about, looking at photographs of Grant embracing various lovers, not all of them blokes... though some of the girls bear a striking family resemblance. He checks out the clothes in Grant's dressing room: Nicole Fahri, Balenciaga, Yves Saint Laurent, Christian Dior... Pity Grant's so much taller. Still, it doesn't take long to put aside a collection of clothes that fit, as well as a nice pile of valuables.

The come-down from the crack is starting to get to him and he finds himself on hands and knees, raking his fingernails through a silk rug to look for a crumb of crack he might have dropped. This is ridiculous, he reminds himself, remembering that he's left the crack downstairs. He needs something to take his mind off the comedown.

Back in the living room, he unbuttons his Stone Islands, removes Grant's gag, slips out his cock and notices Grant's eyes widen with awe as he forces it into his mouth. Tams has a disproportionately large member for his frame and he's impressed on how much has been swallowed up by that slightly goofy mouth. As long as he doesn't look down, it's blinding.

After he's done the business, he smokes another stone, let's Grant have a suck on the pipe and resumes his tour of the house. He's not thinking too much about the future, but he's got a vague three-day plan, possibly longer. Just so long as he can keep Grant trussed up and reasonably content, he'll be able to burgle him while rinsing his bank accounts at his leisure.

He's starting to prang again; there's that horrible buzzing noise in his ears and he keeps getting distracted by all the eclectic artwork hanging on the fashionably patterned walls. When the wallpaper between the paintings starts moving, like intricate formations of marching ants, he bundles both lots of booty into some enormous Pinel &

Pinel suitcase, then returns to the living room to plunge his dick back down Grant's throat and alleviate the symptoms for both of them.

Once Tams has gathered up everything that he can easily flog and lugged it out to the boot of the Porsche, he's surprised to hear the sound of birds singing. The first golden rays of dawn are gleaming onto this exclusive district of London. Going back inside, he drags Grant up to his boudoir and ties him spread-eagled to the bed. Then he covers him with some super-luxuriant quilt, sticks the TV remote in his hand, gives him a drink of water, and gags him up again. It's not long before he's cruising away in Grant's powerful set of wheels to make a start on that bank account.

It turns out to be an excellent arrangement. For the next few days Grant is rewarded with unlimited bondage, rough sex and a break from work, while Tams makes various forays into the outside world to empty his accounts and spend the contents in ways he's only been able to dream of until now. Grant really appreciates the tasty titbits from Fortnum and Mason that Tams bring back, never realising how they're costing him. If ever he kicks up a fuss, Tams simply withholds the crack and he's good as gold again. He doesn't know that it's crack exactly, the silly poof, 'cause Tams has told him, truthfully enough, it's a very pure form of coke.

On the second day, the telephone starts ringing and doesn't stop, so Tams takes it off the hook. On the third day, several callers come to the door, but go away again. On the fourth day, Tams comes up with a plan to have Grant inform anyone who might be concerned that he is taking a spur-of-the-moment holiday. But somehow he's having such a good time, and Grant seems to be having such a good time too, (not that he lets Grant open his mouth unless to swallow things) that somehow it doesn't seem important. He's got a nice stash of money to last him a couple of months, not to mention a whole new wardrobe of designer labels, back at his flat in Peckham, and well, he really oughta to get going... except he's caught up enjoying the high life. He's feeling powerful and significant, exactly the way his bastard of a dad seems to feel every day of his life.

On the fifth morning, the house is raided. Tams and Grant are enjoying a rare sleep at the time and are surprised to be awoken by three uniformed police officers trooping incongruously into their lavish surroundings. Hurriedly, Tams yanks down Grant's gag and sets about untying his wrists under the bedclothes. 'Don't say a fucking word,' he whispers.

'Grant Fortescue?' asks one of the policemen. 'Excuse us for intruding. We've had reports of your missing whereabouts.'

Grant massages his suffering jaw then clears his throat.

Tams crosses his fingers under the bedclothes. The words that are about to come out of Grant's mouth could seriously screw up the next decade of his life.

HMP Belmarsh

Break dancing

Dr No's gone on holiday. There's a new quack on duty and a queue of hopeful convicts stretching halfway along the spur to see him.

A con I did a favour for a couple of weeks ago paid me back with a couple of his epilepsy pills, and they worked so well I've decided to become an epileptic, although I'm not too sure what an epileptic is.

'So what are your symptoms, mate?' I ask him casually. He's a tongue-tied sort of a fella, not much of a one for descriptions, and I'm a bit baffled when he pitches himself to the floor and starts shaking like a washing machine on full rinse mode with his tongue hanging out.

'It ain't funny,' he manages to say, watching me double up with laughter.

'Oh shit, so *that's* epi... epil... epilexy... You have the fits,' I say, shaking my head at my own ignorance. 'Sorry mate, for a minute back then I thought you was having a heart attack and I was gonna have to resuscitate ya.' At this thought, we both start laughing until we can barely breathe. After a while, he says I'd better leave him alone before I really do bring on a fit, because the pills don't always work one hundred percent.

That was yesterday. Today, I'm off to court for a driving offence I can't remember committing. It might be something to do with the time I accidentally overtook a police car at a hundred and twenty on a motorway. Whatever, I know it'll be a long day.

I'm woken early, to grey sky and dogs barking, only to sit around in a dog box for a couple of hours before being wedged in a sweat box in a meat-wagon, which gets

166

stuck in traffic for a further hour or two. I sit about in court half the day and, when I'm finally called up, I plead guilty to some completely different misdemeanour involving stolen goods. The judge can't give me a fine or any more bird, because I'm doing a lengthy sentence already, so he slaps on six months to serve concurrently.

On the way back, we get stuck in another traffic jam, giving me a further two hours to curse yet another complete waste of time, effort and expense at the behest of Her Majesty. By the time we pull up to the prison gates, I'm desperate for more of that con's pills. They must chill you out pretty good if they can stop a full-blown epileptic fit, I reckon, plotting where I'm going to stage my own convulsions. In Reception would be good; plenty of room and lots of witnesses. But what if everyone were to crack up and set me off too? I'd be fucked.

Then again, the new doctor might not be like Dr No. Dr No would take one look at me quaking on the floor and foaming at the mouth, and prescribe me some nice Ibuprofen. The new doctor might actually take me seriously.

Hanging about in Reception waiting to be escorted back to my house block, I notice a group of cons huddled together. I can tell by the atmosphere brewing around them that they're up to no good. One of them throws a glance towards the safe behind the jump and I notice that the door hasn't been shut properly. All of a sudden my senses are on alert and I'm itching for these fellas to finish whatever they're up to before the screws turn up.

'You dozy wanker!' one of them shouts angrily and starts shoving both hands against another con's chest, making him stumble backwards across the room. Nothing too theatrical, they don't want to set any alarms off. The screw on duty looks up from his paperwork with a sigh and goes over to break it up.

By this time, the angry con has propelled the other fella right over to the door and the screw doesn't notice one of the others hurdle lithely over the counter, open the safe, and start dishing out the money to the other cons. Within seconds they're rolling it up and bottling it; much safer than putting it in a safe, with the door left open, when there's lots of thieves about.

There's so many notes being passed round that no one objects when I get in on the act and roll up as much as I think I'll be able to handle. Still, it's a fuckin' tight squeeze. For about ten seconds we've got our hands in our pants, and are making silent, constipated grimaces.

The problem with the dozy wanker miraculously resolves, and the screw stomps back to his place. He's still cursing the vagaries of his job when he notices that the door to the safe is ajar. We're all trying to act innocent but can't resist a peek to see the look of dismay on his mug. We can almost see him kicking himself as he gets out his whistle and gives it a hopeless blast.

The screws that were on their way get a sudden move on and set about looking the business. We're all lined against the wall and strip-searched, trying not to laugh because that money has as good as disappeared off the face of the earth.

'Ever heard the story of Captain Hook and his buried treasure?' someone sniggers, allowing us all to release a fit of helpless laughter.

Back in our cells, some of us are having trouble retrieving our takings.

'Gives new meaning to the words 'dirty money!' Someone bellows from the other end of the landing.

I'm laughing so hard with my finger stuck up my arse that the stash wiggles of my reach. I have an alarming vision of not being able to shit for days, then having to go to hospital to have my wad surgically removed. I'd be the laughing stock of the Marsh for the next half century, which is about as long as a joke can run in these places. Eventually, after contorting myself into all sorts of ludicrous positions, while my cellmate almost does himself an injury laughing, I manage to pluck out the notes, one at a time, and give them a little rinse under the tap.

I'm in luck. The doctor's queue has whittled down for dinner and, just as I was hoping, the new doctor is a complete mug.

'Yes, a long history of ep... epi... epilexy,' I nod, gravely mimicking the grave nods that he's been giving me since I started explaining my predicament. 'Had it on and off since I was a kid.'

'I see,' he says, frowning at my medical notes. 'However, I don't see any previous prescriptions for Rivotril...'

'I thought it had cleared up, doctor,' I say sadly. 'Something about being stuck in here, you know, with all the peace and quiet and nothing much to do... Must have chilled me out,' I lie atrociously. Dr No would be turning on his beach towel if he could see me now. 'But lately, with that court case and having to go to hospital 'n' all, you know what it's like, the fits have started up again...'

'Do you remember your previous dosage?' he asks, pen poised over prescription pad.

When I've managed to stop choking, I gasp, 'Er... four a day, doctor.'

'Four a day,' he says putting the ink on paper.

I can't believe my luck. Still, what a muppet! I should have said six, or better still, eight. Oh well, don't want to jinx it; maybe I can increase the dose next time I see him.

'Thanks, Dr Yes,' I smile. Some other wit must have coined that term already because he frowns wearily. Poor bastard must be exhausted, trying to make it up to all Dr No's neglected patients.

I stride back to my cell, whistling. I've got a week's supply of happy pills and a hundred and ten quid, that I hadn't been expecting, to spend on drugs. All in all, it hasn't been a bad day.

Fly is the best cellmate I've ever been banged up with. He's a fat little lad with a dry wit, and only has to drop a couple of his off-the-cuff observations to have me cracking up. Most evenings he gets the night screws chortling and doing him favours they wouldn't do for anyone else.

During the night, Fly is not such a great cellmate. His name says it all; he sleeps with his mouth wide open. In the summer he's a sitting target for random flying insects. He's a nice fellow though, tries to wait for me to get to sleep first, otherwise his snores keep my eyes wide as saucers and my teeth on edge. Sometimes the thunderous rumbles coming from his bed intrude on some delicious dream I'm having, making me want to reach over and punch him.

I took a Rivotril last night and felt as contented as a baby wrapped in fluffy blankets in a cradle. Didn't hear so much as a whisper all night long. Fly took two and couldn't get up this morning so I ate his breakfast while he snored. When he finally came round, he said he'd never had such a delightful snooze in all his life, so after lunch, we take four each and settle down to see what happens.

For the first time ever, I don't jerk into consciousness when the gates clang open and footsteps go thundering along the landings. Dinner passes by unheeded, and when we finally manage to peel open our eyes at about one o'clock the next morning, we're both starving. Luckily Fly's got a cupboard full of goodies thanks to his generous private spends, so we gorge ourselves on Hula Hoops and Bounties and laugh about how good it would be to sleep away our entire sentences, waking once in a while for a midnight feast.

An hour later, we take another three pills and watch the ever-present grey walls of a convict's life fade out to La La Land. From time to time, the screws try to rouse us, but it's too much bother so they leave us dead to the world.

A few days later we've run out of pills and are wide-awake at four in the morning. We've also run out of stuff to laugh about and things are starting to look shit.

'Maybe I can get some of them pills, 'arry,' Fly's voice interrupts the silence.

'Yeah, but you ain't got epilepsy,' I frown in the darkness.

'Nor 'ave you, twat-face.'

He has a point, but having made such an authentic impression on the doctor I've sort of convinced myself that I *am* an epileptic. 'Don't you think it would look a bit fishy if we both got the fits?'

'*What!*' Fly snorts. 'Those screws wouldn't notice a coincidence like their own shit coming out smelling like a Christmas dinner.'

'Maybe,' I say dubiously.

By six a.m., with no sleep and nothing to do, we're ready to try anything. Fly climbs out of bed and lies on the concrete floor for a trial run. His tongue lolls out the side of his mouth and he makes a few bizarre grunting noises while shaking his limbs and wobbling like a fat dollop of jelly.

'Stop laughing,' he snaps. 'Do I look the part?'

'You look like a fuckin' idiot,' I laugh, gasping for breath.

'Bollocks,' he grunts 'What am I doing wrong?'

I'm glad that the con with epilepsy showed me what a proper fit looks like, otherwise I'd have thought Fly looked the business. 'Nah, mate, you've gotta do it like you're completely out of it,' I advise him. 'And don't make those demented noises.'

'What d'ya mean, completely out of it? You wouldn't catch me doing this if I was in my right mind, would ya? Bollocks. You'd better show me.'

With misgivings I lie down on the cold concrete next to him, roll my eyes up into their sockets and start to jerk as if I'm receiving five thousand volts of electricity up the rectum. My crazy jerks come to a halt when a helpless guffawing starts up next to me.

'That was a proper fit,' I say, feeling put out. 'It ain't funny.'

'Right, right,' he snorts. 'Whatever you say. Just hit the bell.'

I press the emergency bell and we wait for a minute or two. I press it again. 'You'd be dead by now if this was for real,' I tell Fly, who is on the floor.

At last a pair of footsteps comes stomping along the landing and a voice sighs, 'All right, all right, what is it now?'

Fly launches into his fit just like I showed him. One look at his gormless face shuddering on the floor, and I've got tears spurting out of my eyes and an uncontrollable attack of giggles. The hatch shoots open and a pair of eyes peer in. I'm bent over Fly so the screw can't see my face.

'Quick, get the doctor!' I yell. 'He's having a fit! I'm trying to stop him swallowing his tongue!'

The screw marches off, returning shortly with two other screws and a yawning doctor. Fly was glad of the break but now he's at it again, jerking his limbs like his life depends on it. I'm sitting on my bed with my head in my hands. 'He's in a really bad way,' I manage to splutter.

As soon as Fly is carried away on a stretcher I crawl into bed with the blanket over my head and give myself up to the hysterics. At last I fall into a deep sleep, only to be woken up five minutes later for breakfast.

A couple of hours after breakfast, I'm peering over the landing in bleary-eyed disbelief. A nurse is escorting a grinning Fly back onto the spur. He's wearing prison pyjamas and a pair of nice comfy slippers he must have grafted from the hospital wing. Spotting me, he slips out of his pocket a packet of pills, same as mine, and slides them away again before the nurse notices.

I suppress an amazed whistle. That stupid, shuddering, tongue-lolling performance of his has got us back in business.

Tam's Dad

Top of the game

Their accents sound out of place in this trendy West End minimalist hotel. They don't give a toss. Their money's as good as those snobs at those other tables, glaring down their chiselled noses at them from time to time. None of those stuck-up twats have ordered the caviar, at £250 a pop, or the Dom Perignon at £300 a bottle, or the petit plats of crudités and fois gras mille-feuilles and flaked truffle parcel thingies lying untouched on the table.

They always meet somewhere different, the more outrageously expensive the better. Bob Tamsworth doesn't want anyone thinking business is going downhill. And business is what they're here to discuss; or it would be, if only Eric would decide to fucking show up.

Bob looks like he's just stepped off some one-hundred-metre Sunseeker yacht, with his pristine white trousers and his deliberately casual, scuffed espadrilles. His midnight blue silk shirt is unbuttoned to show the deep all-over tan which has eroded his once handsome face into a series of miniature canyons, branching into a series of tributaries at the corners of his ice blue eyes.

There's no flies on Bob Tamsworth. He doesn't suffer fools gladly, and Eric's no-show is starting to create an atmosphere of unrest amongst the five associates from various parts of London with their deep voices and broken noses. They've each visited the toilet for a discreet snort, and are back in their seats, waiting.

The way that Bob's twirling his champagne glass in his fingers doesn't bode well. Bob considers even a minute's tardiness to be a sign of disrespect. He was here half an hour early. So was everyone else. Eric is only five minutes late, but everyone knows that, to Bob's mind, that's thirty-five.

Eric doesn't get it. He seriously seems to think he's a mere seven minutes late when he arrives with his jaunty stride and overload of gold jewellery. At a distant table, one of the chiselled-nosed women stares from his wide-striped shirt down to his patent leather shoes as if he were trailing a dog shit footprint across the minimalist-design rug. Even Barry, with his Burt Reynolds moustache and lady-killer eyes, whose legendary unpunctuality has reduced numberless stood-up beauties to tears, was here at 11.30 on the dot, never mind that his wife had to hand him his clothes in the taxi.

Eric sits down, tossing the South London Press onto the table with such force that the flaky truffle pâtés shiver in their parcels. By way of apology, he beams. 'Fuckin' traffic round 'ere. Awful, innit?'

Bob raises an eyebrow. In one measured movement, he adjusts his sleeve to regard his Rolex, swipes Eric's paper off the table, and blots out Eric's stupid grinning mug with it. Now that Bob's had to wait, he will make everyone else wait while he reads the paper.

Everyone glowers at Eric, whose phone begins to ring. While he faffs about, trying to get it out of his pocket, the toffs at the other tables turn to listen in astonishment.

'Answer yer feckin' phorn!' rings out the irate Irish accent of Eric's pre-recorded ring-tone. 'Come *on,* would'yer, meete? D'yer tink I've got all bleedin' daaay? Jest *annser* that feckin' phorn before I break yer feckin' ...'

'Ha Ha,' says Eric, switching it off and dropping it casually on the table, where everyone will be able to see that it cost him a few bob. 'Me cheeky little grandson put that one on. Funny ain't it? He adds, blushing.

In the lull that follows, Bob rustles his newspaper and Barry rubs his nose, checking out of habit for signs of powder. Teddy looks at his watch then hurriedly makes out he's examining his liver spots, in case Bob's watching from behind his newspaper, which he probably is. Teddy doesn't want those cold blue eyes piercing his and that gravely voice going: 'In some sort of a hurry, are ya Teddy?'

At last Bob turns his page with a loud tut-tut to no one in particular and mutters, 'So much mugging going on these days. Fuckin' dreadful.'

A wave of relief circles the table, everyone nodding wisely as if bowing to the great man's philosophy.

'Diabolical,' agrees Eric. 'Never used to 'appen in our day like it does now.'

Bob leaves Eric's comment hanging in the air until it has gone quite stale, then shakes his head, saying, 'It's all down to the drugs. As I always say, it's all right with the puff and the coke 'cause they don't cause no crime. But that other gear is for scumbags.'

Everyone nods again while the crime-lord folds his hands with a self-righteous sniff.

'Well, I reckon it's them dirty Turks bringing in the nasty that does it,' remarks Eric with a sanctimonious sniff of his own. 'They should be 'ung up and shot.'

Teddy raises his eyebrows. 'What even Yassy?'

The associates stare questioningly at Eric. They've all worked with Yassy, and he's about the friendliest Turk you could wish to meet, right down to his happy-go-lucky Cockney accent.

'No, not Yassy, he's OK. But the rest of 'em,' Eric mutters hurriedly.

'What about Yassy's family?' asks Teddy.

'No, not Yassy's family, they're OK too,' Eric scowls. 'Drop me out now, you know what I mean.'

Eric picks up a flaked truffle parcel and guiltily returns it on the plate. That's another faux pas, because Bob hasn't sampled the food yet. At the same moment a voice comes from behind the South London Press, making Eric freeze.

'No. What *do* you mean, Eric?'

'Scag, that's what I'm on about,' says Eric, flustered. 'Scag and crack and crystal meth. It's fuckin' disgusting, and anyone involved in it should get hurt.'

'Anyone involved, eh?' comments Dickie, who's the oldest amongst them and by no means the smartest, but can recognise an opportunity to jump on the bandwagon when he sees one.

'Yeah, and anyone who takes it, too,' Eric gabbles, not liking where this conversation is heading.

'Don't your son take a bit of crack now and again, Bob?'

An air of foreboding descends on the meeting. Tam's crack habit is a no-go area. Dickie is taking a risk mentioning it, but he must reckon he's merely waving the red flag in front of his fellow matador, Eric, who's now exposed to the bull with nowhere to run.

'Yeah, he does, as it 'appens,' Bob says icily. 'I've warned George not to wash it up and smoke it. I don't mind 'im snorting it, like you, you greedy bastard.' He lowers his paper and looks Eric directly in the eye.

Eric winces, glancing away in relief on spotting the arrival of the waiter. A handsome young Frenchman wearing the trendy grey polo-neck non-uniform of the hotel bows discreetly at Bob's side.

'Is everything all right for you, sir?'

The astronomically-priced food lies untouched on the table. Bob dismisses the waiter with an order for more champagne.

When the waiter has gone, Bob tosses the paper on the table and takes the bottle out of its bucket, wiping it carefully on the napkin so as not to stain his immaculate trousers. Everyone watches guardedly while he fills the glasses at the table. None of them can remember Bob ever pouring his own drinks.

Eric realises he's in trouble when his glass remains empty. He's itching to go to the bog for a snort but suspects that would be tantamount to signing his own death warrant. It doesn't take much to piss Bob Tamsworth off, and Bob has just made it abundantly clear that he knows about the missing kilo of Charlie which Eric thought he'd got away with a couple of jobs back.

Eric glances around, starting to sweat. He can see Bob's jaw working up and down, and Bob's not eating. He kicks himself for being seven minutes late. If only his saggy-arsed wife had remembered to set his watch fifteen minutes fast like she did last time, he would have been OK; wouldn't have made that stupid comment about Turks either. Come to think of it, doesn't Bob have a mistress out in one of those ports he sails to...? Bodrum or somewhere...? Oh, fuck, yes... of course. Stunning girl she is; endless golden-brown legs, and smart, too, even though she's Turkish. Made Eric feel like a gormless prick just by smiling at him. His eyes dart wildly about as he tries to think of something to distract Bob from the inevitable words of doom that are about to drop from his mouth.

'Ain't that George?' he gasps, just in time.

At first glance, the face staring out of the newspaper on the table bears little resemblance to Bob's son, but the observation does the trick. Bob shifts his penetrating gaze from Eric to the newspaper headline, which reads: 'Do You Recognise This Man?'

Underneath the headline is a photograph of a youngish fella standing next to some shelves of crisps, with a hat pulled low over his eyes and what might be a gun poking through his jacket. Before Bob snatches it up to look more closely, Eric deduces two things. The first is that this is indeed Bob's son, and he has committed a hold-up on a petrol station.

Without a word Bob clicks on his mobile and dials a number. He listens for several moments. His expression doesn't change, but his eyes harden into freezing slits of blue.

Eric's second deduction is that he's off the hook. At least for now.

HMP Horfield

Banged up in Brizzle

Don't know how the hell this happened, but I got carted up to Bristol for some long-overdue court hearing involving handling of stolen goods that I don't even remember handling, and I was nodding off in the cattle truck on the way back to London when, lo and behold, I saw outside the window in big black letters: HMP, and I thought bloody hell, that was quick! Only it was HMP Bristol, not Belmarsh, and suddenly I was being told to shift my lazy arse out the van.

True, when I went up before the Marsh Gov a few days ago, (owing to a run-in with a screw over the matter of a visitor with a small present for me) the governor was muttering something about booting me out of his nick for being such a raving nuisance on his drug charts. Turns out he wasn't just ranting, or giving me a warning. I really must be a raving nuisance 'cause I've been ghosted a hundred miles west to make it hard for me to get visits.

It's succeeding. No one I know can be bothered to trail all the way to the West Country to help fill my never-ending drug requirements. Seems my last governor didn't say much to recommend me, 'cause the head honcho here has put me on the life wing, so I'm stuck with a bunch of A Cats who have little to lose if their blood should boil over from time to time.

If the governor of Belmarsh thought he's blocked off all my angles by sending me up here, though, he's mistaken. He's just shifted the problem to Bristol.

A couple of days in, I buy some tobacco and track down the dealer on the wing. He's a slim black fella with his hair scraped back in neat cornrows and he's called

'Jazz.' Used to be a musician on the outside but doesn't play nothing in here, just lords it over his own private canteen, which is so loaded it's spilled over into the cell next door. It's a thriving business. Borrow something and you're obliged to give double back.

No one messes with Jazz. I know this because when he took a shower this morning he left his gold Rolex lying on the side in full view of every bandit in here.

In the deafening silence of his cell, I give him the tobacco and he hands over two small wraps.

'Thanks, Jazz,' I beam. No reply.

My arrival here was like walking into one of those remote country pubs where the volume gets turned down on every conversation as all the punters turn to stare at you. The volume still hasn't been turned all the way back up. I'm holed up with a bunch of violent strangers who speak with unfamiliar North Somerset accents, and so far I've been made to feel about as welcome as a visitor bringing along the Bubonic Plague from London.

To top it all, two things go wrong almost as soon as I set foot in this clink. First of all, my lovely sister, Eva, who's the only person who's faithfully stood by me all these years, tootles all the way down on the train at first visiting opportunity and does her level best to cheer me up. She even shows me some pictures of her three adorable children. I'm assuming they're adorable; I don't actually look at them. My sister's got nothing interesting either tucked in her cheek or hidden in her bra, and I'm too busy scanning other visitors for signs of illegal substances to give her photos more than the briefest glance. It's only when Eva jumps to her feet and marches away, stuffing the photos back in her handbag, that I realise I haven't listened to a word she's said.

At the door, she directs me a look so full of pity and disgust that I yell out, 'I'm sorry, Eva!' making everyone stare at me. But it's too late. The feeling of self-hatred that hits me is intolerable.

The second thing that happens is that I get a 'Dear John' letter from Dawn. Almost every sentence delivers a horrendous blow. She's gone straight, she tells me. (Punch in the head.) She doesn't want our son having a junkie for a dad. (Punch in the chest.) She's moving out of our old home. (Punch in the stomach.) She will never tell me where she's going, or with whom. (Kick in the balls.) I will never see my son again. (Finish me off with a flurry of kicks, anywhere you like, while I'm writhing on the floor.)

Mentally, I'm so beaten up that I start losing the plot, sliding down the slippery slope that stronger cons than me have gone down before. More than ever, I crave heroin as my brain starts to crack from all the guilt, the self-hatred and the jealousy.

If I was a free man, I'd track Dawn down, kick out that fucking lottery-winner she's probably shacked up with, and shower my beautiful son with presents and kisses… Or perhaps I'd just go and get wasted. Makes no difference what I'd do; I can't fulfil one single urge in here.

In a single cell surrounded by strangers, there's no escape from the dozen voices that have taken up residence in my head. I'm just about holding it all together, but only, I suspect, because I still have the means to get my hands on a bit of smack.

As soon as I've smoked it, the dozen voices back off.

The next morning they start up again. The canteen doesn't open for six days, so I pay through the nose for some more tobacco and head back to give it to Jazz.

I've been up for three days and already I've got myself into a couple of fights, so on top of the usual aching bones and the bad, bad thoughts clanging round my brain, I've got throbbing bruises and pounding headaches to keep me entertained through the endless nights. If I laid off the gear for a bit I'd get over the withdrawals. But here I am again at Jazz's door with no tobacco, no money; nothing but a pocketful of lies and promises.

He looks right through me as I sell him the lies and shower him with the promises. Eventually he throws me a wrap to shut me up.

'Thanks Jazz, mate,' I grin using the word loosely, because he's the sort of mate I'd like to feed through a meat grinder. I saunter back to my cell, trying to look like I don't care about the heavy dramas I'm about to have on my hands.

Canteen Day comes round and Jazz gives me a list of stuff to get him.

'Sorted, mate,' I nod, knowing full well I'm not going to get very far on the £2.40 left in my account. 'Worry about that later,' being my general plan of action, I buy some tobacco and head back to my cell for a smoke. Jazz is leaning against his door, watching me with his impenetrable gaze.

'Sorry, mate, they fucked up my spends!' I shout up to him with a shrug.

He says nothing; just walks into his cell and closes the door. I walk into my cell and slam my door. I've got no friends, no one to give a toss when I find myself having to face the Jazz music.

I'm so on edge, waiting for it to happen, that when my door opens I'm flying at my visitor like a coiled spring with a head butt to the nose. The unsuspecting black con falls against the door, accidentally locking it. As he holds his gushing nose, it strikes me that maybe he didn't come to do me damage, maybe he came by to ask for some sugar. How the hell would I know, when I feel like I've been sent to some foreign clime where no one speaks my language?

I'm throttling this black con's neck with one hand while yanking his head with the other, and I snarl into his blood-wet face, 'If you've come in 'ere to have it with me, I'm telling ya, I will kill you.'

'No, mans, no. Me's just comes to tell you that Jazz wants to see you,' he blubbers. 'Mes no wants no trouble.'

I let him go and press the buzzer, waiting until a screw lets him out. Then I sit on my bed with my head in my hands and regret not hurting him properly, because now he'll be back any minute with his pals.

This Bristol lingo has been doing my head in. For some reason, people round here put an 'L' on the end of words ending in a vowel, while leaving the 'L' out of words which actually do have an 'L' in them. On top of that they talk real slow and their grammar is up the spout. So when a Bristol con says, 'I be from the Bristowe ariel, I be,' he means he's from the Bristol area. Yeah, even though he sounds like he's from another planet. And even when he's trying to sound hard, he comes out with something like, 'Shut yer mouth, you bloody gerrrt idut, you.'

I'm sick of this hell. It's not prison I can't handle, and it's not the prisoners either, not even these unfriendly fuckers. It's living without gear. Unless by some miracle Jazz continues to tick me after his cronies have beaten me senseless, I know there'll be no more drugs for me in this shit hole.

I walk down the landing to the pool table and stand about with nothing to do, listening to a couple of cons nattering in the background.

'Ark at 'ee, 'ee can 'ardly walk, mind.'

'Well, I zays to 'im, give I the fifty quid! And wivvout fuurver ado, 'ee did what I done asked 'im, like.'

'Reallay? I'm proper 'ungray.'

'Me's too. Starrrrvin', I be.'

I glance round, expecting to see a couple of old-time country fellas having this conversation, but no, they're younger than I am. They give me a filthy look when they notice me staring. I turn my attention to the pool game. A couple of cons are languidly knocking balls in various directions. Stephen Hendry versus Hurricane Higgins it ain't. Watching them play, I'm reminded of a scene from the film 'Scum' Where Ray Winston makes an effective weapon out of a sock and a pool ball.

Back in my cell, I'm hunting around for a sock to accommodate my stolen pool ball when out of nowhere, a black mist comes at me and something smashes into my head. Again and again the black con's blows pound into me and I'm watching my blood trickle onto the concrete, closer and closer, until I'm face down in it on my knees.

My door bangs open.

'Waz s'atter with yous, then?' says a screw, his dim-witted accent making me scrape my face out of my blood. Lying not far away is a bloodied plastic jug. So *that's* why I've got a splitting headache.

'Are you always this stupid?' I mutter. 'Or are you making a special effort today?'

'Come agins? The screw frowns as if I'm talking Portuguese.

'Oi fells downs, didn't Oi?' I scowl.

Not noticing my damn fine impersonation of him, the screw quips, 'Well, yous seem to fall down quite often, don't yous?'

I must be a dead ringer for Frankenstein. Got two black eyes and my head stitched together with what looks like several boot-laces. As soon as I'm led back to the lifers' wing, I take advantage of my gruesome new looks to yell, 'I'm back for you, Jazz, you fuckin' slag! Where are ya? I'm gonna have a go on your fuckin' trumpet!'

And I'm looking forward to it. I'll take on that sleek black fucker and die killing him, if I have to. A life without gear is a life with nothing to lose!

My fighting talk gets me dispatched temporarily to another wing, leaving me full of pent-up aggression. I'm banged up for the night in a two-up with a skinny, tattooed skinhead whose teeth are so yellow it looks like he's never used a toothbrush. Turns out, he's so thick he probably doesn't know how to.

From the top bunk, he watches patiently while I go through the drudgery of making up my bed. Cons are invariably nosy bastards and eventually he asks, 'What's 'appended to yous, then?'

I frown at him for a moment. 'Are your parents brother and sister?'

He looks at me blankly while his brain ticks slowly over.

Putting aside my prejudices, I'm about to tell him what became of my face when he remarks, 'That Jazz is aa gerrrt 'arrrd barrrstard.'

Hmm. Gossip flies on prison grapevines, even in a hostile dump like this.

My cellmate frowns dubiously at the scabs forming on my head. 'You ain'ts got that Aids, 'ave you?'

'Fuck off, you moron,' I snap, glaring at his jaw in a way that makes him withdraw warily over the side of his bed.

The screws are at my door first thing in the morning with a nicking sheet. 'Fight with person unknown,' it reads.

'Bollocks!' I say ripping it to shreds and tossing the pieces over my cellmate, waking him up with a jump.

The screws hoist my arms behind my back because they've heard that I'm trouble, and escort me along the landing.

'Hey! Wake up, you fuckin' scumbags!' I yell, trying to yank as many West Country convicts out of their slow-witted dreams as possible.

'You're welcome to your shitty prison, you brain-dead, half-breed bumpkins!' It's all coming out now. If I don't get kicked out of this prison I'm as good as dead.

Suddenly they're all waking up and yelling at me with their dumb-arsed accents.

'Gets back to London, yous fresh piece of shite!' someone roars.

'Shut yer trap, yer bloody gerrr twat!' yells someone else.

A couple of cons point to my stitches and double up with retarded laughter as if they haven't seen anything so funny since Bob the fucking Builder dropped his hammer on his foot. I lurch towards them, wobbling my forehead with my fingers the way I practised in the mirror last night, sneering at them with a truly macabre expression. They step back, aghast, making the extra pain worthwhile.

I'm locked up with a bunch of other cons waiting to go in front of the governor. I shove a couple of them off a concrete bench and lie down. They sidle away, not prepared for a tear-up with potato head before breakfast.

The governor reads out the fucked-up charge with what looks like a smirk. Why's he laughing at me, I wonder, glancing round to see the same stupid smirk on everyone's faces. Why does everyone round here seem to be having a laugh at my expense? For the life of me I can't remember cracking any amusing jokes just now. So are they really laughing at me or am I imagining it?

I can't take it any more.

'Stop laughing at me, you 'fuckin' sheep-shaggers!' I scream, making a run for the governor. He pulls himself back in his chair, startled, I make a grab for his throat, determined to wring that fuckin' smile off his face. Just as my hands close round his double chins, one of my arms is seized and twisted painfully behind my back. Even if it hadn't been the one that not so long ago had got clobbered by Meathead's mate, it renders me instantly and exasperatingly helpless.

Still, at least I manage to gob at the screw who's got me in the arm lock. All the while I'm being dragged out and beaten; I keep my mind focussed on that big, moist blob of yellow phlegm sticking to his forehead.

The wound in my head breaks open, those big bastard stitches powerless to keep it together, and I'm dragged down the Block leaving a trail of blood to mark the way.

I've been in solitary for days now, not sure how many. I'm not eating because the screws have been poking their fingers and spitting into my food. At least, I think they have. Maybe I'm paranoid; I don't know anything for certain.

Thoughts are bombarding my brain like fireworks going off. 'Why,' thoughts are the worst; they never stop: *Why* am I stuck in this dump? *Why* can't I stop using? *Why* is life such a heap of stinking shit?

Then along come the answering thoughts; thoughts that don't answer anything but raise another shit-load of questions in their place: *Because* you're a piece of scum. *Because* you deserve it. *Because* no one said life was going to be fair. *Because* you're a useless criminal who got caught and has to face the consequences. *And because* you're worthless.

In between all this nightmarish ranting come the **Despair** thoughts. These are the ones that stab me where it hurts the most: 'I can't bear this any more! I want to escape, out of this cell, this prison, my head! *I just want to fucking die!*'

On the fifth or sixth day, I start punching my fist into the wall. It stops the thoughts for minutes at a time; if I'm lucky, an hour or two. But the thoughts always come back, mugging me, choking me, dragging me down into hell with them. I want to cut off my own head and tear out my heart and gouge out my eyes, because all they think and feel and see is shit. Unbearable shit. I punch the wall until my hand is a raw, pulpy mess.

Tears pour out of me. I'm sliding down the wall in such a pathetic way that I'd punch myself out of sheer disgust if I was someone else, looking at me. But there's nothing I can do. I've been taken over by some complete wreck of a human being who just wants to sit about and wallow in a pool of his own snot.

'Why? Why? *Why?* '

My stupid, plaintive shriek echoes against concrete, mocking me.

'There's no answer, you fool,' shouts the evil cunt who lives in my head. 'Get off the floor you stinking, worthless scumbag.'

'I can't,' I blubber, wiping mucus away with my sleeve while tears cascade down to my lap. 'I can't fuckin' move!'

'Course you can move, cunt-face. Stand up and get a fuckin' grip!'

'I can't,' I blubber, wiping mucus away with my sleeve while tears cascade down to my lap. 'I can't fuckin' move!'

'Course you can!'

I can't work out which voice is which and it doesn't stop talking, taunting me, driving me mad. So whose is it? It can't be mine, because I'm in control here, right? *Right?* But, if I'm the one in control, then why can't I so much as lift one fucking finger when I tell myself to? Try as I might, I can't *make* myself do one fucking thing right now. And suddenly I'm staring stark raving lunacy straight in its empty, endless, scary face.

'Who am I?' I groan. 'Is there one of me or two? Which is the real Harry Shaw? *Who the fuck am I?* And who the fuck is Harry Shaw anyway?

I'm sure everyone down the Block can hear me, even through the double doors separating me from the rest of the world. Probably half the chokey can hear the sound of a man losing his marbles. But even if they can hear me, no one gives a toss. I don't blame them because I wouldn't give a toss about a sorry piece of shit like me either.

Eventually a screw opens my door. He stares down at me as if he's never seen such a pathetic relic of human scum in his life.

'You's being shipped out,' he sniffs.

For a moment I look up, my eyes full of watery hope.

'Where to, guv?' I manage to utter.

'Cardiff,' he grins and my hope shrivels to despair. I'm desperate to head back to London, not travel further west into unknown territory.

'Cardiff's where the *proper* sheep-shaggers live,' he informs me, referring to the insult I made in front of the governor. 'Round these parrrrts, we just lets 'em give us a nice b'owjob,' he chuckles, obviously thinking himself a proper chap. 'But don't yous worry, they's got the rea' thing up Cardiff. If yous don't mind me sayin' so, you looks like a bit of a sheep yourseff!

I open my mouth to let out one of my usual scathing ripostes, but nothing comes out.

The screw leads me out of the Block. I'm quite certain we don't have to take this particular route, I think to myself, as we head towards the wing where the prisoners I offended a week ago are straining at the leash to get their own back. Someone's tipped them off. They're belting out the East Enders theme tune at the tops of their voices.

'Cockney Boy's off to the sheep shaggers!' someone bellows.

'Just say 'baa' and you'll find a nice, lush farmer!' yells someone else while a few of them start lobbing missiles at my head. A damp piece of screwed-up paper pings off the back of my neck.

'Aw right, aw right, that's enough of that,' beams the screw, walking on ahead so that he doesn't get hit.

'All right, treacle? 'Ow's yer father? Some wit hollers from the top landing.

'You'll 'ave a lovely time down Wa'es. They hate you fuckin' Londoners down there!'

'Yeah, you'll be lucky to gets shagged, *mate*,' sneers some black con, probably a pal of Jazz, leering at me through the bars. 'More likely to get sheared alive. Ha ha ha.'

'*Dng... dng...d...d...d...d...d...dng!*' someone mimics the final cliff-hanger moment of an episode of EastEnders, which for some reason goes down a right storm.

I say nothing as I shuffle after the screw with the whole wing in hysterics. Normally I'd have a put-down for every one of their lame insults. But the bravado's gone out of me. I don't know where it's gone, but it feels like it's never coming back.

HMP Cardiff

Welcome to Wales

As soon as I'm led into reception and one of the screws remarks, 'What have we *hure*?' and another screw quips, 'Doctor been practising his patchwork quilting on you, boyo?' with their accents from hell, I decide I'm going to hate this dump.

It's a sprawling Victorian eyesore that exudes an atmosphere of pent-up frustration from all the hapless convicts fate has plonked here over the past century and a half. But the main reason I hate it is that, after making a couple of enquiries on my way here, I discovered it's almost impossible to score gear. I don't know what it is with these Welsh criminals that the monotony of prison life doesn't make *them* desperate to pursue the joys of the brown stuff. I haven't met them yet. So I'm thinking maybe it's the growing up in lonely, rainy valleys that makes them immune to the boredom.

It doesn't help either, that as part of my welcome bed-pack, I'm given a pillow as bulky and as bouncy as a tea towel folded in half.

'What's this then,' I wonder aloud. 'Did its last owner drive a steam roller over it in his dreams?'

No one laughs; I assume they're having trouble with my London accent. But I think I detect a muffled smirk when one of the screws helpfully swaps my so-called pillow for a brand new one. I've never been lucky enough to be issued a brand new pillow before, and I don't connect the screw's sucked-in-lipped chortle with the pillow swap-over until a few hours later when I test it out in my new cell. The other one, I wouldn't even have

192

noticed under my head; this one is like trying to cuddle up to a breezeblock.

'Whassa matter, princess?' asks the same helpful screw, strolling past my cell with his hands behind his back, as he watches me jumping up and down on my spanking new headrest, trying to make it more pliable. 'You trying to learn gymnastics, or something?'

Not a great start to my incarceration in the place they call 'Cairdeff.' Still, perhaps the lack of scag round here explains why these cons get so bloody excited about Fridays.

Having arrived on a Thursday, I don't get a chance to build up the baffling levels of anticipation for Friday that's creating an atmosphere of camaraderie amongst both the Rhonda Valley Cons and the Cardiff Boyos, who normally detest each other. But the high spirits start to rub off on me when, standing in the dinner queue, I hear the belly of the fella in front of me rumble, which sets mine off, making us both laugh. It's my first inkling that maybe life in here won't be so horrific.

There's a fresh-baked aroma in the air which I've never smelt in any other prison, and instead of doling out the usual frazzled fish cake and flaccid white chips, the servery lads are grinning, 'Come and get it, boyos!' as proud as a bunch of cordon bleu chefs.

I haven't eaten properly in weeks and I'm salivating while watching the bloke in front get his tray loaded up with a piece of fish that's triple the size of a fish finger and chips that are positively crispy. And instead of the snot-coloured mush that generally passes as the vegetable side dish, real little bright green peas. I'm so amazed that, while my own tray's getting loaded up, I snatch a glance at the fella behind to remark, 'No wonder you boyos are in a good mood,' and turn back only to see a ladle of clay-coloured slime swamp my crispy fish and chips and drown all the little peas.

'What the fuck?' I'm devastated.

'Curry sauce, Bloody lovely, initt, boya?' grins the con behind me. 'Now 'urry up you, I's bloody starrrving.'

Back in my cell, I scrape the gunk off a few chips that haven't been too badly hit. My cellmate comes in with his tray, grinning.

'Cor blimey!' What's the matter with you, me old fruitcake?' he says in his best cockney accent. Then in his usual voice, 'Dorrn't you get no curry sauce with your fish and chipsies down Alberttt Square, you poor boyo?'

'Don't call me fucking 'boyo!' I growl. 'Christ, I knew I was going to hate this place.'

My cellmate tucks into his curried fish and chips with relish. 'You can't say that on a Friday, mate,' he says, wagging his fork at me. 'Any other day of the week you 'ave my sympathies.' His voice has a musical quality I can't help liking. 'If you don't want me to call you 'boyo,' you'd better tell me your name.'

'Harry.'

'Pete.'

Peter swaps a piece of his fish that hasn't been smothered to death for a bit of mine that has. Gradually the tension that had been gnawing away at me all the time I was in Bristol ebbs away until I find myself feeling, if not happy, at least pleasantly relaxed. And not a single drug in my bloodstream. Surprise of surprises, after staring into a bottomless pit of desolation from which I doubted I'd ever return I've been banged up with a decent bloke at last, and he's Welsh and doesn't look the sort to fancy a sheep. Though you never can tell.

'I supporrrse you think we're all sheep-shaggers down hure,' he says as if reading my mind. It takes me a moment to work out that 'hure' means 'here'. 'Like we boyos think you're all sooty-faced chimney sweeps, innit?' His eyes twinkle as he reaches over to dip a chip in my sauce.

'Talking of sheep,' I laugh, 'what d'you call a Welshman with a sheep under each arm?'

He shakes his head disapprovingly. 'A pimp, of course. You can'ttt be telling thorrse sorts of jorrkes around hure. You'll get your silly barrow boy 'ead kicked in. Why do Welshmen wear buttonfly jeans?'

'Go on,' I grin.

'Because a sheep can hure a zipper at a hundrrred yards,' he says, polishing off the last of his drowned chips. 'There's thousands more where tharrtt came from. Why did the Welsh farrrmer drive his sheep to the edge of the cliff…? Because they push harder tharrtt way.'

I'm laughing so hard I barely notice a forkful of curry-flavoured batter slide down my throat. It's not so much his jokes that crack me up, but his wide-eyed delivery, as if he's at a loss to know how anyone could laugh at a joke involving a Welshman and a sheep. But some part of him seems to recognise that I've been down in the dumps, and wants to cheer me up. A dozen or so sheep jokes later when I'm choking on my curried peas, which don't taste so bad after all, he says, 'Have you hured about the latest Welsh sex aid?'

'Ah, I knew you'd have to run out of sheep jokes sooner or later.'

Again, that pitying frown of his. 'Velcro gloves, innit?'

By now I'm nearly pissing myself laughing and when Pete frowns reminiscently I'm half-hoping he's going to change the subject and give me a break. 'What's the worst thing about having sex with a sheep?'

He's right, there's thousands more sheep jokes than I ever imagined existed.

'I dunno, dread to think!'

'Breaking her neck when you try to kiss her.'

At last I manage to keep a straight face long enough to say, 'Ah, it's great to meet ya, Pete. I was dreading being banged up with a Welshman, but we're getting along like a bleeding 'ouse on fire. What you in for, mate?

Suddenly he's the one shaking with laughter and it's my turn to stare at him, mystified.

'Ah, that's fuckin' breeelliant, tharrrt is,' he says, 'I'll have to share thaarrt with the boyos. Hey, Jimmy!' he yells. 'Tell my cellmate Harry hure what I'm in forrr!'

From the next cell, a Liverpudlian voice rings out, 'Pete's in ferr fockin' arrrson!'

Pete cracks up. 'No wonder we're getting on like an 'ouse on fierrr!'

Pretty soon half the landing is laughing at my inadvertent joke and a wave of camaraderie sweeps over me. This I wasn't expecting either.

I try out a proper joke this time. 'What do you call a clairvoyant midget who's just escaped from prison?

In the silence that follows, I wonder how many Welsh cons are waiting for my punch-line. After a few seconds I put them out of their misery. 'A small medium at large!'

A round of chuckles breaks out on either side of my cell, then my joke gets passed swiftly along the landing. Seems to be going down quite well considering how clean it is, so I try out another.

'How does a Welshman commit suicide?' I shout and wait for a bit. 'He takes a sniff of his armpit.'

This time the silence has a distinct edge to it. The cons in the adjacent cells aren't so tickled by this one.

I wait for one of them to let out a swearword before adding, 'How does a cockney commit suicide? He tells this joke to a Welshman.'

It takes a bit of time, but this one goes down even better than the first one.

'Proper lad that cockney boyo, innit?' someone observed.

Pete happens to be one of the most popular boys on the wing, and because he likes me I find myself in with a ready-made circle of friends. These Welsh cons haven't heard half the jokes that were circulating Belmarsh before I left, so for a few days I'm relegated to the role of fucking comedian. Making people laugh has always given me a good feeling; and these Welsh cons seem to be a bit more innocent than the London lot.

Two days after Fish and Chips Day, Jim the Scouser from the cell next-door, storms into our cell with a face so livid that half my tea sloshes into my lap on its way to my mouth. Jim's a big fella, always wearing tops that are too tight in order to show off his muscles. Hurriedly, I cast my mind back over recent events to make sure I haven't done anything to piss him off.

'Fockin' 'ell!' he roars.

'Calm dooone, Jimmy boyo. What's the problem?' Pete asks in his concerned way.

My fockin' bairrrd's coming on a fockin' visit tomorrehhh, all the fockin' way down from fockin' Mairseyside. It's all fockin' boochkked and she's bringing me a fockin' pearrrssell and I've been fockin' loochkking forward to this for a fockin' fortnight,' he says in an accent that's so full of throat-clearing noises that I'm trying to translate the words underneath them.

'Then those fockin' screw-focks told me I'm being fockin' moved tomorrehh fockin' afternoooon and the fockin' screws won't let me on the fockin' phone to let me bairrrd know in case I fockin' well try to fockin' escape! Marrrkk my waaaairrds, there's going tairr be a fockin' maaaairder around here.' He takes a deep sniff and says finally, 'They're not going to stop me from getting me gear and that's that. Over me dead body.'

Pete and me exchange glances. We're guessing he must be serious because he's stopped swearing.

Jim stomps out of the cell without waiting for a response.

'Poor sod is that Jimmy, aaaaye,' sighs Pete.

I nod as if I care too, but really I'm thinking about what will be in Jimmy's parcel and how I might be able to get hold of a bit.

That night I'm woken by a terrible roar from the cell next door. I sit up with a jolt, blood pounding through my ears. A minute later there's another roar, followed by the sound of footsteps hurrying along landings and a terrible, agonised whimpering. Then the sound of someone chucking up in the toilet.

'Oh, my God, he's reeeeally gone and fuckin' done it this time,' I hear Pete groan in his bed.

'What?' I ask. 'Who?'

There's no answer. After a while, I hear a few muffled sobs and Pete groans, 'I can't stand it in hure. It's getting to me, reeeeally it is.'

Suddenly I'm hit by a wave of revulsion. Silly wanker, breaking down in front of me; falling apart like a hysterical bird. My muscles are tense; my breath is coming in ragged gasps between clenched teeth and my fists are itching to do him an injury. It's like having that miserable fucker Don back in my cell all over again, sobbing and heaving until I chucked the razor at him to do himself in.

Suddenly it dawns on me why I want those pathetic sobs to stop. Clear in my mind is an image of my mum, ploddin' round the house doing the housework with

198

tears dripping down her sodding face. I'm about nine years old and I've just come home from school and told her that I got the prize for the best story in class. I'd opened up and written something so different from my usual half-arsed efforts that the teacher had looked at me with respect and written 'Excellent' in my book. I went straight home to tell my mum and she didn't hear a word I said. I knew it when I watched her mop her tears off the sideboard with a duster while looking straight through me. Right then, I felt like a nobody. If my own mum couldn't be happy for me, then what was the point in trying to make her proud?

That's why I hate people crying. That and my dad drumming it into me that 'only girls' cried. It makes me feel helpless, worthless and ultimately, murderous. Pete's only in for eighteen months. Silly wanker, should hold himself to-fucking-gether.

For a long time I lie there, my face contorting into evil grimaces in the darkness. I want to yell at Pete just like my father yelled at me until *nothing* could make me cry. Not even Grandma kicking the bucket.

I like Pete.

Right now I want to crush his skull under my foot.

I like him though. He's the closest I've had to a friend since Fly, who was good for a laugh but probably didn't give two shits when I got shipped out to Bristol.

Eventually Pete drifts off to sleep leaving me wide-awake, torn by conflicting feelings of disgust and a sort of horrible grudging admiration that Pete actually does give two shits about people.

Then again, I remember, and the memory makes me cringe. It was only a couple of weeks ago that my own wheels were falling off down the Block at Bristol. Pete wouldn't laugh at me for that. But I couldn't tell him about it. I can't talk about *anything* to anyone. Not that I want to anyway. I'd choke on my own stinking self-pity.

Finally, at about three o'clock in the morning, I arrive at some sort of a conclusion. Maybe it's not Pete who's the pathetic one around here; maybe it's me.

Next morning, Jim's cellmate Nick comes round looking like he's had a sleepless night too. Nick's a decent fella, as skinny and angular as Jim is huge and muscular, and everyone feels a bit sorry for him, having to share a cell with a huge, manic depressive body-building scouser.

'What 'appened, boyo?' asks Pete sitting him down. 'I never *hured* such a fuckin' agonisin' scream in all me life.'

'Thattt were Jim,' says Nick, 'afttter he asked me ter break his leg, aaaye.'

Turns out, there was no way Jim was going to let the screws mess up the visit with his bird, so he asked his cellmate to stamp on his shin. First time round, it didn't break. Jim's a hard nutter but even *he* felt it was too painful to have another go. So he stuck his other leg on the bottom bunk and told Nick to jump off the top bunk and do a proper job this time.

Nick was more worried about missing Jim's leg than actually snapping a bone. Nevertheless, he climbed up and threw himself down with all his weight. The sound of shattering bone made him rush to the toilet and throw up, leaving poor Jim to hobble across the cell and get on the bell for help. He's all right now though; loaded up with painkillers, and he'll almost certainly get that visit he's been raving on about.

'Looks like he won his bartttle then, innit?' Pete says admiringly.

I'm shaking my head, speechless. I thought *I* was bad around a bit of gear, but I'd never break a leg for it. At least I don't think I would.

For the rest of the morning I lie on my bed, brooding. Are there any winners in this drugs game, I wonder? Only the dealers that don't get high on their own supply, I decide. Until they end up in here.

With the Rhonda Valley lot and the Cardiff Valley Boyos at each other's throats and hurling abusive nicknames at each other, I find myself falling into a neutral spot somewhere in the middle. Next to the Rhondas with their skinheads and tattoos, and the *Caairdeffs* who have dreadlocks even though they're mostly white, I'm just 'That Flash Harry from London,' or at worst, a cockney Rag 'n' Bone man from Walford. Now and again I play both roles for a laugh.

It's all beginning to get a bit too good to be true when Thursday rolls round again. Thursday is Toad in the Hole Day, just as it was at Belmarsh; sausages made with so many gristly bits you wonder if you're chomping on the pig's kidney stones, scrotum, ground-up teeth, or even if it really *is* a pig. As if to disguise the fact that we're eating pulverised corpse, the bangers are encased in a thick, rubbery tomb which is then drowned in a glutinous brown slurry, that tastes surprisingly good until it leaves behind an oily after-taste, making you want to scrape your tongue all night long.

Anyway, it's not very popular, and everyone's looking forward to their fish and chips tomorrow. There's the threat of a few punch-ups in the air; so when a short, stocky, Irish bloke gives me the evil eye in the dinner queue, I know there's going to be trouble. He's glanced my way a couple of times but I've been cruising on my wave of popularity and he's kind of fallen off my radar until now.

It's when I've got my hands occupied with my tray that he makes his move. 'Jazz torrld me to give yee this,' he hisses in his Irish traveller's accent, slamming his fist into my face. I'd been half-expecting it, and just manage to hold onto my tray. The pain ricochets round my jaw but I put on a big grin as a screw steps in to break us up.

'What's going on hure, boyos?'

'There's no trouble, guv,' I tell him. 'You forgot the beans, mate,' I remind the server, who's wincing and cradling his own jaw with sympathy.

'Yee tink yer a big man, do yee?' Traveller sneers from behind the screw. 'God help yee, 'cause yee are one dead focker.'

'Why don't you piss off back to your bog?' I say, with a smile.

'You ain'ttt going to let him away with tharttt, is you, Cockney boyo?' the Rhonda Valley con behind me says in disgust.

'Not on your nelly,' I growl, making him chuckle. I return to my cell, just managing to stop myself slamming my tray into Traveller's thick Paddy face and grinding its contents into his eyes.

'I hope I'm not going to be haunted by that Jazz cunt wherever I go,' I say with my mouth full of rancid batter.

'Jazz cunt?' Pete says thoughtfully. 'Are you talking about thartt Jazz bastard over in Birzzle? Dorrn't you worry about him, 'arry, we dorrn't like his music round hure.' He sets his half-eaten food aside with disgust. 'Ive got a way of helping you get thartt Irish prick barrck, if you're interested.'

Ten minutes later we've hatched a plan. Traveller is a cleaner, up to all sorts of tricks, no doubt, so we'll use that to our advantage. Pete's going to bribe another cleaner with some tobacco to persuade Traveller to clean out our cell. Pete looks at me with concern. 'Would you like me to hold him down for you?'

It's my turn to look at him with pity. Obviously my reputation hasn't preceded me out here, so I mention my days of boxing glory back when I was a teenager. 'You keep outta the way. That Paddy wanker won't know what hit 'im.'

'Better give me some ringside seats for tharrtt,' Pete grins.

Later, when we're lying in our bunks waiting for sleep to transport us far away from our concrete walls, I start to feel the familiar ache in my bones and a longing for something to fill the insatiable yearning in my being.

The emptiness started gnawing away at me the day my Grandma died. 'Granny Guinness' we used to call her. It seemed to do her a world of good, her three bottles of Guinness each night. There was a lot of stress in my household, what with Dad spending long holidays at Her Majesty's ever abundant generosity and my Mum falling apart in his absence, so I spent a lot of time with Gran. If it hadn't been for her, I would have grown up thinking that life was shit all the time.

Thanks to Grandma, I got a taste of a life I wouldn't otherwise have known existed, with cuddles and stories at bedtime and one short but never-forgotten trip with buckets and spades to the seaside.

Just after Grandma died, Dad sat me on his knee in some prison visiting room and told me he was going to be away for a long time, and that I was the man of the house now. Maybe he was trying to make me feel important. Or maybe it was his misguided way of telling me he loved me. But, from that day on, I walked around with the weight of the world on my shoulders, thinking it was my job to take care of my mum and little sister and the baby that was on the way; thinking that I was the one that had to hold it all together, even though I was only seven years old.

Eight years later, I'm arriving home from school when my mum bustles me into the front room, all silly flustered smiles and nervous faffing about. My dad's sitting in the best armchair – my armchair – while a bunch of rough-looking geezers sit about on the extra chairs brought in from the kitchen, drinking whisky and eating the nibbles my mum keeps handing round with her hastily-painted fingernails and a breezy smile like she's been throwing spur-of-the moment parties all these miserable years.

Eight years, I've been the man of the house, just like I promised, but suddenly I'm having to relinquish this title to a man I hardly know with a gruff voice and a hardness about him that comes from years of being cooped up with other criminals. Now he's putting his arms round me and kissing my forehead and calling me his Champ.

He's praising my left hook even though he's only seen it from the newspaper clippings that my mum's sent him, and I'm thinking about demonstrating it for him now, right into his solar plexus. All the crap now that he's out, with his pals coming round to congratulate him, and money being thrown about. There was no money flying around during the last eight years, apart from a few scores thrown our way at Christmas.

Looking at them now with their jokes and their camaraderie, talking about the good times as if they were yesterday, I see a bunch of hypocrites. And the biggest hypocrite of the lot is my mum, bustling around as if everything's normal, even though she's been crying in her bed for years. Rage builds slowly up in me. I feel like showing the lot of them a few of my prize jabs and hooks.

But I hold it all in, just the way Dad taught me when Grandma died, just before he got sent back to the shovel. Dad went berserk at the sound of my crying; it was like torture for him.

'Listen, son, we all miss Granny Guinness, but she's kicked the bucket now, so no use in crying over it,' he'd said.

But still I couldn't shut up, grief-stricken I was. So he made it very clear, unforgettably clear, that the sound of crying *did his head in.* I never cried again. I held it all in until it festered and bubbled and started spewing out under the lid, and then I'd launch it at my next opponent in the boxing ring. All these years later, the same festering grief is bubbling up under its lid, waiting for me to launch it at the next available victim.

Traveller.

My body might be lying in bed in Cardiff, but my mind is back in the ring. The ref's holding up my hand while my photo gets taken. My mum, my sister and my little brother are amongst a sea of grinning faces in the crowd. The cheers are roaring in my ears and I'm drinking it all in.

Somehow, I know that I'm going to have to savour this moment forever. Through all the hurt and the pain that I will cause myself and others over the years, I will hold onto this little piece of comfort... All through the years until tonight, when I fall asleep beating the Traveller to a pulp in my mind, again and again and again.

I'm standing behind the door, fists trembling with anticipation.

'He's coming,' Pete mutters, then shouts cheerfully, 'Yeah, in hure, mate, those nutters left a right mess, aaaye.' A moment later there's a thump and a scuffle and Traveller flies into our cell to slam against the wall. Fear and shock flood into his eyes as he realises he's been had.

'He's all yours, Harry,' says Pete, locking the door and leaping onto his bed.

'This first one's for Jazz, you fuckin' prick,' I tell him. His fists fly up to protect his face, too late to prevent a jab that bursts his lower lip, sending blood cascading down his chin.

'Please don't hurt me,' he pleads, but I've no sympathy. I'm going to break him, bit by bit; rekindle that triumphant glow I used to feel in the ring.

It's as if the moves have never left me. With my left foot forward, I pull back my right arm and throw a beautiful, twisting punch right between his uselessly-raised fists. It catches him square on the chin. Satisfied to hear his jaw crack, I follow up with the left hook that I used to practise so often. It smashes into his cheekbone. There's no pain in my knuckles; nothing but cold hatred as my fists tear down on his body with right hooks and lefts, his chin coming down almost in slow motion.

I'm desperate to get that feeling of unadulterated jubilation I used to feel as a kid. It's not coming yet. Perhaps I'm not hitting him hard enough. He's on the floor, but still I don't stop. I'm using my feet now, stamping on his face until a mixture of blood and teeth come out of his mouth. Pete jumps off his bed. He's been telling me that perhaps I've done enough damage, but I haven't heard him.

I stand back, catching my breath, surveying the motionless mess on the floor. Travelling Man won't be travelling nowhere for a while.

I want to get that feeling I used to have when I threw my gloves in the air and the crowd roared their appreciation, but all I feel is slightly sick, watching a slick of blood spread slowly towards my feet.

I press the bell and wait for the screws to escort me down the Block. I'm ready for the bastards, and if they've got a problem with what I've done, I'll punch their fuckin' lights out too.

The screws take one look at the mess on the floor, however, and lead me away with a slap on the back. 'Good on you, boyo,' says one of them. Traveller obviously wasn't very popular around here.

Much as I'd like to soak up the praise, his words ring hollow. I don't feel triumphant. I don't feel glorious. I feel worse than a fuckin' animal.

I'd been kidding myself that things were looking up in here, that maybe I could get by without drugs; that being popular and cracking jokes and looking forward to fish and chips on a Friday could substitute for a good dose of H.

Anyway, it's fish and chips tonight and I'm missing it. I'm back down the Block barely a week since I set foot in this place, and it's hardly any time after that before I'm sliding down that one-way slope into bitter, dark despair. I'm remembering all the shitty things I've ever done. And when I'm not remembering all the shitty things I've ever done, I'm remembering all the shitty things that were ever done to me. Soon I will be on the floor, punching the walls.

All I want is to use.

The Governor of Cardiff wasn't so chuffed about the mess I made of his travelling convict. He let me rot for a couple of weeks down the Block while Traveller pressed charges, until one of Pete's mates got a message through Traveller's thick ear and into his deficient brain and the case got dropped. There was nothing the governor could do but take thirty days off my remission and pass me onto whoever would have me.

He sends me to the last place in the world I want to go. Bristol.

I've been locked up in a dog box in the Brizzle reception for the better part of a day, waiting to be processed. I'm losing the will to live. My hands are battered and raw and my head is throbbing from where I've bashed it against the wall so many times. The darkness is closing in as I anticipate walking down that stinking landing with all those West Country cons whistling the EastEnders' theme tune and ripping the piss out of my accent. The only good thing that could possibly come of this would be to get sent back to Jazz's wing so I can kill him. Then one of his mates will do me in, and that will be the end for both of us.

Eventually a screw unlocks the door.

'Fuckin' prob'em yous are, Shaw,' he sighs. 'They don't like yous in W'es and no one wants yous in Bristowe neither. Get your kit, you is off to The Mount.

Not the friendliest of screws, but I almost leap up and hug him. Back to London! Well, almost... Hemel Hempstead gets loads of Londoners sent in, so I'll be back amongst my own kind. No more listening to cons while struggling to decipher their every fuckin' sentence, a polite frown on my mug like some bastard tourist.

The meat-wagon to The Mount might be crawling along in the slow lane, but I'm speeding to freedom. The black gloom has lifted and it feels almost like I'm being sprung.

'Girls and Boys' by Blur is playing on the radio. I nod my head to the beat.

'You all right in there?' the Securicor guard asks quizzically, staring at me through the mesh which separates me from the driver's cabin. 'Whatch'a so 'appy abaaatt going to The Mount for, eh?' He has an infectious smile and I'm over the moon to hear his London accent.

'On my way home, mate,' I grin, momentarily shocking myself for being so friendly to someone who works for the system. But the sun is shining and lush green countryside with a few cows and haystacks are flipping past the windows and what the hell, he's only human and probably doing a job so he can scrimp by and pay his bills, just like most of the population.

He laughs and turns up the music so that I can hear it in the back. The speakers blast out: '*Streets like a jungle, so call the police.*'

'Call the police,' I smile, 'fuck the police' nodding my head to the beat. The guard turns it up even more.

Yeah, fuck the police for stitching me up and presenting their dodgy evidence, I think to myself. Fuck them for getting me put away for seven instead of the four or five I should have got.

A new song comes on and I'm merrily tapping my feet while the guard sings along up front to The Clash. *'Fighting the nation. Police and thieves in the street, oh yeah...Oh yeah. Scaring the nation with their guns and ammunition. Police and thieves in the street. Oh yeah. Fighting the nation with their guns and ammunition.*

Ha ha. The DJ on the radio is on my side. The Securicor men are on my side. And I'm heading back to civilisation and as many drugs I can get my hands on. Everything's going my way. There must be a song about that, too.

HMP The Mount

Down the tubes

Supposing HMP Bristol was a hostel in a bad part of town, whose managers lock you in your room with your own keys, then sits around in reception having a laugh at your expense, and supposing that HMP Cardiff was a shabby Victorian B & B with no room service and no mod cons, then HMP The Mount is a holiday camp. It's surrounded by pleasant gardens and it has all sorts of activities to take your mind off your bird. At least, until you come up against the brutal railings which make it hard to escape.

Having been built in 1987, it hasn't had the chance to accumulate the layers of tension and doom that descend on you like a cloud when you cross the threshold of the ancient Victorian wicks.

There's an optimistic feel about the place. Quite a few of the cons are taking classes, workshops, even university degrees. Some of them, inspired by TV home-improvement shows, do up their pads with interior decorating zeal. Even the cons doing life sentences seem to have made jail their home and are making the best of a bad job and getting on with it.

This is all a far cry from the days long before prison gyms. A hundred and fifty years ago they had the real thing; tread-wheels and cranks. Instead of putting in ten minutes or so on the running machine, convicts were forced to spend at least six hours a day traipsing the equivalent of 8,640 feet, which would be like climbing the Eiffel Tower eight times without stopping. Apart from the fact that the prisoners knew they were treading the wheel for no purpose whatsoever, the guards could up the ante by altering the resistance of the wheel whenever they fancied.

They could also tighten the screws on the hand-driven cranks (smaller versions of the tread-wheel) set into the prisoners' doors, which is why guards are called 'screws' to this day.

Still, some things don't change; we're still sandwiched in a square box with no choice as to our roommate, who for all we know might be a chain-smoking, bible-bashing, classical music-listening psychopath, who on the outside severs his enemies' necks with piano wire.

My new cellmate actually enjoys doing time in here, the nutter. Trevor tells me I'm wasting my life. I laugh at him because he's the one finishing off the twenty-year stretch, but in my heart I know the joke's on me. Trevor's a normal enough fella, even though he's finishing off a sentence for murder. He gets up in the morning and he's got a fucking spring in his step, with projects to work on and grades that are constantly improving.

For one mad moment, I looked at Trevor and saw myself doing a computer course or an English Lit 'A' level, and fuck knows, maybe writing some short stories and getting all excited about my marks like a kid.

But that was before I bumped into a mate of an old mate, who hooked me up with some of that brown powder that I almost, but not quite, forgot I'd been missing in Cardiff. Now, of course, every spare bit of my brain power is being used up on planning, scoring and using.

Planning, scoring, using.

'You know, H,' says Trev, making a sideways dig at my habit. 'I bet you've got a few hidden talents. Why don't you come to the woodwork room tomorrow? Make something with your bare hands; take your mind off that shit for a while?'

He's watching me heat silver foil, making a blob of powder melt into barely enough oil for the briefest foray into heaven.

'Drop me out,' I groan. I can't remember the last time I made anything useful with my bare hands, apart from fashioning crack pipes out of everyday prison utensils. I chase the fumes from the fizzling powder through a tube. I inhale like an animal taking its last breath, until finally, there's a twinge of relief from the constant hell of being a devotee to smack.

'There's a letter for you, mate,' says Trevor, sticking his nose back in his New Scientist magazine.

I'd been so intent on using, that I hadn't noticed a letter addressed to me with HMP Belmarsh stamped on the envelope. Unlike Trevor, who's doing his bird like royalty, with convoys of friends and relatives piling regularly into the visiting room and sending him Birthday, Christmas, Father's Day, and We Just Fucking Love You cards, I hardly get any post. My sister's the only one who remembers my birthday. My brother sorts me out from time to time, but you can never rely on a heroin addict, although he assures me there's a parcel in the post arriving any day now.

I make myself comfy on my bed and get ready to savour every word of my letter. It's from Danny. He tells me, with relish, how he didn't get caught for eight whole weeks after that crazy ball point pen-stunt he pulled on the taxi driver taking him to court. After eight weeks of shooting up every mind-altering substance he could get his hands on, he made the mistake of gouching out on the wrong set of steps early one sunny morning. I can just see him sitting there, blissed out, the real world seeming very far away, especially the words, 'West Kensington Police Station' directly above his head.

He describes his walk of fame into Belmarsh wearing a cat-suit with a great bloody yellow stripe down the middle to mark him out as an escapee, and how he swallowed his embarrassment to hold his hands high while everyone cheered him like a returning hero.

He mentions a riot that got started after I left, all instigated by him if I'm reading correctly. Then there's some other mischief he got up to, all written in screw-baffling code, make me work hard for my laughs. And in the middle he's written, 'By the way, your mate Fly wanted to send you a joke. But he's dead, he went and hung himself.'

I stop laughing and hurriedly scan the rest of the letter for some explanation. There isn't one. The fat little lad whose ridiculous observations used to send me into paroxysms of giggles, would have been the last person on earth I'd have expected to top himself.

I lie back on my bed with the wind knocked out of me. The high I got from the heroin has just fizzled out.

'All right, mate?' Trevor asks from behind his mind-boggling magazine.

'Don't feel that well, Trev,' my voice manages to mumble while the rest of me goes plummeting into a pit of desolation.

If I can feel this bleak after a use up, I can barely imagine how I'd feel if I hadn't had one. News of Fly's suicide has swept the rug right out from under my feet.

For a moment I consider telling Trevor about the abyss that's rushing up to greet me. I know he'd try to understand because he's a decent bloke, but then he says in his kind-hearted voice, 'Go see the doctor, H,' and I know he wouldn't understand.

'You know what docs are like, Trev,' I say, turning my face to the wall.

Trevor carries on reading his intellectually-stimulating publication while I sink further into the pit. Remembering how me and Fly cracked up while shivering dementedly on the floor of our cell, I'm gutted. Profound thoughts of life and death invade my mind, accelerating my descent. Thinking of Fly swinging from some bars with piss and shit dribbling out of his trousers, what a waste of a life!

Then again, we all have to die sometime, I tell myself angrily, so what's the difference between now and later? What's the fuckin' difference?

All of a sudden, the answer is clear. No difference at all!

I know exactly how Fly felt, and what he did makes total sense. If we're all going to die anyway, why not dispense with the pointless bit in the middle, like skipping to the end of a crap book to make sure that it turned out just as badly as you knew it would?

My mind flits back to Don stabbing at his wrists with my razor. Abruptly the idea of suicide fills me with revulsion. No matter what, I'd never do what that pathetic fucker did!

But then what…? If I can't die, then I have to live with myself. I'd rather be dead than spend another day with myself!

My head's in turmoil. I can't live with me and I sure as fuck can't live without me… which doesn't make any fuckin' sense. And who is this me who can't stand me? Is there one of me, or two? Oh fuck, here we go again. Spiralling out of control, heading for the loony bin.

There's no answer to these questions. They send me shuttling back and forth, between the me I think I should be and the me I can't fucking abide. And if there's a real me, and an imaginary me, then that makes two of me and both of them are a whirling around and around in a vortex of hopelessness.

I don't know where these stupid thoughts are coming from; I just want to get out of my head. That's what heroin is for. Only it isn't fuckin' working. So where does that leave me? In a deep, dark hole with no way out.

I'm not sure whether I've just let out a tell-tale howl of madness but when I sit up, Trevor and a screw at the door are staring at me oddly.

'Parcel for Shaw at reception,' snaps the screw.

That's it! My mind floods with relief. I just needed a bit more of the brown stuff, that's all! I'm up and out the door and following him like a dog that hasn't eaten for weeks. I hadn't been expecting my drug-addled brother to get his parcel in the post quite so speedily.

We traipse along landings, then out through the yard where a dry wind is sending leaves scuttling round in circles. I don't notice the leaves or the yard or the distant landscape, my mind is intent on one thing only as my feet trudge after the screw, step for step.

The prison is quiet and I'm the only con about. I must be the single lucky recipient of contraband today, I tell myself, salivating at the thought of a proper dose of bliss, perhaps three or even four. Depends on whether my brother got to the post sooner in the day rather than later.

I follow the screw through reception until he comes to a halt at the gate of the parcel office. I watch eagerly through the gate as a screw with buck-teeth and a gormless expression rummages painstakingly through the alphabetical cubby-holes. Do I see him exchange a wink with the other screw, or am I imagining things? Eventually I'm summoned inside. The door is locked behind me and the screw departs, leaving me alone with the buck-toothed screw. He holds a slim brown package out to me.

I reach for it, looking forward to squirreling it back to my cell.

I'm not sure why they've locked the door behind me. Doesn't matter; they've got their silly rules; no point trying to work them all out. The parcel does not come away in my hand. It remains wedged in the iron-like grip of the buck-toothed screw.

'What do you say?' he asks pointedly.

What do I say? Shame your old man didn't make you wear braces on your fuckin' teeth. That's what I want to say.

'Oh yeah, thanks guv,' is what I actually say, pulling on my package. It remains glued to the screw's fingers.

'That doesn't sound very polite. Not after all the trouble I've to find your parcel amongst the many, many packages that get sent in to you ungrateful convicts.' His lips close around his protruding teeth, giving him a bizarre, philosophical expression.

I take my eyes off him to glance at the virtually empty cubby-holes. I'm being taken for a ride.

'Say it properly, like your mother taught you,' he says like some sanctimonious school teacher.

There's no fuckin' way I'm going to be any more polite to this cunt! That's my first thought, anyway. My second thought is to say whatever the hell he wants and get out of here, with no pride but my package intact.

'Thank you for going to all that trouble, guv,' I say, relieved there are no other cons around to witness me humiliating myself.

'Sir,' says the screw, 'not guv.'

'Sir,' I manage through gritted teeth.

'Very good,' he says with a self-satisfied air. 'Now, let's just see what's in your package shall we?' He snatches it out of my grasp then sets about opening it with a paper knife, meticulous bastard that he is. I watch him, imagining stabbing the paper knife up his nose and deep into his warped brain.

'What have we here?' His mouth widens into a Cheshire cat beam as he pulls out a magazine. 'My, my. A disgusting, dirty porno?'

My brother would never be dumb enough to smuggle in both porn and drugs at the same time. In fact, it would have looked suspicious if he *hadn't* sent me a girlie mag. Fiesta is about as pornographic as the Mills and Boons my own granny used to read.

Starting at the back, Buck Teeth rifles slowly through the pages, leering at the pictures. I'm starting to sweat. I hope to God it tickles his fancy, otherwise I'm fucked.

His fingers run blithely across the glossy pages to poke about in the creases, yet still I hold out the hope that he won't find anything. I might have had a wank over it later, but I wouldn't touch it now that he's had his stinking fingers all over it.

'Oh dear,' he frowns, after flicking right to the front of the magazine. I feel a tentative surge of relief. 'Not really doing it for me, this one.' His Cheshire Cat smile creeps back across his face. 'Perhaps the centrefold will be more interesting.

Now I know I've had it. My face freezes with hatred. I imagine, like hundreds of cons must have imagined before me, giving this screw a punch that will knock his teeth into their proper position. And then landing him one that will drive them so far inwards they'll cause a traffic jam going down his throat.

I've stooped as low as I will go. It doesn't matter what I have to do; I will jump and bite and punch and kick, but he is not getting my little piece of heaven!

Like an old movie that I've watched time and again, knowing the outcome, yet hoping in vain that it will somehow turn out differently, I watch him unfold the double centrefold. He pulls out a long, thin piece of cling-film and holds it up to the light, his moronic beam stretching from ear to ear.

'Good heavens! How did this get in…?

In a flash I've snatched it out of his hand. Wrenching down my prison jeans with one hand, I roll the cling-film into a ball with the other.

His Cheshire grin switches to a furious grimace. 'No way are you bottling that!' he yells grabbing my arm and forcing it around my neck.

Suddenly alarm bells are ringing and footsteps are pounding along corridors. I'm on the floor. Buck Teeth is kneeling over me, tugging my arm out of its socket trying to choke me. My feet are scrabbling against the table legs for leverage, and my free hand is forcing the package up my bum. I'm gritting my teeth and trying to breathe while my face starts to pop. He can choke the life out of me with my own arm if he likes, but he is *not* getting my gear.

The package is still protruding out of my arse and we're rolling back and forth on the floor. Buck Teeth is growling and huffing, his hand making wild grabs at my bare buttocks. It would be laughable if we weren't both so deadly serious.

Just as I'm about to pass out, a couple of back-up screws arrive. Buckteeth stops his desperate attempts on getting my parcel from my arse and tightens his grip on my neck instead. By some Herculean effort, I just manage to ram my third finger into that magical place where the sun don't shine, spiriting my package to safety. My arm free at last, I slam my elbow into Buckteeth's blubbering belly.

Buckteeth lies gasping on the floor while the other screws lay into me with their batons.

I'm writhing about on the floor, flinching under the blows. My throat is on fire and I'm almost certain my shoulder has been dislocated, when the memory of my fat little friend, Fly, flashes into my mind. He seems to be urging me; trying to tell me something.

I suddenly realise that the only way I'm going to stop the screws from hurting me anymore, is to do something drastic, I start to writhe around on the floor, making them think I'm having a full-blown epileptic fit.

The screws move away, leaving me alone and one barks. 'Oh fuck, we've got a shaker. Call the doctor!'

I've got 'em, the fucks, I laugh to myself, just like Jimmy the Scouser with his broken leg. I'm beat up and I'm hurting, but I've got one over on them and that buck-toothed bastard getting his sick thrills from taunting a desperate human being.

A doctor gives me the once over, then gives my shoulder an agonising little swing and declares me fit and well. Probably went to the same prison training camp as Dr No.

I'm not having it. I demand some Rivotril, eight fuckin' pills a day this time. It's been a long week for him and he scribbles out the prescription there and then. A few minutes later I'm being half-shoved and half-dragged down the Block, same as I was at Belmarsh, and at Bristol, and at Cardiff. It's only a matter of time before I'm out of The Mount too.

I'm locked in a cell with nothing but a bed and a Bible. As soon as the screws' footsteps have receded, I pluck out the roll of cling-film and lay out a line of heroin on the back of my hand. I bring it up to my face and snort it up my nose.

Moments later, I've gone to heaven and I didn't have to read the Bible to get there.

I stand before the governor of The Mount, with two serious-faced screws on either side of me. I'm bruised and ugly. One of them growls at me to tell the governor my name and number, then the governor reads out the charges against me.

'Let me see, Shaw,' he sighs, 'you have been charged with smuggling drugs into prison, disobeying orders, assaulting a prison officer, failure to...'

'Guilty, sir,' I say just as he's starting to warm up.

The governor doesn't like being stopped in mid-flow. It seems to remind him that I'm not just a name and number. I'm actually standing in front of him. He looks up from the charge sheet with an aggrieved frown.

'Belmarsh, Bristol, Cardiff... Seems you're a bit of a nuisance, aren't you, Shaw?'

I don't know what he expects me to say. But I know exactly what he's going to say.

'Yeah, I'm a total bleedin' nuisance, guv,' I mutter under my breath. 'Why don't you take thirty days off me and put me on closed visits and ship me out as soon as you like?'

He gazes unseeingly at me for a long moment. Then he shakes his head and says, 'I'm taking thirty days off your remission and putting you on closed visits. You'll be shipped out soon.'

'Where to?' I ask, sounding a bit too eager.

He shrugs expansively. 'Could be anywhere. Don't think your reputation's travelled as far as Scotland yet. Perhaps we could persuade them to have you. A few hundred years back, you'd have been thrown in the dungeon and we wouldn't have these problems,' he jabbers, frowning at his paperwork.

'Yippee, I love Scotland,' I tell him with a big grin, '*Always* wanted to go there.'

The very next morning, I'm off on my magical mystery tour in a meat-wagon bound for Who Knows Where. Seems like The Mount Governor couldn't bear to have me on his books a minute longer. No one will tell me where I'm going and there's a couple of other cons being taken to court, so I'm being driven around in a sort of limbo, looking through the drizzly windows at mile after mile of suburbia. Outside, people are sheltering, their unsmiling faces under caps and umbrellas. I'd gladly take their place.

There's a song playing round and round in my head. *'You never know what you've got till it's gone.'* It's an old classic that Joni Mitchell did a version of after they paved over her paradise; but she might just as well have been singing about the cushy motel room I just checked out of at The Mount.

Suddenly I want to smash through the reinforced windows and yell at the passers-by, 'Cheer up, you fuckin' muppets! Stop moping around in your clouds of self-pity! You're free, you arseholes. Don't you realise? You're free!'

My nails are cutting into my palms. Eventually, I slump back in my seat. Half of them wouldn't know what I was on about. The older we get the more we live in our own self-made prisons, and it starts when we are young. After a few weeks of being out there, I'd probably forget how lucky I was too.

HMP Pentonville

Dreams and Nightmares

Going through the gates of HMP Pentonville for the first time is a bit like walking onto the set of a horror movie; then realising it's for real.

Opened in 1842, it was built as a monument to the belief that prisoners should be isolated from each other in order to erase all traces of individuality. The thick walls between cells prevented communication and even the guards were forbidden from talking to convicts. This belief in sending convicts up the wall with loneliness has gone through a reversal since then, but the walls are as thick as ever and the old oppression lingers on.

On my way here, I'd been having a laugh to myself while the van drove further and further away from Scotland, and further and further towards the middle of London. I was thinking – yes! Back in the thick of it, in my home city! But one whiff of these grey stone walls, the colossal dreariness of the place, and I know this ain't home sweet home.

The Mount was like a university campus compared to this. On top of all the interesting workshops I opted out of, it had lush green gardens that we were actually allowed to stroll around. The closest I ever got to taking in the country air was to hot-foot it across the lawn a couple of times to score. Now I'm banged up like a factory animal in a Victorian fortress, whose grounds consist of a concrete yard with a few weeds in the corner.

Doesn't take me long to settle in though, one prison's grindingly dull routine being much the same as any other, and soon I'm up to my usual antics, using all my wits to get enough smack to keep me just about ticking over.

I've been here a couple of months when I hear about a couple of new cons on my wing. News on the grapevine is that they're friends on the same burglary beef, so I'm surprised they've been banged up together. Mackey is a shortish black guy with rapidly shifting eyes and a mischievous grin; by contrast, Roland is tall and skinny with a perpetual scowl, except when he's having a dig at Mackey and his face lights up like a cheeky kid's. Right now though, there's nothing cheeky about Roland, and Mackey isn't grinning. They're going through the hell of prison cold turkey.

I'm paying them a visit because they need someone to help them score. 'You're lucky to get shacked up together,' I point out, trying to cheer them up. 'Normally the screws split mates up if they can.'

'Mates!' scoffs Mackey.

'We ain't mates,' groans Roland at the same time. 'I hate the bastard.'

'If he's a mate, who the fuck needs enemies?' Says Mackey drowning out whatever his pal just said. No wonder the screws threw them in together. They must have thought it would be funny to watch sparks fly.

They're lying on their backs in the middle of the afternoon with sweat seeping out of their pasty skin. Being heavy needle-users, they're clucking abominably. Can't keep still for a second, twitching and groaning and rubbing their aching limbs. Roland on the top bunk and Mackey on the bottom each happen to throw me an imploring glance at the exact same moment, making me wince.

'I'll let you know as soon as it comes in,' I say hurriedly, 'Shouldn't be long, this being Pentonville.'

As B Category prisons go, Pentonville has to be one of the easiest places to score outside of a Brixton council estate. Unfortunately, things are a bit dry today, and Roland and Mackey might have to wait a little longer than they expected when they declined to accept medication on arrival. They've opted to rough it out so that they'll be allowed to have visits without a couple of screws standing two inches away, eyes glued to their every orifice.

'It's unbearable, man. Excuse me, mate,' groans Mackey blowing his nose. I look away, not quickly enough to avoid seeing a stream of green goo shoot out of both nostrils. Mackey tosses the snot-soaked tissue into the air. It bounces off the ceiling and lands on Roland's pillow.

'You dirty bastard!' shouts Roland flicking it across the cell in disgust.

'Serves you right for wanking all night,' says Mackey thrusting his hips up and down against the mattress and causing the rusty old bunks to squeak like mad.

Roland throws me an apologetic glance. 'You know what it's like, doesn't take two minutes to knock one out when you're clucking.'

'Yeah, I know what you mean.' I remember all too well how every nerve ending shoots alive when you're withdrawing from gear, making you want to do the hand shandy till kingdom come.

'At least I can still get my dick up,' Roland sneers at his mate.

It's obviously a sore point he's hit on.

'Right, that's it!' says Mackey. He plucks a big lump of snot out of his nose and flicks it with expert precision towards a spot slightly to one side of the smudge on the ceiling where the snot-soaked tissue just bounced.

'Yuck!' screeches Roland, lurching aside as the green grolly shivers on the ceiling directly above him. Mackey leans out of bed to watch with delight as the

224

bogey dangles, getting heavier and heavier at the bottom. He breaks into evil snorty laughter as the slimy glob scrapes itself off the ceiling, pulling the rest of itself down with it until splattering the pillow right where Roland's head had been.

'Right, I'm off,' I say, leaping out the door.

'Wait! Give 'im the money, Roly,' begs Mackey, mopping his sodden brow.

'All right, all right.' I linger reluctantly beside the door while Roland drags his skinny carcass out of bed and fumbles about in his filthy trainers.

'Hurry up, you wanker,' says Mackey, only to scream as Roland's cum-soaked boxer shorts slap against his ear. Glaring triumphantly at Mackey, Roland holds out a crumpled score. Gingerly, I take it in the tips of my fingers, hold open my pocket with the other hand and drop it in.

'You two deserve each other,' I say, grateful to leave them to entertain themselves during their long cluck ahead, knowing full well how each hour will stretch into unbearable infinity.

I stroll down the landing to Gavin's cell. Gavin's one of those tedious cons who never gets bored lifting weights up and down all day long. What's different about him is that he's always getting his cock out of his trousers; he just loves the noise his Prince Albert makes when he clunks it down on a table. No one asks him not to because they don't want to get picked up and used as a bench press, or sent flying over a landing. I hope he'll get done for indecent exposure one day.

'What you laughing about?' comes a growl from behind a thick book entitled, "The World's 1000 Worst Crimes."

'Wouldn't want to interrupt your studies,' I tell him, 'but I've found someone who'll go on a visit for ya.'

'Oh yeah?' he says slipping a bookmark between the pages and carefully setting it down; total neat freak that he is. Gavin's got tattoos all over him, even one that spells "Becky you'll always be the love of my life" across his shoulders, the idiot. I'm sure he's a closet homo.

Gavin's last package was confiscated and he's been put on closed visits, but now he's expecting a large delivery and needs someone to fetch it. It's what we all do when we get screened off from our visitors; we get them to visit other cons instead. Not too nice for them to travel halfway across London for a chat with some stranger in a clink, but needs must. I put Dawn through it a few times before I came up with that jeans trick. She had to meet up with some right horrible criminals thanks to me.

Trouble is, Gavin hasn't found anyone he can trust yet. I'd go on the visit myself, but the screws are watching me like hawks. Besides, it's going to be a large package and there'll be enough for all of us.

'How d'ya know you can trust 'im?' Gavin asks suspiciously.

I think back to Roland tossing his sopping boxer shorts at his friend.

'He's alright, mate,' I say, nodding persuasively. 'Top notch bloke.'

'Aw right, if you say so, 'arry. You'll get your cut. But if he fucks up, you'll just get cut. Know what I mean?

'Yeah, I know what ya mean,' I laugh, adding, 'you've been reading too many true crime books, mate, haven't ya?'

Later that day, a consignment comes in. Roland and Mackey are in no fit shape to score for themselves, so after I've skimmed a bit off the top, I pay them a visit to put them out of their misery. They're barely able to move, got the shakes and the shits and that gnawing, rat-eaten look I know so well.

'You're a fuckin' life-saver, Harry!' gasps Mackey, opening the wrap which contains barely enough to keep them hanging on until tomorrow.

'Yeh, thanks Harry, let me know when I can return the favour, mate.' Says Roland, struggling into a sitting position and collapsing against the wall. Soon as he's recovered his balance, he's leaning over his bunk to make sure his so-called mate gives him his fair share.

'That's what they all say,' I chuckle, handing over some foil. It's good to do favours. At least it's nice to get my name pronounced right for once. 'Actually, there is a favour you can do me.'

Next afternoon, Roland's waiting for me in his cell, wearing a clean shirt and jeans, with his face freshly scrubbed. Looks like he's spat on his trainers and given them a bit of a wipe too. He's all excited about getting a visitor, never mind that it'll be a total stranger. Mackey's been talking him through it all morning like a trainer prepping a forgetful boxer.

'Don't worry, all ya gotta do is keep your eyes on your visitor like you're 'avin' a deep conversation, then wait till the screws are outta the way and ram it up your arse swifto, got it?'

'Yeah, yeah, I got it,' says Roland nervously wiping his brow.

'Stick it all the way up,' Mackey insists. 'Have ya greased up yet?' he asks, grasping the back of Roland's jeans to check for himself.

Roland smacks him away. 'I've stuck baby oil up my chad and stuffed three fingers in, so fuck off.'

I wish Mackey would leave his pal alone and stop making him so fucking nervous. 'You'll be fine, Roland,' I say reassuringly. 'If anything goes wrong, you'll just have to swallow. But only swallow it if you've got no other option.'

'Yeah, don't swallow it whatever the fuck you do,' nods Mackey who seems to have a habit of repeating everything twice. 'Do not swallow it. Don't swallow or we're fucked.'

'I'm an expert at this, you mug. I'm a fuckin' magician,' says Roland hunching his shoulders up and down, geeing himself up. 'One second it'll be there and the next it'll be gone. Poof! Vanished!'

Footsteps approach along the landing a screw says, 'Visit for Dwight.'

'It's sweet then,' says Mackey, looking none too convinced. 'We're all sweet. Sweet!'

Roland walks into the visiting room feeling like John Wayne stepping off his horse after a long, sweaty ride across the desert. He's regretting being quite so liberal with the baby oil. Hopes it's not seeping through his jeans. You never know, the girl who's coming to visit might be a bit of a looker, and Roland's heard a few stories about couples falling for each other across a crowded prison visiting room.

The screw behind the desk tells him which table number to sit at and Roland scans the room looking for his place. Roughly three quarters of the visitors are female. Half of those are mingers, and the other half are either preggers or trying to keep a brood of kids under control. Apart from that, there's one complete stunner who has just come in and is striding to the drink dispenser, pink stilettos clacking, magnetising everyone's eyes to her shapely legs.

'Third row,' the screw says loudly, snapping Roland out of his reverie.

Roland makes his way to his seat, unable to take his eyes off the stunning brunette. Even from this distance he can see her dazzling fingernails clasping two Styrofoam cups of tea. After all that panic earlier he's gasping for a cuppa.

He reaches his allocated seat and sits down with a squelch. Hurriedly, he glances round to make sure no one has heard him. One of the mingers at the next table glares at him with disgust. He glares back, thanking his lucky stars that he didn't do that in front of the stunning girl. Subtly lifting one buttock, he squeezes his arsehole and gets it tightly under control as she sashays towards him with two cups of tea.

He hopes she's got the package in her mouth. It won't help much with conversation, but what an opportunity for a snog! If he plays things right and thrusts his tongue into her mouth a couple of times, it'll take her ages to transfer the package. And by then, who knows... those lust chemicals might have started to flow and perhaps she'll reach up to grasp the back of his neck like in one of those black and white movies that his mum used to make him watch as a kid, and pull him towards her for a proper...

'Hiya, babe!' she calls out, smiling at him with lovely white teeth.

Doesn't look like she's got no package in her mouth, he thinks with dismay. Maybe it's in her bra, he decides, cheering up again. Feeling a stirring in his loins, he watches as she walks past him, sets down the cups of tea and throws her arms around the lucky bastard sitting directly behind him.

'Roland Dwoight?' says a man's voice.

Roland doesn't want to hear it.

'Roland Dwoight?' the voice asks again.

Roland tears his gaze from the voluptuous hindquarters of the girl-who-doesn't-know-what-she's-missing to find himself gaping up at a muscle-bound fella with veins popping out of a vast neck. He's holding a

229

single can of Pepsi in one gigantic hand, and it's not for Roland. Roland's heart sinks as fast as his last mobile phone sank into a toilet (when he answered it a bit too eagerly.) Things could hardly get worse, except when two screws march over to stand behind Muscle-neck with their arms hanging stiff on either side of their flies.

'It's Dwight, all right?' says Roland, wondering what sort of exercise could build such unnecessary beef in a fella's neck. 'What's your name, mate?' he whispers.

'Mark, mate,' the visitor mutters under his breath then says loudly, 'Long time no see, eh?'

Roland frowns. The geezer sounds like he went to some posh boarding school, and yet he *looks* like he grew up on some breeding ground for criminals. All is made clear when his visitor opens his mouth to reveal a huge package weighing down his tongue. There's no way Roland's leaving that behind.

He leans forward rather too quickly, making his greased arsehole play tricks with him. Muscle-neck grimaces on hearing a wet burp under the table. The screws watch closely.

'There's no other way round it; you're gonna have to kiss me Mark, mate,' Roland whispers.

Muscle-neck shakes his head; manages to mumble, 'No fucking way.'

Roland doesn't hear him. He's already got his hand round the back of that massive neck, and no amount of muscles can stop him pressing his mouth against his visitor's with his eyes squeezed shut. For one horrific moment, Roland senses all the muscles in his visitor's body tense with outrage. At the same time, he is excruciatingly aware of the bristly feel of the skin against his lips as well as a nauseating smell of Brut and something else… uurrrgh… banana-flavoured high protein shake!

Just as Roland's about to retch, the biggest, hardest tongue he's ever snogged forces itself into his mouth. His first reaction is to shove it out with his own tongue. But, thank Fuck he doesn't, because suddenly there's about three hundred-quid's worth of heroin in there, and now *he's* the one with the great lump in his mouth trying to act normal.

'What 'ave we 'ere, a couple of homos?' one of the screws frowns suspiciously.

Muscle-neck had been looking relieved on being able to breathe properly again. Now though, the veins start throbbing indignantly at the sides of his neck while his fists clench up.

'Just good mates,' says Roland, astounding himself with his plumy voice.

The screws frown sceptically.

The sweat that has broken out on Roland's brow starts dribbling down his temples. There's no way he can get that juggernaut of a package out of his mouth and bottle it with two screws watching his every breath. And if he waits for the strip-search he might as well slit his throat right now, 'cause Mackey will never let him hear the end of it. That's if Gavin lets him *live* to hear the end of it. And, as if having a chat with a homophobic brute wasn't hard enough, now he can hardly squeeze a word out edgeways.

There's only one way out of this situation. He grabs Muscle-neck's Pepsi and takes a swig, half of which shoots out the sides of his mouth on contact with the huge lump in his throat. The package slips against his tonsils and comes to a halt, making his eyes water. He gulps down some more Pepsi and starts gagging. Through blurry eyes he sees Muscle-neck and the two screws watching him with deep suspicion.

'Looks like he's swallowing drugs,' says one of the screws. 'He'll have to go on forty-eight hour shit watch. Open your mouth, Dwight!'

No fucking way! It's as if Roland can see the rest of his life flash before him, and it doesn't last very long. With a sudden stroke of genius that would surely make Mackey proud, (and possibly make up for screwing up that burglary on the pub,) he gives an almighty swallow which brings the package down to the level of his Adam's Apple, then rubs his lips in disgust.

'You fuckin' faggot!' he snarls disgustedly at his visitor. 'Keep your dirty, stinking lips to yourself!'

Suddenly there's a noisy scraping of chair legs and Muscle-neck, who's come all the way from Dagenham to meet up with a scrawny scaghead, is clambering over the table to throw punches at Roland, one of which gives him a wonderfully distracting nose bleed. The screws are hanging off Muscle-neck's elbows, trying to bring him under control, and in all the mayhem the notion of drugs being swallowed seems to fly clean out of everyone's heads.

Roland swaggers heroically back to his cell where I'm waiting with Mackey and Gavin.

'What happened to your nose, you twat?' asks Mackey.

'Never mind his fuckin' nose. Where's my smack?' demands Gavin. Suddenly the veins are standing out of his neck and his LOVE/HATE knuckles are clenching up, giving Roland a horrible déjà vu.

Meanwhile, Mackey's tossing handfuls of salt into a jug of water and saying, 'Calm down, calm down, I'll get him to sick it up. It's sweet, mate, everything's sweet.'

'Nah, wait a minute,' cries Roland as Mackey shoves the jug under his nose. 'I can feel it. It's stuck in me throat, look!'

Me, Mackey and Gavin peer at a large lump in Roland's throat.

'That's your Adam's Apple, you muppet,' says Mackey.

'No, it ain't, it's right there, can't you feel it? It's a fucking big lump!' Roland insists.

'I'll squeeze it out of him,' says Gavin reaching towards Roland's neck with outstretched hands.

'No, wait!' yelps Roland, leaping out of the way.

'Maybe we could try the Heinrick Manoeuvre,' I suggest and the others look at me blankly, except Roland, who doesn't like the sound of that. 'It saves people's lives when they're choking,' I explain, stepping behind Roland and positioning my hands around his waist.

Gavin frowns doubtfully. 'If that doesn't work I'll reach down his throat and get it out myself.'

'What the fuck are you doing?' wails Roland, trying to escape.

'Hold still, mate,' I say and with all my strength bring my fists up together into his solar plexus.

A moment later, Roland's on hands and knees, winded and gasping for breath, and Mackey, ever the optimist, is searching around the floor for the package which surely must have flown out of his throat.

'It's still in here,' Roland manages to wheeze, throwing me an offended look.

'I'll give ya a kick up the arse. That'll make it come out,' says Gavin, eyeing Roland's skinny rump.

'Gavin, why don't you stand outside and make sure there's no screws about?' I say hurriedly. 'We'll get him to puke it out, don't you worry, mate.'

Gavin glowers suspiciously at all three of us as if we're in on some crazy conspiracy to outwit him of his goods, then stomps outside to guard the door. Mackey drags a bucket under his mate, who's crouching doggy-style on the floor, and grabs the jug of salt water.

'I hate being sick,' says Roland.

'Yeah, but think about all that lovelly-juvelly 'eroin,' says Mackey.

I'm regretting not guarding the door myself, but it wouldn't have done to have Gavin making Roly accidentally choke to death on his own drugs. Roland glugs down the water and throws it straight back up with a horrific retch. Mackey peers eagerly into the bucket to see nothing but bile.

'That's better,' gasps Roland, 'it's not stuck in me throat any more.'

'Right, well this time give a fucking good heave,' says Mackey, filling up the jug and chucking a huge handful of salt into it then mixing it up with a spoon. Roland swallows as much as he can take before his stomach retaliates, spewing out the salty mixture with a ferocity that makes Mackey dive out of the way. This time, the watery bile hits the bucket so hard that half of it sprays straight back out, but there's still no sign of the package.

'I've got an idea,' says Mackey, grabbing hold of his pal's ankle. 'Grab his other leg, mate. A bit of gravity should help it come out.'

Reluctantly, I help Mackey heave Roland into a handstand with his head positioned over the bucket. 'Quick, stick your fingers down your throat, Roly!' urges his mate.

For a long while, as the gruesome retching noises ricochet off the concrete walls, I wonder why I'm not laughing. I've laughed my arse off at this sorta thing in the past. But now I'm not even smiling. I feel like I'm watching some sort of torture scene out of the Dark Ages.

A stream of bile gushes out of Roland's throat and a thick string of snot from his nose, a small amount of which makes it into the bucket. Mackey gets his feet soaked, but I let go of Roland's leg just in time for me to escape and for him to splash in a heap of bones into the puddle on the floor.

Mackey regards his friend with disgust. 'We're just going to have to wait for you to shit it out.'

Feeling like a doctor pepping up the nerves of an expectant father, I go outside to break the bad news to Gavin. 'It'll be out in the morning, mate. These things tend to come in their own time.'

He doesn't take it too well. I watch him storm back to his cell, his great thick neck swinging from side to side as if he's looking around to tear someone's head off.

It's long gone bang up for the night, and Mackey and Roland aren't talking. That is, Mackey is talking but Roland has a pillow over his head and is trying to drown it all out. They're both clucking again. Mackey's method of dealing with the aching limbs, the shakes, the sweats and the clouds of despair, is to talk his way through it, unlike Roland, who hasn't got a method. He's just thinking about dying.

'You should've bottled it while you'ad the chance, is all I'm saying,' Mackey's voice drones on. 'Like I told you, if you couldn't do it at the time, you should'a waited till you got round the corner, and then we wouldn't be in this mess now, would we? You could have pretended you had an itchy arse – I got one all the time, mate. I should have done it meself. Me mum always used to say: 'If you want a job done properly, do it yourself,' and she was right, she was.'

235

Roland throws himself over onto his other side arousing a racket of rusty squeaks.

'If you'd done what I told you, you'd be high as a kite, mate. High as a bloody kite. High... as... a... kite in the sky.'

Roland tosses himself back onto his other side.

'D'ya wanna go for a pony yet?' Mackey asks him for about the fifth time. 'You must be dying to go by now, ain't ya?'

An agonised mumble comes from under Roland's pillow.

'A pony,' Mackey patiently explains in case his thicko friend can't understand him, 'is a pony and trap; crap. Did you eat all that brown bred I got ya?'

A disgusted groan comes from the mattress above. 'Yeah I ate it, and all those cold fucking baked beans and the three pieces of Weetabix.'

Mackey frowns into the dark. 'What, and you still don't want to go?'

'No, you cunt.'

Mackey bites his tongue for a moment. In his mind, the more he asks Roland if he's ready for a dump, the more it'll make Roland need to go. Still, maybe he's been laying it on a bit thick.

'Well, let me know when you do, is all I'm saying,' he mutters, getting out of bed to smooth out the foil again; making sure everything's ready for when Roland feels the urge.

It's cold in the cell this early in the morning. They didn't get much sleep. Mackey kept one eye wide open and glaring at the mattress above him for most of the night, and Roland could feel it burning into him. Their soaked mattresses feel about as comfy as a bed of nails against their overwhelmed nerve-endings. When the

236

servery opens up for breakfast, the sound of clanking pots and scraping trays tortures their tender eardrums.

Roland leans out of his bunk, daring Mackey to open his mouth. Roland's been holding it in for a minute or two, trying to make the bastard wait. But now he's got the shits for sure, and anyway, he needs this as badly as Mackey. He jumps off his bunk, yelping as the floor hits his feet with some kind of vengeance.

Mackey's out of bed like a shot, laying out sheets of newspaper. That done, he grabs his plastic knife, ready for when Roland has finished, although Roland can do that part himself.

Roland slides off his boxers and crouches, holding his knees. A long squirt of semi-fluid shit splatters the paper. Mackey, bending down for an inspection, is amazed to see steam rising out of it.

'Fuckin' hell that stinks,' he says grabbing his nose. 'Did a rat crawl up your arse and die in there or something?'

'Smells better than your festerin' dumps,' mutters Roland, straining his wasted muscles until another turd encounters the paper with a splat.

'Go on, look through it then,' says Mackey, handing him the knife.

Roland takes the knife and turns round to inspect his dump. His brown-stained arse swings past Mackey's face by an inch, making Mackey gasp with disgust. 'Wipe ya fucking arse, mate!'

'Na. Wait a sec,' says Roland, all excited. 'I think this might be it!'

'Oh no, it's just a lump,' says Roland, disappointed.

'It's gotta be in here,' says Mackey scooping up the crap and slicing through it like he's making ice cream. After a full minute of scooping and gagging, Mackey finally decides he's had enough. He sits hunched on his bed, sulking.

Roland collapses on his mattress, leaving his pile of shit in the middle of the floor.

After a while, Mackey says through his pinched nose, 'Gavin ain't gonna be happy.'

'He'll just have to wait.'

'There's a nice single cell coming up today and I might have to move into it.'

'You dog.'

No sooner have the doors been unlocked for breakfast than Gavin bulldozes his way into their cell, veins throbbing in his temples. 'Where's my drugs, you slags? Fuckin 'ell, what's that stink?'

Roland and Mackey shoot out of bed, guilt-ridden. Roland sets about clearing up the mess.

'They're still in 'is belly, but don't worry, mate,' Mackey explains hurriedly. 'Nothing to worry about, Gav, it ain't nothing to worry about. I'll get onto the doc right away for some laxatives and flush it outta him. Get hold of some bran flakes too... maybe those prunes with custard they serve up of a Wednesday... He'll be shitting himself in no time. No time at all, mate.'

'Too fucking right; he'll be shitting 'imself by the time I've finished with him,' snarls Gavin, casting a suspicious grimace over the pair of them. Apparently satisfied that they are genuinely clucking, and not gouching out on fluffy clouds of bliss, he stomps out, slamming the door behind him.

Over the next twenty-four hours, Roland and Mackey endure the worst cluck of their lives; the worst because the antidote to it is so close, and yet so far.

'Where the fuck could it have got to?' groans Roland, rubbing his stomach in the clockwise motion that

238

Mackey has instructed him to follow on advice of the doctor, as an extra aid to the laxatives he prescribed.

'Maybe he said anti-clockwise,' mumbles Mackey. 'Start rubbing in the other direction, Roly'

'Won't that make it go back up the other way?'

'I don't fuckin' know, do I? I heard about this bloke once, who swallowed a package on his way to the nick and it burst open in his stomach and he died from the overdose.'

'Great. Thanks.'

'What a fuckin' waste,' says Mackey, staring at Roland gloomily.

'Yeah, what a fucking waste of a life,' agrees Roland.

'Your life ain't going nowhere. I'm talking about the smack, you mug.'

'That's it, you ain't getting none now!' A vengeful look comes into Roland's eyes, then he folds his arms behind his head and says, 'I heard about this other fella once. Swallowed his drugs on the way to the nick and they never came out. He checked through his shit every day for months. Then, one day he forgot to check, and just as he flushed the loo he saw a shiny bit of plastic swirling round and round. He reached in to grab it just as it got sucked down the toilet.'

'No fucking way,' says Mackey with a groan.

'You're the mug; you'll believe anything,' says Roland with a glimmer of his old cheek, but only a glimmer. He turns over, causing a zillion nerve endings to start up a rumpus of complaint. For a long while, he stares silently at the wall. Eventually he murmurs, 'Tell you what, mate. I'm never going through this again.'

'You what, mate?'

'I'm never putting myself through this shit again. It ain't fucking worth it.'

Mackey frowns uncomprehendingly. 'Soon as it comes out, you'll be shooting it up just like old times. Everything will be sweet, mate. Sweet.' He says encouragingly.

'Maybe. But after that it's over. I'm sick of being a junkie!'

'Why's that then?' says Mackey, dreading the end of the conversation. But Roland's got nothing more to say and try as Mackey might, he can't get him started again.

A couple of hours later, Roland heaves his aching bones out of bed and staggers along the landing on a mercy mission to ask the doctor for some Methadone. Passing Gavin's cell, he spots, 'The World's 1000 Worst crimes' lying neatly closed with its book mark on the table. He hurries past, relieved that Gavin's not in.

Suddenly there's a great, thick arm around his neck, his feet have left the floor and he's flying in an arc into Gavin's cell with the door clanging shut behind him.

'*Where's my drugs, you skinny fuck?*'

A mad face with popping eyes is leering so close to his that Roland's bony snout collides with Gavin's fleshy bulbous one. Inches from his stomach, just outside his line of vision, Roland hears an unmistakable click which sends a shiver of dread down his spine.

'You've got ten seconds to tell me what you did with my drugs,' Gavin snarls into his ear, pressing the sharp point of his switchblade into Roland's stomach. 'Otherwise I'm going to open you up like a fuckin' chicken and sort through your innards till I find it myself...! Jesus Christ, what's that fuckin' smell?'

Roland doesn't know whether to be embarrassed or ecstatic. For the first time since he was a little kid, (or at any rate, since his headmaster caught him red-handed in the girls' locker room sniffing a pair of frilly knickers,) he's shat himself. There, on the floor, in the middle of the

240

fluid dump that has trailed out from his trouser leg, is Gavin's package.

HMP Pentonville

Doing Time

I'm sitting on the patch of weeds in the corner of the yard with my eyes shut and the September sunshine beaming down on my head, dreaming of lying in a hammock somewhere on the East coast of India. It'll be bliss. I'll be swinging in the stifling sunshine under some palm trees, with a drip-feed in my arm delivering a constant supply of heroin; not the adulterated junk we get round here, but the pure, sweet nectar straight from the poppy. I've never tried it but I've heard it's a bit like dying and sailing to paradise on a magic carpet. I won't need for anything as long as I live, and when it comes my turn to kick the bucket, it'll be with a blessed-out smile on my face.

'I know that look. Dreamin' about what'ya gonna do when you get out, are you 'arry?'

The voice drags me back to the real world just as a gust of wind blasts across the yard, making me shiver. I open my eyes to see Deano grinning at me against a background of barred windows and grey stone walls. Deano is tall and athletic and covered in a fine mist of sweat after his jog round the yard.

I shut my eyes again, trying to block it all out. No harm in drawing him in on my happy fantasy.

'I'm moving to India. I'll buy a poppy field, and one day a week I'll pick my flowers and turn them into finest grade heroin. Rest of the week I'll be in my hammock in Limboland, till I die with a great big smile on my face.'

Deano laughs. 'Dream on, silly bollocks. It doesn't work that way.'

I keep my eyes squeezed shut while the edges of my ideal world curl up like a burning photograph. Deano has lit a match to my dream, and for some reason, he's determined to watch it burn.

'You can never get enough smack into your system to be happy. You can stave off feeling shit for a while, but it catches up with you, and in the end it fuckin' kills you.'

A scowl settles on my face, like the cloud that has just moved in front of the sun, casting a desultory gloom over the yard.

'Oh, yeah? How would you know? All you do is get high on your own endorphins, exercise freak!' I cast a sideways glance at the muscles rippling in his arms as he lies down with his hands behind his head. My muscles used to ripple like that, once.

'Used to be a junkie, meself,' Deano says to the sky. 'Dealt it to feed my habit. For about a year... year and a half... I was doing really well, always had enough smack. At one time I was booting up five grams a day.'

I let out a whistle of admiration tinged with envy.

'It never felt like enough, though. I was getting through five, six grand a month and I still wanted more. Anyway, just *supposing* you ended up in India and could feed your habit as much as you wanted,' he says rolling his eyes with derision, 'you'd soon bust your veins. Then you'd have to have an IV straight into your groin, yeah? That's the biggest vein. You'd end up with a massive hole, though.' He sniffs and shakes his head. 'And being in a hot country with all sorts of diseases lurkin' about in the water 'n' that, it'd soon go septic. Your immune system would be so fucked you'd pick up malaria or some shit and not even know you had it, unless you came off the gear for a couple of days. *Then* you'd know you was ill, all right!'

243

This is horrific. I don't want to hear any more. But somehow I don't want him to stop.

'And all this time you'd be wasting away 'cause you wouldn't be eating or exercising. You wouldn't want to get out of that fuckin' hammock to take a piss, mate. Oh! And by the way, just in case you think you'd be in Cloud cuckoo Land, let me tell you something. Your body would get so used to the smack that the best you'd feel would be sort of all right, like if you'd never taken it in the first place. That's if you were lucky.'

He lets this information sink in while my chest starts to hammer. I've had my fears and doubts about my drug use, but no one can convince me that life isn't shit without a bit of gear to give it that golden glow. I've always held out the belief that if only I could get a clean, reliable supply, I'd be sorted.

Deano's shaking his head as if he can read my thoughts. 'It's all the up-and-down shit, the relief of having it after not having it, that makes you think it's so fuckin' great.' He shrugs and lets out what sounds like a sigh of total relief. 'It's a prick-tease. That's all it is. A fuckin' prick-tease.'

There's a bloke wearing a tracksuit bottoms pacing up and down next to the wall. I've been keeping a watchful eye on him in case he's waiting for an over-the-wall-delivery, but now I'm collapsing on the grass next to Deano feeling exhausted. For years, my love affair with heroin has held out such beautiful promise, as if it's been saving the best for last. But somehow, now I've aired my dream of giving myself up to heroin's beguiling embrace, I can see how I've been duped.

Staring into the greying sky, an excruciating emptiness seeps through me. I catch a glimpse of Deano, and he's smiling. Something's not making sense. He fell under smack's alluring spell too; so how come he's looking so happy without it?

I sit up, chest pounding. 'Deano, how did you get off it? I'm sick of living like this. I'm willing to do whatever it takes.'

Deano sits up and glances around the yard. His eyes light up.

'Good timing!' he laughs and points to a man with a clipboard talking to a con from behind the mesh. 'Ask that fat bloke over there. Tell him you want to get on the RAPt wing. It'll be the best thing you ever did.'

His words seem to pick me up and I'm running across the yard as if through no will of my own. I wait impatiently for the fat bloke to finish with the other con, then gabble, 'Excuse me, mate, could I have two minutes of your time?'

The fat man turns to me with a concerned smile. 'I'm Gordon. What can I do for you?'

I step back, not used to being addressed so politely.

'I'm going to be honest here like I've never been honest to anyone before.' The words tumble out of my mouth in a rush. 'I need to come over to your wing and do something about my drug problem.'

It's the first time I've admitted to having a problem, secrets being held deep in my family. As for a drug problem, until a few minutes ago, mad as it might sound, I didn't realise I had one. I thought that *not* having drugs was the problem.

Gordon asks my name and number and puts me on his list.

'How long will it take?' I urge him.

'At the moment, the waiting list is two months, Harry. But I'll see what I can do.'

I hold back a gasp of dismay. 'Please do that, because I don't know if I can last that long.' And I mean it, knowing it's only a matter of time before I either implode and go fucking insane, or explode in a moment of rage and seriously hurt someone.

Gordon looks me sincerely in the eyes. 'Leave it with me.'

I wander back through the yard, thoughts whirling through my mind. I feel strangely excited but also suddenly furious; furious because it's like a veil has been lifted and I can clearly see how I've wasted so many years of my life fixated on a temptress who promises the earth at the cost of her lover's mind, riches, body and finally, soul.

From the corner of my eye, I spot a small, glistening package fly over the wall. It lands on the grass not far from where Deano is still sitting. Swiftly, the con that I'd earlier noticed pacing twitchily by the wall, whips down his trousers and stuffs the package up his arse. It's all done so quickly that there's only the briefest flash of his hairy bum before he's slipping into the crowd. He doesn't get very far, however, before a couple of cons intercept him.

Suddenly, he's being yelled at to drop his trousers. He yells back, tries to make a run for it. There's a scuffle. Other cons swarm forward on smelling the scent of fear and fury in the air. I sense it myself. I'm being propelled along with the crowd, feeling an urge to see blood fly. I watch punches rain into the con from several directions and catch a glimpse of blood before my view is blocked.

Screws are running everywhere. A whistle is blown. It echoes around the yard, sending pigeons scattering upwards. The screws are pulling and shoving at anyone in their way, swinging their batons and screaming at us to get inside. Our adrenaline is pumping and the excitement feels good, a welcome change from our constant boredom. I'm carried along with the crowd heading back inside, knowing there's going to be more violence any minute now.

The conversation I just had with Gordon flies out of my mind. This time I want to be in on the fight. I want to feel the thrill that comes when my fist or my foot connects with living, feeling flesh. It can't be just anyone though; it has to be someone who's got it coming. Someone who deserves to get fucked up. The rage that's permanently trapped inside me is starting to boil over.

We're crowding onto the tarmac path leading inside when an old cellmate of mine from back at the Marsh slows down and mutters in my ear. 'Hey, 'arry, I know you don't like nonces.'

My ears prick up. Nonces? I can't fucking stand them, and Lenny Hatcher is one of the few cons who knows why.

'See that bloke behind you?' says Lenny. 'He's a bacon. Screw said he raped his two-year-old step daughter.'

That's it. That's all I need to hear. My rage has an outlet.

I glance round, following Lenny's line of vision to see an older fella with an intelligent-looking face and stooped shoulders hurrying behind us. He looks nervous.

I can barely wait as Lenny hangs back, positioning himself to throw what I recognise will be a left hook. Even though he senses it, the nonce doesn't see it coming. The blow thunders into his jaw and by the way his mouth sags I know it's broken. He slumps to the ground while Lenny walks on with a crazed grin.

The con's horizontal, so I'll have to use my feet. I step in quickly, burying my foot deep in his belly before he has a chance to double up. There's a satisfying squelching sound, which I follow up by stamping down hard on his leg, making him let out a pitiful yelp.

'There ya go, you fuckin' nonce!' I scream and follow Lenny, glancing behind to see the cons behind me take over, turn by turn, exacting retribution for whatever grievances they happen to harbour. They heard what I said, and if they didn't it doesn't matter. With the screws distracted outside, it's the best chance they're going to have of getting a thrill in this place with no sex or excitement to alleviate the tension. I'm happy for the bastards.

Through the blur of kicking feet, I catch a glimpse of the con gazing blindly to one side. Tarmac is embedded into his face along with the red stuff, as unreal to me as ketchup, oozing onto the path.

He had it coming.

I'm buzzing. Power and triumph are pumping through my veins and I feel great. I feel a little bit sick too, but quickly remind myself that anyone who messes around with a two-year-old deserves to die. I feel better at once. In fact, I wish I'd killed the fucker. Hopefully the cons behind me will see to it, and that twisted bastard will never walk again, let alone plunge his filthy…

There's a lump in my throat and I'm awash with rage. I want to rush back, toss the other cons aside and finish the job myself. I lean against the wall, taking deep breaths, trying not to lose control.

Thoughts of stamping on the nonce's face assail me. But first, I want to break the nose that bore down over that little girl's face. I want to smash the mouth that said twisted things to her. I want to gouge out the eyes that leered down at her innocent gaze, before he smashed her skull into tiny fragments with a paving slab. Most of all, I want to jump on the flaccid dick that he tried again and again to force inside her before she started screaming and wouldn't stop.

I'm running towards my landing, tears rushing to my eyes. Everything's a blur. Can't recognise which cell is mine, they're all the fucking same anyway… Where is it? Oh where the fuck is it? I've got to get into my bed with the blanket over my head and block out the memory of what that pervert did to my beautiful cousin. The way he snapped off her life, like I'd like to snap off his fingers, one by one, and laugh at his pathetic screams.

Somehow I've made it to my cell. My chest is hammering and thoughts are blasting round my brain; violent murderous thoughts. I laugh a bitter laugh. I'm in the right place for this. I'm in prison. I'm a criminal with a history of violence. Only I don't really deserve to be here. Not yet anyway, because I didn't get the chance to kill the monster who molested my beautiful, ever-smiling, fourteen-year-old cousin.

Blood's pounding through my veins and I can barely breathe. All prisoners have been returned to their cells and the prison is on lockdown. I bang my head with its incessant thoughts against the wall. Then I get a better idea and press the emergency bell. I wait restlessly for a screw to escort me to the doctor. The screw can see that I'm shaking; that I'm a danger to myself and others, and takes me at once. The doctor isn't stupid either, he gives me Valium, no questions asked.

When I come out of the doc's, the landing is empty. The screw that escorted me has been called off on some emergency, so I swallow the Valium and start pacing along the empty landing, waiting to be let back into my cell. There's a suppressed, almost guilty atmosphere in the prison, and for once the constant racket is subdued.

'Shit! I didn't mean for it to get out of hand like that.'

'You can't beat yourself up about it, mate. These things happen.'

The voices are coming from the screws' office a few feet away. I know they haven't heard me and creep closer, compelled to know what they're talking about.

'He's been beaten badly. He's in the hospital now.'

'He probably 'ad it coming, mate.'

'No, he didn't though. I didn't like the git, but he didn't deserve that!' The screw lets out what sounds, weirdly, like a sob, making my heart miss a beat. It sounds like there's been some sort of horrific mistake.

'What was it he did to piss you off, exactly?'

The screw's voice is so low I barely catch it. 'He said something about how an ignorant piece of scum like me wouldn't be able to get a job anywhere else because I wouldn't be able to read the 'Entrance' sign on the way in, or some shit like that.'

The other screw whistles through his teeth.

'So I said, without thinking too much, right in front of his cellmate. Well, you're in the right place, scumbag, for raping your two-year-old step daughter.'

'Fucking 'ell,' exclaims the other screw. 'You said that in front of that nasty little fucker, Hatcher?'

'Yeah. I thought he knew I was just having a dig.'

'Doesn't look that way, does it?'

'Now there'll be a fucking enquiry, and if he dies, I've had it.'

I don't need to hear any more. All I can think, over and over and over, is how, when my foot went into that man's belly, it made a nasty squelch, not like it was connecting with fatty flesh but more like I'd punctured his bladder or something. Then that horrible yelp he gave.

I speed silently back to my cell and wait for a screw coming from the other direction to let me in. Last thing I need is that other screw knowing I could get him put away in his own nick where he wouldn't last two fucking minutes.

My cellmate Geoff's 'All right, mate?' hangs in the air as I hurl into my bed and pull the blanket over my head.

The Valium's only just starting to kick in. All I can think about is how I got the wrong fella, and how maybe if I hadn't yelled out the 'nonce' word, all those other cons wouldn't have put the boot in and he'd still have a decent life to look forward to.

I'm beside myself with remorse. That intelligent-looking gent might only have been in for tax evasion or some stupid mistake by the police. He could have been completely innocent for all I fucking know. And now he's going to die, or be in hospital for ages.

It's all my fault, and if I didn't hate myself before for all the grief I've caused Dawn and Tom, my Mum, my sister and so many others, I do now. I hate myself in spades. If I had a knife I'd stab it straight into my stomach because I'm such a cunt.

I want to use. Heroin is the only thing in the world that could take me away from this tortuous, writhing pit of guilt. With heroin I could be the worst person in the world and still she would welcome me into her soft embrace and dry my sweating brow and tell me she loved me, no matter what.

But, wait a minute, says a logical voice in my schizoid brain. You trusted Lenny; you thought his information was good. Besides, it's not your fault you're angry about your cousin. You were only trying to avenge her death the best way you knew.

Yeah, I was avenging Alice's death, I tell myself. Just got a bit confused, that's all.

The Valium's beginning to work.

Just got a bit confused, I try to convince myself over and over again, until falling into a feverish sleep.

All night long, I'm tormented by Alice's killer. He's doing a life sentence in Grendon protected from the prisoners who'd mete out their own form of punishment on him in other jails. In my dream he's got a huge, comfy cell with a sofa, a fridge full of beer and a gigantic TV screen, and instead of a narrow bunk he's got a king-sized four-poster. Even the bars on his window are made out of sticks of multi-coloured seaside rock, with flowery curtains draped on either side.

He's lying in his great big fucking bed, all cosy with its fluffy duvet and plumped-up pillows; he's lying in that great big bed and he's laughing at me. From time to time I think I glimpse a little lump in the bed beside him, a little girl's plait here, a little girl's foot there, peeking out from under the duvet.

'You got the wrong bloke, you twat!' he guffaws. 'It's me you're after! Here I am, come and get me!'

I make a lunge for him, only there's a fucking great paving slab in my arms and it's weighing me down. Much as I'm desperate to smash it over his repulsive face, I can't quite summon the energy to move one step closer towards him.

At last, I manage to gather enough strength to heave the slab above my head. My heart surges with glee. I'm going to kill him. I'm going to make sure his wicked, warped grin never scares another little girl ever again.

I bring the paving slab down with a triumphant yell. It echoes around the cell and along the landings and into the yard outside, making the pigeons fly upwards with a great flapping roar. Just as the paving slab is about to squash the bastard I notice, too late, the intelligent fella looking up at me, the one we hurt coming in from the yard.

He looks at me in terror. A pitiful yelp comes from his throat, followed by an unbearable squelch as his bladder bursts open. I'm engulfed with searing, soul-crushing guilt.

Over and over again, I kill the wrong man, and each time I hate myself more, until at last I wake up, drenched and shaking. My voice wails out into the emptiness and my cellmate groans, 'Shut up, will ya mate?' and I'm seized by the most bitter self-loathing a person has ever had to endure.

For two days and two nights I lie in my bed, not eating, tossing and turning with bad thoughts running through my mind. Geoff tries to snap me out of it, but it's useless. The screws try to drag me out of bed, but I let out such a howl they don't bother. Finally, one of the screws escorts Lenny Hatcher into my cell and shuts the door behind him.

'All right, mate?'

I open one of my eyes and close them again. Lenny's got a gloomy look on his face and he seems uncomfortable. He draws a chair up to my bed and speaks into my ear.

'Listen, 'arry, that bloke I said was a bacon?'

'Yeah. How d'ya know he was a bacon? You know you can't trust the screws in 'ere.'

'That's what I've been thinking meself,' says Lenny. 'But don't beat yourself up about it, mate, it's all checked out. Maybe he didn't rape a two-year-old, I don't know. But he's outa hospital and on the numbers, word is he asked one of the other bacons last week if he could get some kiddie porn smuggled in.'

I wipe my face with my sleeve. 'You sure about that, Len?'

'Yeh, mate. Certain.'

Two days later we're still on lockdown, only being let out for food, visits and emergencies. There's nothing to do but pass the time talking bollocks with our cellmates.

I'm back to my chirpy self, almost. What Lenny said about that con we beat up, I don't know, maybe it was true and maybe it wasn't, but I had to believe it for my own sanity.

Geoff's a decent enough bloke; wouldn't score two points on a pub quiz but didn't bother me while I was going through hell over the bacon, and didn't ask too many awkward questions when I woke up in the night screaming. He's coming up for parole soon and we chat about all the stuff he's planning to do when he gets out. In no particular order, he's going to go for a pint and a curry, have a shag (probably have to splash out on one 'cause he's been in so long he doesn't have any offers.) He's going to the movies, take a long, hot bubble bath, enjoy a daytrip to the seaside, all the usual crap.

Out of the blue I'm feeling a longing for all those normal things too, things I hardly ever think about 'cause I'm always telling myself that the only thing I miss is an unlimited supply of smack.

'How 'bout you?' he asks when he's completely run out of ideas.

'Me?' I've got no chance of parole. Lost so much remission it looks like I'll end up doing my whole bird.'

He shrugs helpfully. 'I know a couple of cons in here got parole when they found God. Just go to chapel every week and make out you're turning over a new leaf. That's what I did. It was boring listening to the fuckin' sermons, but I just twiddled me thumbs and thought about all that stuff I was just telling you about.'

Great. I can already see myself sitting in chapel thinking about scoring heroin, just like I do everywhere else. My thoughts flit back to the RAPt programme. I hope there'll be a place for me soon.

In the meantime, I suppose it wouldn't hurt to get a chance at parole, even though it's the oldest trick in the book. Another six hours on lockdown with a cellmate who ran out of interesting subjects of conversation two days ago, and I'm ready to give anything a try, even religion.

'Right, I'm gonna give your 'God' idea a go.'

Geoff looks at me incredulously, 'when? now?'

'Yep, right now. Don't laugh, whatever ya do.'

I press the bell, and when a screw eventually consents to come by, I say in an urgent whisper. 'I need to see a priest, guv, something mad just happened.' I know he won't be allowed to refuse me.

'A *priest*? You're not Catholic, are you Shaw?'

'I mean a minister,' I say hurriedly. 'Or a vicar or whatever the fu... I mean, whatever they're called. I'm serious, guv.' Geoff suppresses a snort behind me and I force myself to keep a straight face.

'All right, Shaw, I'll see what I can do.' The screw slides the hatch shut with a sigh. He returns twenty minutes later with a vicar and lets me out so that I can talk to him privately on the landing.

Seeing the vicar's dog collar, I swallow uneasily, remembering all the blasphemous things I've ever done, like using pages of the Bible to blow my nose, wipe my arse, inhale drugs, make paper aeroplanes... that sort of thing.

'Thanks for coming, mate... sir. I saw something last night. I don't know what it was exactly, but it appeared out of nowhere,' I tell him, making it up on the spot. 'It changed me...'

The vicar is listening so patiently that, for a moment, I consider telling him about my problems with nonces, or my problems with drugs, or my problems with

Dawn and my son, just for the relief of letting it out a bit. But I can't. Secrets run deep, and all that.

Geoff's sniggering loudly in the background, so I close the door. 'I think it may have been an angel or something, some kind of calling, urging me to go to church.'

I know the vicar's trying to work out if I'm having him on, but giving me the benefit of the doubt he says, 'Well, some people do see things sometimes, especially in times of difficulty. Perhaps you need to pray for guidance.'

This isn't quite the response I was hoping for. 'No, it was more like a light,' I say, putting on a bewildered look and getting into my story, 'hoverin' over by the toilet...'

'Did it sit down and have a shit?' I hear Geoff giggle behind the door.

I lead the vicar along the landing by his elbow. 'take no notice of my cellmate. I don't think he believes me.' I don't think the vicar is all that convinced either, but I'm grateful to him for addressing me with a kind look in his eyes and a friendly hand on my shoulder.

'Well, my son, all I can say is that it might help if you pray about it. Ask God for help. He always listens even if you don't always recognise His answer. I'll put your name down for church this Sunday, and you'll know if it's the right thing when you come.'

'Thank you, sir,' I nod, not knowing what else to call him and feeling a bit shamefaced for trying to pull the wool over his eyes.

Back in my cell, Geoff erupts into hysterics. Between gasps for breath he cracks joke after joke about my incredible revelations. I try to join in, but they don't seem all that funny.

I've never prayed before and don't know how. But when Geoff goes quiet for a minute, I shut my eyes and send out a fervent thought:

'Please help me 'cause I am fucked!'

It's all I can think of.

A couple of hours later, when Geoff's laughter has died down to the occasional chuckle, and I'm staring at the cracks on the ceiling just like I always end up doing, footsteps come clomping along the landing. I sit up in surprise when our door clangs open.

'Pack your kit, Shaw, you're going over to C Wing,' says the screw. He has the same voice as the screw I overheard admitting his part in the nonce incident a couple of days ago. I have a fierce urge to grab him by the throat and pound his head against the bars until he confesses to his stupid comment and its consequences.

I rein myself in. I'm shocked. It's only been four days since I begged Gordon to get me on the programme. He must have known I was in earnest, unlike just now when I was winding up the vicar. Then again... maybe that encounter with the vicar turned out to be more than just a prank. Maybe that prayer I yelled out in my mind has actually been answered.

Feeling a bit dazed, I gather up my stuff, exchange goodbyes with Geoff, and follow the screw over to Crackhead Wing.

HMP Pentonville

The beginning of the end

The screw hands me over to another screw at the entrance to C wing. This one's cheeks are sucked inwards in a sort of permanent holier-than-thou expression, a look intensified by a pair of arched eyebrows situated high on his head that reminds me of some patronising, toffee-nosed aristocrat.

He leads me up some stairs, throwing me a sneer that almost punctures my bubble of excitement. In all the prisons I've been in, I've never admitted to a screw about having a drug habit. As I trudge after this mocking dick, I half-wonder if someone's stuck a label on my back reading 'junkie.' Later I will find out that this particular screw's name is Butler and I'll cheer myself up imagining him dressed up in a stiff collar and cravat, coming to my cell to empty my piss pot.

He directs me into a two-up identical to my last one, except for a hefty black bloke lying on the top bunk. Without a word of welcome to my new gaff let alone an introduction to my latest roommate, the screw gives a disdainful sniff then bangs his baton a couple of times against the bars to make sure they haven't been sawn away.

As his self-important footsteps echo into the distance, I start making my bed, just as I've done hundreds of times before. It would be easier to tuck the sheets down the side if the bloke on top would budge his hefty arse for a minute. He's ignored my heavy sighs, and when a couple of growled curses haven't done the trick, I'm seething.

'Do me a favour and get off the bed for a minute, will ya?'

No answer.

I try the friendly approach. 'Mate, you might not feel like talking, but I need to make my bed, and I'm not that fucking strong that I can move you too, so will you please get off?'

I peer over the top bunk to see my cellmate staring at the ceiling with a trance-like expression. Great. First day of my brand new life and I'm stuck in a box with a fucking zombie. I try the less-friendly approach.

'Mate, I'm getting fucked off. All I want to do is put my covers on, lie down and read a book. I won't say another fuckin' word if you get off, I promise.'

Suddenly he's jumped down from his bed and is looming over me, the whites of his eyes dazzling against his dark face.

I glare steadily up at him. 'I don't want no trouble. But if I was to hit you I'd more than likely break your jaw.' This is all I need, I'm thinking, to be shacked up with a zombie who turns into a nutter intent on a tear-up.

'Yeah?'

His first word to me is snarled right into my face. I watch his eyes flicker while he mulls over my comment. As we glare at each other and the seconds tick slowly by in the deafening silence that follows, the irony of the situation hits me. Here are two men about ready to have murders over making a bed!

A laugh bubbles up and I can't hold it. It diffuses the tension instantly. My cellmate laughs out loud along with me, and it's not long before I'm bent over, holding my stomach, and he's doing the same, leaning against the bed for support. Still laughing, he helps me make the bed and shove it against the wall.

'I'm Harry. What's your name, mate?'

He stops laughing and a dejected look crosses his face. 'Owen.'

He climbs back onto his bed and the joke is over. Something about the way he said his name makes me suspect he hates himself. It's an odd thought and I pick up my book, pushing it to the back of my mind.

As soon as I walk into the pre-admissions group next morning I spot a familiar face with dirty blonde hair.

'My God, if it ain't Roly!' I grin. Roland grins back and an awkward moment ensues while a million words that neither of us could admit to are exchanged between us.

'You too, mate?' he says at last.

'Yeah, me too. What happened to your mate, Mackey?'

'Still using.'

I think back to Mackey and me holding onto Roland's flailing ankles while he puked out a gallon of salt water. Now it all makes sense. That must have been when Roland had decided that he didn't want that life anymore.

There's a short, stocky Irish fella writing with chalk on a blackboard and it feels as if I'm back at school. A cheeky little kid's voice keeps piping up in my head, 'Go on, throw something at him when he's not looking!'

Seven cons are sitting in a semi-circle in front of the blackboard. I look round at the others and recognise that longing, unfulfilled look in their eyes, same as mine. Sitting between Owen, who's staring fixedly out the window, and Roland, is a cool-looking mixed-race fella called 'Tyrees' who stands out at once because of his dazzling green eyes. Then there's a dwarfish but tough-looking Glaswegian, Jake, unfortunate name of an alkie. He's fidgeting in his seat, can't keep still for a minute. Next to him is a fat guy called Terry sitting all laid back like he's in his armchair in front of the telly at home.

Finally, there's a good-looking black fella who gives me a respectful nod. His name's 'Winston.' I won't forget that name in a hurry, 'cause while the rest of us are wearing trainers, Winston Churchill himself couldn't have had shoes better polished than this con. It's the first group meeting for three of us, and there's a strong sense of anticipation in the air.

'My name's Liam. I'm a peer supporter and I did this programme a year ago,' says the Irish bloke in his broad Dublin accent. He's wearing prison clothes; otherwise I'd never have guessed he was a con. He's got a sort of kind and helpful innocence about him that seems more suited to being a care worker in the outside world.

'You'll 'arll be going on the programme soon, when spaces become available and when you're ready. I take it none of you were forced to be here in any way?'

I shake my head along with everyone else. Glancing around it strikes me that all these cons have reached the end of their ropes, like me.

'RAPt stands for the Rehabilitation for Addicted Prisoners Trust, and it's based on the twelve step model some of you probably know about. It's a very powerful programme, so it is. Over half our graduates remain drug-free after six months, and eighty percent remain crime-free.'

Bloody hell, those words have hit me like a crack on the back of the head. Drug-free and crime-free? I find myself exchanging a mystified look with Roland. It's one thing to be knocking the drugs on the head but we didn't know we were going to be tackling our criminal proclivities too.

In his warm Gaelic accent, Liam explains, 'We believe dat all thorse who have become invarlved with croime trooogh deir substance misuse, should be supparrrted to toon deir lives around.'

261

'Who decides which of us gets on the programme first?' asks the black fella who is immaculately presented, as far as prison clothes will allow. He's rake-thin though, and has a famished look about him.

'Well, Winston, that's up to me. The people I tink are ready are the one's I'll pick.'

'I've been here a coupla weeks already. How come you haven't picked me yet, Liam?' asks the fat bloke, beaming as if he's just told one of his funny jokes. He reeled off a couple while we were waiting for Liam to arrive, all in his deadpan manner which is a good technique. His jokes ain't all that though, so when he comes out with the punch lines it's kind of like getting an unexpected surprise.

'Well now, the counsellors have given me the responsibility to decoide, Terry, and if you pay attention here and listen, it won't be long till you go up.'

The fat fella's grin fades. 'Bollocks,' he mutters under his breath.

Somehow, I know he's got the wrong attitude. He's thinking the sooner he gets on the programme, the sooner he can bullshit his way through it and get sent to a D-cat prison. Something tells me this ain't going to work that way.

'Programme? Are we gonna be on TV, then?' asks the fella whose dazzling green eyes pierce out of a smooth, milky-brown face.

Liam laughs. 'More will be revealed, Tyrees. More will be revealed.' He turns to the board and draws a large circle. I'm beginning to like this Liam. He's taken the trouble to remember our names and he calls us 'people' rather than cons.

'There's a hole inside each of us that is empty.' Liam explains drawing a bottle and a syringe in the circle. 'We fill it with drugs or booze or... al sorts of tings...'

Terry nods wisely. 'I remember the first time I used alcohol as a substitute for a woman.'

'Yes, Terry, alcohol is often used to...'

'Ah ha, yes, very good Terry, ya got me going for a minute there, so you did. Can any of you tink of any others?'

'Nicking great big wadds of cash,' suggests Winston.

Roland puts forth, 'Sex,' which arouses a couple of dirty sniggers.

'Be honest now, Roly,' says Tyrees, 'you're talking about watching the same porno over and over again, ain't ya?' Roland shrugs bashfully while we have a good laugh.

'Pills,' says Terry. A picture springs instantly to my mind of him jiggling his enormous bulk round a dance floor.

'Gamblin', says Jake, twitching on his seat like he's desperate to toss some money into a fruit machine and send the controls spinning.

'Excellent,' nods Liam, sending a wave of positive energy around the room.

I want to join in but can't think of anything. On the outside, when I wasn't filling the hole with drugs, I'd be rushing around making money, spending it, being busy, busy, busy and doing anything as long as it took my mind of the emptiness.

'Er... how about smoking?'

'Very good, Harry,' says Liam, which gives me a weird feeling; 'good' and 'Harry' not generally being used in the same sentence.

'Lots of people tink that smoking isn't a serious addiction like alcohol and drugs, until they troy giving it up!'

We're not allowed to smoke in this room but suddenly we've all got twitchy fingers.

'Chicken and an egg were lying in bed,' Terry says casually. 'The chicken was smiling and smoking a ciggie. The egg was looking miserable. The chicken took a deep puff on its fag and said, "Well, I think we answered that question."'

Liam waits for the slowest amongst us to work out the joke before continuing. 'Now that we're clean we need to fill the hole with sumting else. That's where the RAPt programme comes in. First of arll, we have to break down our denial about our addiction. After dat, we will examine obstacles to our recovery, and behaviours which led to failure in the past...'

I notice Owen staring out the window. His mind seems to be constantly consumed by something. Catching my eye, he flinches then rivets his gaze to the floor.

By the end of the session, I'm eager to rush through the preliminaries and get onto the programme itself. I haven't used in almost a week, but Tim's been talking about finding peace in our heads, and the idea of peace in my mad, whirling brain has shunted out all thoughts of getting high. As everyone leaves, I sidle over to him for a word in his ear.

'How can I make sure I'm one of the first to get on the programme, mate?'

He smiles as if he can read my addict's mind. 'Listen and learn, Harry.'

Well, er... would it speed things up if I got you some canteen on payday?'

He laughs and slaps my back. 'All in good time, you'll go up as soon as you're ready, I promise. Arll in good toime.'

'Yeah, yeah,' I frown, still trying to think of an angle, because there's not a con in all the shovels I've ever been, with the possible exception of this one, who doesn't have a price.

On the landing I catch up with Winston, who's loitering at the top of the stairs while the rest of us go down to eat.

'What's the matter, mate? Aintcha hungry?'

'Hungry?' He looks at me like I'm mad. 'What, with the food they serve in here?'

'Why, you used to eating in gourmet restaurants or something?' I joke.

'Actually, yeah,' he retorts. He sounds like a real East End lad, and frankly I'm a bit surprised. 'Don't worry about me, mate. Go eat your mechanically-recovered chicken deep-fried in engine oil, and re-hydrated potato granules. That's what's on the menu today.'

My belly rumbles. 'Yum, yum, my favourite!' I laugh all the way down the stairs. A thought flashes across my mind that one day me and this fuss-pot Winston will go to some posh award-winning restaurant and reminisce about the shite we got served up in the slammer. I don't really believe it though; it won't occur to me until much later that some of the blokes I meet on the RAPt wing will become the closest friends I've had.

The iron stairs rattle as they must have for well over a century as cons troop down to the ground floor, which houses the drug addicts who've recently been dragged in from court. They look beaten and tired, as if a life spent keeping a habit going on the outside wasn't hard enough, it's just got ten times harder in here.

'Hurry up and get your fucking food!' barks a screw, making the new cons look round in surprise, since everyone is waiting in a reasonably orderly line.

'Stop pissing about! Get your fuckin' food, then get a fuckin' move on!' yells the screw, shoving some unwitting con in the back. He's got black eyebrows that ascend diagonally from his nose to his temples, reminding me of some crazed cartoon character.

I glance round, amazed. How come no one's yelling back at this slag? My eyes latch onto Owen's and he hangs back to enlighten me: 'Mr Blake. Proper dog.'

'If he ever talks to me like that,' I say glaring at the screw and hoping he notices, 'I'll bite off his nose and he'll have an even uglier fuckin' mug.'

'I wouldn't talk like that around him if I was you,' says Owen, which is quite a long sentence for him. He doesn't elaborate.

'Urry up, you dirty bastards!' shrieks the screw shoving along some new con who's fallen behind in the queue by a couple of inches.

'Jeeeesus. What's his problem?' mutters the con.

Blake descends on him, eyes blazing and cheek muscles working furiously. 'You're my fuckin' problem! You! You Junkie!' he screams, inches from the incredulous con's face. 'I've got my on you, Smith!'

We've got a proper one here, I think, remembering that screw called Butler with the sucked-in cheeks who escorted me to the wing like something he's scraped off the bottom of his boot. Those two are probably great pals, I reckon. Sure enough, I spot the very same wanker watching his colleague's proceedings from the landing above, hands on hips and eyebrows lost in his hairline, getting a hard on from strutting around all day in his stupid uniform.

But Blake, he's in a different league. I've seen his sort in prisons all over the country, Northern Bollocks and Buckteeth being just two examples. There seems to be one of them in every prison I've ever been to, usually some low-ranking reject from the army, booted out for being too twisted. But this one's the worst yet. This one obviously eats, breathes and shits being a screw.

'Filthy scagheads should all be shot,' he comments to a screw passing the other way. Then he swaggers alongside the queue, lifts his leg and starts tapping his baton on his steel toe capped boot, then smashing it against the bars for the sheer effect of making some clucking convict leap halfway out of his skin.

The queue moves slowly towards the servery. I'm starving-hungry and all wired up, thinking about slamming Blake's face into a wall and making his silly-faced screw-pal jump out of his skin at the noise of his friend's head cracking open. So, on feeling a tap on my shoulder, I spin round, ready to floor someone.

The fella with the green eyes from pre-ads is frowning at me quizzically. 'Are you the one who did Brick in Belmarsh?'

Brick? What the fuck is he talking about? An image comes to mind of some huge bastard slamming a brick down on some hapless fucker's face. Gradually the face behind the brick becomes recognisable, but I always thought of him as Meathead.

'You done him with hot water then stabbed him,' Tyrees adds helpfully. He's a handsome bloke and the thought flashes through my mind that he won't be after I've hit him a couple of times.

'Yeah. I did,' I say. 'You got a problem with that?'

'Well, he's my mate.' The green eyes gleam, waiting for some kind of reply.

Fuck me! Is there no end to Meathead's mates? I wonder, feeling an uncomfortable twinge in my right arm as I remember what another of Meathead's mates did to it. I take a few steps forward, nearly at the counter now.

'Look, mate, I'm here to try and sort my life out and I don't want no dramas,' I warn the fella. 'But let me tell you one thing. Your mate pushed me into a corner and he deserved what he got.'

'OK, I'll drop it for now 'cause I'm here same as you,' says Tyrees, gazing levelly back at me as if to let me know that he can match me, punch for punch. 'But I'm not sure how I feel about it.'

I barely notice as a pile of chicken nuggets and mash are dumped on my tray. 'Not sure how I feel about it.' His words hang bafflingly in the air.

I don't feel anything, I think to myself. Hatred and fury and plunging into the deep, dark abyss a few times not included, I haven't felt for years.

I carry my tray to my cell, shaking my head in bewilderment. Halfway there I break into a great big grin. I'd been expecting the fella with the green eyes to feel sort of like swinging a lump of wood at me. But he's not sure how he feels! Ha ha.

Neither the fuck do I.

Owen is a man of few words and he seems to have used them all up for the day. After lunch he fell into a deep sleep on his bunk, leaving me with a thousand uninterrupted accusations for company.

'You're no shitting good.'

'Thought you'd make loads of money did ya? Get out of that scummy estate you grew up on?'

'Yeah, well you wasted it all on smack, scumbag.'

'You couldn't even look after your own kid.'

'You'll never amount to nothing. You're a waste of fuckin' space.'

The blame goes on, eating away at my new-found resolve and mocking me for my optimism, until at last the cunt they call Mr Blake unlocks the door. He struts in, thumbs hooked in his belt, sniffs the air a couple of times and pulls a face of such disgust that I'd burst out laughing if I wasn't so fucking depressed.

'Time for your touchy-feely meeting, girls.' He turns on his heel and stomps along the landing with a smug chortle.

I tap the still-comatose Owen lightly on the head to rouse him gently from his place of escape. Gradually his serene expression hardens. His eyes dart around the cell, widen with recognition and then slowly glaze over.

That night there's a gathering for everyone on the programme. About forty of us are crowding into the main meeting room. In front of me, Terry swears under his breath, and behind him Winston does the same, then it's my turn.

A good-looking businessman in his mid-thirties is waiting to greet us. He's wearing a well-cut suit in gun-metal grey, a stylish shirt and tie, and sleek shoes that look like they cost a packet. His tanned face is freshly shaven, save for a super-neat line edging his jaw and sweeping over his upper lip. Fuck me! This is a taste of the Good Life, right here in the middle of the stinking Ville.

'Bet nobody bats an eyelid at you on the outside,' laughs Paul, who's one of the counsellors.

There's an expectant, almost holiday-like atmosphere in the room. I glance around, searching for something in the other cons' faces, some sign that I'm on the right track.

'Plenty of birds batting their eyelids, last time I looked,' the suave fella tells Paul in a broad Cockney accent. I glance at Terry and we both breathe a sigh of relief. For a minute there, we were thinking the stranger might be some philanthropic businessman looking to give us some condescending lecture about pulling our socks up and maximising our potential.

I notice Winston staring inquisitively at the fella's shoes.

The businessman clears his throat and announces, My name's Steve and I'm an addict.'

'Nor weeeey! Yee's jist getting us at it, meete!' exclaims Jake, leaping out of his seat with his usual rampant excitement. It's exactly what I'm thinking too. Jake sits down but I swear he's got his bum hovering a couple of inches above the seat.

'I spent most of me life robbing and thieving,' Steve continues. 'I ended up living on the street and I've done stuff I ain't proud of,' he says, unconsciously rubbing his knuckles. I've been in and out of these nicks plenty of times... Wormwood Scrubs, Brixton, Wandsworth, this dump.'

I tear my gaze off the businessman to glance round the room. I've never seen a bunch of cons so fascinated by anything, at least not since the big baps cum-shot mag that filtered through the system a couple of weeks ago.

'For the last year I was at Wormwood,' Steve recalls, 'I was getting drugs maybe twice a week, if I was lucky, but I was thinking about them every minute of the fuckin' day. I couldn't have a normal conversation 'cause my mind was ninety-nine percent focussed on using, leaving fuck all to be witty about. I was always saying, 'Yeah, know what ya mean,' and nodding away like I actually gave a shit, but I never 'ad a clue what the other person had been going on about.'

There's plenty of nods and grunts around the room. I'm wondering how many conversations I've had with cons who have completely ignored every word I've said, when Steve jerks me back to attention.

'Then I had my rock-bottom experience, right here in the Ville. I expect a lot of you have had your rock-bottoms to have got to this stage. Or what you might call your 'gift of desperation.'

Next to me I notice Roland nodding with his head in his hands.

'What was your rock-bottom experience, mate?' someone asks.

The businessman leans back in his chair with a smile, as if he's been waiting for someone to ask him.

No sooner has he started telling us about his dark night of the soul, than I'm back in Bristol, reliving my own descent into madness. He's talking about crawling around a concrete floor in solitary confinement, screaming his stupid head off, and I'm remembering doing pretty much exactly the same thing down the Block in Brizzle.

It's funny, the more he talks about himself, the more I understand about me. We've all been there, though you'd never guess it to look at us rough-looking villains. We're lapping up his words, especially because most of us wouldn't dare to admit we'd ever crawled around the floor screaming out to the walls for mercy. Even Tyrees, who's a hard-nosed fucker if ever there was one, has a stressed look, re-living some tortuous memory of his own.

Only Owen doesn't seem phased. He doesn't seem to be listening. There's something gnawing away at his mind and my heart goes out to him. Did I just say 'heart?' Fucking 'ell, this programme must be starting to get to me.

Steve describes how RAPt set him on a course of recovery that led, only two and a half years later, to his being the C.E.O. of his own software company. His profits for this year are set to exceed a cool mill.

When Steve stops talking, there's a long, reflective silence. I'm thinking about what amazing heights I could reach if I put half the energy and brains I used into scoring,

271

into doing something useful. I reckon most of us are doing the same.

'Any questions?' Paul asks finally.

'Yeah, I have one,' says Winston. 'Where did you get those shoes, mate?'

To Winston's surprise everyone bursts into laughter. Then Steve finds himself being bombarded with more pressing questions.

At the end of the meeting I'm feeling great. From out of nowhere, a whole new life is opening up without the gloomy spectre of drugs to cast its deep, black shadow over it. Right this minute, anything seems possible.

I stand up, along with everyone else. Then I come crashing back down to earth. From my right, a hairy hand is reaching towards my waist. From my left, a tattooed forearm is closing in on me. As if this isn't bad enough, the roomful of burly convicts launches into some prayer about finding serenity. It's all gone tits up and I'm retreating helplessly towards the door, where Terry and Owen have already beaten me to it.

'Fuckin' bum-bandits,' mutters Terry. I thought I was having problems, but he's looking positively terrified. 'What's the latest chat-up line in a gay bar?' he jokes desperately. 'Can I push your stool in, mate?' We've only heard it a coupla hundred times already but have a good laugh to ease our discomfort.

'Don't want nobody touching me,' growls Owen. There it is again, I notice; the self-hatred in his eyes.

'No one's gonna put no hairy arm round me either,' I say.

All the same, I'm cursing myself for feeling so panicky. I keep this thought to myself though. I really want to get on the programme, and something's telling me that being able to put my arm around another bloke might be part of it.

272

'What ya in for then, Owen?'

'We've been banged up together for over a week and all I know about him is his name and the length of his bird, and that's only because that information is slung up by the door, same as for everyone else. I rest my book on my stomach and lean out of my bed, calling up to the top bunk.

'Anybody up there?'

'Nothing,' he says at last.

'That's a bad bastard to be in for, ain't it?' I sigh. 'And you went and got three years for it too. Did the judge have the 'ump that day or something?'

'Bollocks!' a growl comes from above. For a moment I think he's going to follow it up, but he's gone silent again. I feel like a dentist trying to extract a stubborn tooth. 'Come on, mate,' I pull and twist. 'What'ya get three years for?'

'G.B.H.'

Grievous Bodily Harm. Doesn't surprise me. 'Did'ya win?' I ask, trying to make him laugh.

'Yeah, now piss off. I don't want to talk about it.' I pick up my book and try to read from where I left off, but the emptiness is closing in, and with it return thoughts of using.

After a long while, Owen asks, 'What you in for then?'

Even though I ask the same of other cons often enough, this is one of those questions that makes my lips curl around my clenched teeth, a bit like when a judge asks, 'Do you feel any remorse for what you've done?'

Money laundering,' I say, with a warning edge in my voice for him to leave it at that.

'What, you got done for washing dirty money down the launderette?'

273

So, Owen's sense of humour has made a rare return. 'Yeah, something like that.'

The reason I don't want to talk about it is the same reason that I avoid thinking about it. It's like lifting a stone and exposing the light of day to the dingy, sordid lifestyles of the maggots living underneath. Still, what the fuck! There's nothing else to talk about and really, come to think of it, why am I here? It all seemed so horribly inevitable at the time, but I was heavily into the drugs and booze then, so I suppose I never really questioned it.

I put my hands behind my head and let my mouth do the talking.

'Well, I had to meet someone in Croydon. I was paying him a lump of money for some coke I'd had off him the week before. I booked into a hotel as I'd had a row with Dawn. I wasn't meeting him until the next morning so I spent the afternoon down the pub knocking back double Jack Daniels on ice.

'By the time I got back to the hotel I was trolleyed. I opened the window to get some air and clear my head a bit, and somehow I dropped the fuckin' bag with all the money in it out the window. It wasn't zipped up properly and about a grand's worth of notes went flying away in the wind. So there I am climbing down the fire escape from the fourth floor in broad daylight, hoping no one's watching, but totally out of my nut. I was chasing after these fuckin' notes and plucking them out of hedges and plant pots and I think I got most of them back.

'I knew I couldn't carry on like that, so I bought some crack to wake me up a bit, then went back to the pub 'cause I was paranoid, and had a few more Jack Daniels to calm me down. When the pub closed I could barely see straight but I made it back to the bar at the hotel and carried on with the double Jacks, 'cause I was terrified of going to bed. Terrified of lying there awake. I kept buying

274

the barman drinks so he'd keep the bar open. Fuck knows what we talked about. I kept handing him pinks and he kept dishing out the drinks.

'When I finally got in the lift I was so shit-faced I tried to get into the room on the floor underneath mine. 'Course, the key didn't work so I had to kick the door in. Next thing I knew, it was morning and I was waking up to see the manager coming in with the old bill. I'm on the floor, hadn't even made it to the bed. It takes me forever to suss out where I am. I'm feeling like a bag of shit – one of the top three fuckin' hangovers of my life – and I've had some right fuckin' miserable hangovers, I can tell ya. So, after I'd worked out that I was lying there in the wrong hotel room, for a minute I thought maybe I'd get lucky, 'cause you know how dumb the old bill can be; maybe they wouldn't look in the room upstairs. In the room upstairs was a small bag of coke, about a hundred grand and my phones. I looked at my watch and realised that the coke dealer was due to meet me in five minutes and well, if I got him in trouble too, I knew I'd be well fucked. Turns out they'd been on him anyway and had nicked him already; they were on their way to get me when the manager must have phoned the police, hence normal plod nicking me. As we were leaving the hotel the other mob come running in to nick me too. It wasn't one of my favourite days.'

Owen has been silent all this time and I've forgotten to wonder if he's even listening. I've been reliving the whole mad nightmare as if it had happened to someone else. I'm quiet for a long time.

'So, didya get away with it?' He asks at last, taking the piss.

'Er… Nope!'

'Hmm, didn't think so. Well, sounds to me,' Owen says thoughtfully, 'that, if you'd deliberately set yourself up, you couldn't have done a better job of it.'

I lie there for a long time mulling over Owen's observation. Why the fuck would I deliberately set myself up?'

Slowly what he said starts to make some sort of crazy sense. I'd lost so much self respect by the time I got nicked that I hardly gave a fuck what I was doing. I'm lethal when I'm using. If I hadn't been stopped right then in that hotel in Croydon, I would have carried on the way I was going and ended up killing myself or someone else.

'Tamsworth!'

The roar makes me jump as I head to group with Owen the next day. It's Blake, stressing everyone out with his sergeant major performance. I'd have though I'd be getting used to it by now but there's something in his voice that pinches a raw nerve in me.

'I'd have thought I told you to get your skinny arse over to pre-ads!'

I glance down to the landing below to see a smallish fella with a stylishly slicked-back blonde hair wearing a crisp new issue shirt, neatly-pressed prison jeans and glossy tan shoes. He's sauntering along with one hand in his pocket, and, on hearing Blake's screech, he does a neat about-turn and starts sauntering along the landing in the opposite direction. We wait for him as he jogs lightly up the stairs.

'All right, mate? Friend of yours, is he?' I grin jabbing a thumb at Blake, who's glaring up at the new con as if he'd like to slowly tear out his fingernails.

'Who, Blakey? Yeah, we're great pals,' says the neatly-dressed con turning round to give the screw a joyful wave, which makes him apoplectic with fury.

'What's your name?' I laugh.

'Tamsworth.' His blue eyes glint with a sort of seen-it-all-before intelligence. 'Well, it's George Tamsworth, but don't be calling me George.

'Call me Tams. As in my name Tams and I'm a raving poofter,' laughs Terry.

'Oh yeah? You're the closet bum-bandit,' frowns Tams, his svelte, compact body tensing up with animosity next to Terry's loose, fat one.

'You'd be lucky to get a glimpse of my dick, you salivating homo,' Terry beams, sailing into the pre-ads room.

'Is he one of your friends too?' I joke to diffuse the animosity that has suddenly flared up.

'I've met him a few times on the out,' says Tams. 'Thinks there's nothing wrong with him. But he's got a booze and pills problem that stands out a mile and he can't even see it.'

'Walked into a chicken restaurant the other day,' says Terry in a loud voice. He's standing at the doorway grinning at us. 'I ask the manager: 'How d'you prepare the chickens?' The manager leads me aside, and tells me quietly, "We just tell them straight out that they're going to die."'

Even Tams can't help laughing. No matter what snide comments Terry comes out with, it seems impossible to stay annoyed with him for long.

Liam's talking about powerlessness. The more he gets into the subject, the more his arms wave around. He explains how we each fall into our particular traps, like bees into a beer bottle, or a wine bottle or a whisky bottle. We're struggling to get out, our attempts growing ever more futile as we're assailed by the alcoholic fumes, until we fall into a stupor and don't bother trying to crawl out anymore.

I'm half hypnotised by those waving arms, but now everything's slowing down. Liam's explaining that we have no more power than that inquisitive little bee who likes the sweet, sticky smell of the booze and can't help going to investigate and that once we use, we set off some kind of allergic reaction with the obsession kicking off again.

'Powerlessness means that, when you put the first drink or drug into your body, you don't know when you'll be able to stop,' says Liam. 'You have no power over the first drink or drug and it's the first one that does the damage.'

Powerless. I'm new to this idea and the word knocks me sideways. If we're powerless, then what hope in hell do any of us have? I'd always thought I had power over my life and was just making a few shit choices.

Gradually it begins to occur to me that, if I had no power, then I couldn't help using. When I put that first drug or drink in me it would set off the mad cycle again and I wouldn't be able to stop.

The tons of guilt I've been lugging around with me for so long that I thought it was a normal part of everyday existence briefly lift.

It's the most incredible sensation. It's like the first time I took Ecstasy when it was as if a grey and dusty veil had been whisked away, revealing the world as it really is underneath, all shining and bright, and a club packed with dodgy strangers became a club full of friends. At the same time, I have this distinct feeling, a knowing, that everyone in this room: Winston, Terry, Jake, Roland, Tams, Tyrees and Owen, are crushed under their individual burdens. They're all hurting and they don't know why and it's not their fault. I'm blissfully innocent of putting drink and drugs before anything else and so are they and the best thing about it is that I haven't taken anything to feel like this.

'But how do you stop yourself taking the first drink or drug?' Winston is asking as I come out of my reverie, buzzing with a kind of rapturous excitement. No wonder they call it the RAPt programme, I laugh to myself. All my senses are alert.

'I'll come to that, Winston,' says Liam, 'But if you think of the analogy of a train racing towards you, and you're stuck to the rails and can't move, which carriage is going to kill you?'

'The first one,' says Winston. At the same moment, Owen pushes his chair back with a violent scrape. It crashes into the wall as he storms out of the room.

'I don't want to fuckin' hear it,' he shouts, slamming the door so hard that it flies open again.

'What's the matter with him?' Liam asks me, knowing I'm his cellmate.

'Fuck knows.' I'm about to add, 'Nothing to do with me,' as I usually do in such situations, when the thought occurs that maybe it does have something to do with me. Maybe I'm the one who's supposed to find out what Owen's problem is, this thing that has built an almost impenetrable wall around him.

I feel the eyes of everyone on me as I get up and leave the room.

He's sitting with his knees hunched up in a corner of the landing. Angrily, he wipes his eyes with the back of his hand as I bend over him.

'You all right, mate?'

'Fuckin' trains,' he mutters. 'Fuckin' rails... what's that got to do with taking drugs?'

279

He starts to weep. Real sobs, not like Pete back in Cardiff with his couple of sniffles in the middle of the night. Here we go again; I've got that old familiar feeling of wanting to punch Owen in the head until he can't utter one more fucking sob. But the person, who sits on the floor with his arm around Owen like he's never done to another man before, is not the same person as the one that wanted to hit Pete all those months ago back in Cardiff.

Liam leaves the group for a moment to check on us. 'Are you OK, Owen?'

'I just want to be left alone,' he moans into his cupped hands.

'Ok, then.' Liam turns to go back to the room. 'But you'll both be going on the programme tomorrow, so you will be ready, won't you, Owen?'

I gaze at Owen, silently shaking in his private misery and think back to Don having all those problems over his wife and how I wanted to kill him just to stop his fucking racket. Something else has got into me now. I can't leave Owen like this. If he keeps clamming up he might end up doing something irreversible.

'Did something happen?' I ask quietly. 'Something about a train?' Even as I say it I feel a sort of sickening trepidation.

'No! I told you I don't want to fuckin' talk about it. Leave me the fuck alone if you know what's good for you.'

I sit there, letting his fighting words wash over me. There's so much hatred in his expression that I wonder if he's going to put those huge black hands around my neck and start squeezing.

'He was twelve,' he moans so softly I barely hear. 'But he had a mental age of six. I was supposed to be looking after him, only I couldn't even do that properly.' His face crumples with remorse.

I don't say anything. Just let him get this off his chest in his own time.

'My little brother, Rory,' he explains. 'Sam used to call him Worwry, taking the piss outta him 'cause Rory was a bit slow. 'Worwry, come out here to the end of the garden,' Sam told him that day. 'I got something to show you.' A bird's nest or something. Rory loved nature. He was fascinated by slugs and caterpillars. Used to spend hours lying on the ground watching the fuckin' ants carry chunks of leaves up and down the blades of grass.

For a while, Owen doesn't say anything. He's squeezing his temples so hard I think he wants to crush his own head. He releases the tension with a shuddering sigh.

'They said it wasn't my fault; that it was an accident. But I made a promise to look after Rory and I let him down. First I lost my job, then I lost my girlfriend. I said I'd take care of Rory because he was the most precious thing in my life. I was the only one who could cheer him up when he went on one of his downers, and he was the only one I could bear to be around most of the time.'

Owen's moist eyes gaze at me unseeingly. 'Worwy, follow me,' Sam told him. 'Don't be a sissy. Follow me over the railway tracks. I got something to show you, Worwy.'

Owen's head sinks back into his hands.

'He told him to jump over the live rail. At least, he says he did. Showed him how to do it without touching it. But Rory was so innocent. He would have thought it was all a laugh. Didn't think it was much of a fuckin' laugh when Sam told him there was a train coming.'

'He froze halfway over the rail. Couldn't move. Sam was laughing and laughing, it seemed so funny, he'd been sniffing glue. But even he knew it wasn't funny when the rails started to clatter. Told Rory to get a move on before a train really did come. But Rory was just standing there; his hair was sticking up in a funny way, and when Sam ran back to grab him it was too fuckin' late, the train was coming...'

Owen trails off, shaking his head back and forth like a bear in a cage.

I wait for him to carry on.

'I was up in my room with Josh,' he says at last. 'We'd both done a couple of stones but there was one more. He'd agreed to break it in two, but I was coming down from the last one and he was already trying to light it. I made a grab for it and it went under the bed. We were both madly trying to find it and I dunno... maybe I knew somehow that something was going on with Rory, because I just started punching the shit outta him and couldn't stop. Thinking about it afterwards, it was like I was beating myself up. By the time I finished, he wasn't moving.

'I got nicked. It was the worst fuckin' feeling you can imagine, locked in a cell knowing something fuckin' awful has happened and not being able to do anything about it. I kept screaming out: 'Where's Rory? You've got to find my little brother because he can't look after himself! Let me out and I'll help you find him!' Somehow I knew he'd gone down the railway. I'd always warned him not to.

'They interviewed the kid, Sam; that's how I know what happened. But they couldn't charge him because it was just a prank. Wasn't his fault anyway. It was mine.' He bangs his head against his knees.

I strain my ears to hear him groan, 'I think that kid was pretty fucked up about it too. I know he got the fright of his life when Rory got stuck, sort of like frozen, with one foot on the rail. Said there was this funny smell, like something cooking, and when he looked into his eyes they were like black holes.

282

Whooaa! I don't want to hear this. My heart isn't as closed off as it used to be and it feels as if it's just been stabbed. I think about my younger brother, Dave, and how I would have felt if it had been him dying out there on the railway line. A few minutes ago I was feeling high as a kite, and suddenly I'm back in the pits with my eyes welling up. We're hugging each other on the floor, not caring who sees us. Right now, it doesn't seem in the least bit strange to put your arm around another bloke. Not when life delivers blows like his.

'That's when the train came.'

'You've gotta stop blaming yourself, Owen. Remember what Liam said? You were powerless against the drugs. You thought your brother was safe in the garden; it's not as if you hadn't warned him to be careful. This could have happened to anyone.' I can tell he's being haunted by that image of his brother's smouldering black eye sockets, sucking him in and making him feel guilty forever and ever.

'I'm a piece of shit and I deserve to die,' he groans.

I shake my head, frowning. 'I've said the same thing myself, mate, many times.'

He lifts his head out of his hands and, for the first time, looks me straight in the eye. 'But you're always so cheerful... 'appy-go-lucky, making the best of everything all the time.'

'It's an act, mate,' I tell him with a truth that surprises me. I start thinking back to how I let Dawn and the baby down, and then a hundred other memories of failure and wrong-doing come flooding in. 'Underneath, I'm just as big a piece of shit as you think you are.'

He considers this for a while. I think he's about to say something philosophical when he lets out a sigh. 'Yeah, you are.'

Slowly a grin creeps across his face. I give him a punch on the shoulder. Even though we've still got tears rolling down our cheeks, we start to laugh, and it's just like the day we met, when we wanted to murder each other over making the bed.

On The Up

Now that I'm on the programme proper, I've been moved into a single cell and it's good to have my own space.

Owen's pleased to have his own pad too. He insists that I'm a shit and he's glad to see the back of me. It makes him laugh every time he brings it up, so I'm letting him get away with it. For now.

Roland gets moved onto the programme a couple of days later. We're heading to our group when we hear a familiar voice calling up to us.

'Roly! Psst! Roly n'arry!'

We glance to the landing below to see Mackey's cheeky face grinning up at us. He's looking crusty round the edges but he's happy about something.

'All right, Mackey?' says Roland warily.

'Yeah, mate, sweet. Sweet! I'm going on a visit today. I'll sort ya out later. And you, 'arry.' He's remembered he owes me one.

During the low moments, my mind's been bombarding me to get some gear. Just a little bit to take the edge off. To be at peace in my head. To take away the pain of listening to those horrible evil voices telling me how shit life is, that I will never change, dragging me down to that bottomless pit. I find myself glancing round to make sure there are no screws about.

'Yeah, all right mate,' I'm telling him except that what comes out is, 'Nah, mate, I'm gonna give this a try.' I can't help feeling treacherous.

At the same time, Roland shakes his head. 'Thanks but no thanks Mackey, mate.'

Mackey glances from one of us to the other confused. Then he breaks into a grin. 'Well done. Well fuckin' done,' he says with awe in his voice.

I walk on, smiling. If cons like Mackey can see cons like me and Roland giving it a go, then maybe he'll try it out for himself when he's ready.

'Never thought I'd hear myself saying that,' Roland says quietly.

A couple of days later, Winston and Tyrees are moved onto the programme and so is Terry, even though he's shown no signs of a personal breakthrough, or even of admitting to a problem with addiction. He's been on pre-ads so long that Liam, being the nice fella that he is, has given him the benefit of the doubt. Terry's been warned that he'll kicked off the programme if he doesn't change his attitude though.

But no one really wants to see him go. We'd miss his jokes.

'Did ya hear the news the other day?' he asks, all serious, making Roland go,

'Naw, what 'appened, Tel?'

'Thieves broke into a police station and stole all the toilets. Police say they have nothing to go on.'

We all groan, except Roland, who's gone into hysterics.

'So ya didn't hear about the shipment of Viagra that got stolen last week?' asks Terry, looking surprised. 'Yeah. Apparently, police are still on the look-out for two hardened criminals.'

'Who would like to start the group?' asks Karen as we shake our heads and Roland almost falls off his chair.

Karen is one of the perks of moving up onto the programme. She's attractive in a school-teacherly kind of way with an endearing gap between her teeth. Even though she's careful to wear the most unrevealing clothes, in a roomful of deprived convicts who would fancy a peanut butter sandwich if it was placed in our cells at night, she is, shall we say, extremely popular.

The cons on the main programme are split into three groups. There's about ten in our group. Sat as close to Karen as possible is Jake. The mad little jock is gazing adoringly into her eyes, oblivious that his behaviour bears a disturbing resemblance to that of a psychopathic stalker. Karen does an admirable job of pretending not to notice. I really like her and I vow that, if Jake gets one inch too close for her comfort, I'll fling him across the room like a love-sick teddy bear.

'I'd like to start,' says a con who's tall and muscular, but has the sort of face that only a mother could love. 'I have to get something off my chest.'

'I'd like to start,' says Terry mimicking the ugly con's voice, 'I 'ad a terrible child'ood. Until I was twelve I thought my name was Shut Up!'

Karen waits for the group to stop laughing. 'Start with your name, please,' she smiles encouragingly.

'Oh yeah, sorry. My name's Ian and I'm an addict,' says the fella with the unfortunate face, throwing a warning look at Terry. 'Well... about a year ago I was skint and I needed to get some cash badly so that I could score.'

Terry put on a big yawn and folds his arms behind his head. Everyone else listens to the con with interest.

'I was sitting in my mum's house,' says Ian. 'I was sitting there, clucking, and she was fussing all over me, asking what the matter was and could she do anything for me. I said, 'Yeah, all right, get me a pie and chips Mum, I'm starving.' So she went traipsing up to the chippie with her handbag, knowing there was more to it than that but... but just wanting to make me happy, like she always did, and not knowing that I'd cleaned out her purse before she went, so when she got there she wouldn't be able to pay for nothing...'

'Scumbag,' interrupts Terry, all smiles.

Ian looks at him not with anger, but with resignation, and taking a shaky breath continues, 'I knew I only had five minutes. I was going to write her a note to say sorry, but I couldn't find a pen anywhere, and then I noticed she'd got this brand new TV, so by the time I'd unplugged all the wires...'

'How could you?' Terry mutters behind his broad smile.

'Terry, please let Ian continue,' Karen says gently.

Again Ian flashes Terry a look, but it's so full of self-recrimination that it's almost as if he wants to be insulted.

'I knew she'd be back any minute so I didn't have time for that note and I just made off with the TV and... and... Grandad's watch, which was only worth a few quid. But she'd always treasured it and it was just lying there in the drawer... and I buggered off quick, meaning to call her up and tell her I'd pay her back...'

The face that looks like a bulldog's, only not so cute, crumples with shame. I'm thinking that this poor bastard must have lost the one person who loved him. But serve him right for doing that to his own mother, I reckon, forgetting for a moment all the turmoil I heaped on my own long-suffering mum.

'Course, once I got high I didn't give two shits about me mum...'

'You oughta be ashamed of yourself,' says Terry, his voice hard as nails behind his happy beam.

'Now, now, Terry,' says Karen. 'Please let Ian finish, he's doing so well. How do you feel about this now, Ian?'

'Guilty!' says Ian, dissolving into tears. 'I feel so fuckin' guilty!' He's squeezing his stomach with both hands as if his bowels contain a seething mass of poison, and blubbering.

We all stare at him, disgusted by the display of emotion, but I suspect we're grudgingly admiring his honesty. Fuck knows; everyone in prison is innocent in his own mind, so this sort of sincerity blows us away. Even Owen isn't staring out the window but watching the wretched con with curiosity. Something about this whole situation seems to make us feel better about our own guilty secrets. With the exception of Terry.

'You oughtta shoot yourself, you ugly git,' he says in his laid-back way.

Suddenly there's a scraping of chairs and Jake is on top of Terry with his hands round his neck. 'What are yee so feckin' smug fer, Terry? He screams into his face. 'Who are yee tae sit there takin' the piss outta everybody as smug as y' like? Who the feck dae yee think yee are?'

The sight of the ferocious little jock clinging to Terry's enormous bulk, like a terrier shagging a farmer's shin, causes snorts of laughter to break out round the circle. Try as he might, Terry can't loosen the Glaswegian's clutch.

Karen stands up sternly. 'If you continue this behaviour Jake, you will get a warning.' But much as Jake admires her he hasn't finished yet.

'Ah know what yer feckin problem is, yee fecin' hypocrite!' he hollers. 'Yooou stole off your own ma, didn't yee? Well, didn't yee?'

Quite a few of us are laughing now, and we're all expecting Terry to join in 'cause Jake usually has everyone in stitches with his passionate outbursts. But Terry's gone red in the face and, for once, he doesn't have a comeback. With difficulty he extricates himself from the wee Scotsman's grip, dumps him bodily back in his chair, and storms out of the room.

He doesn't come down to get his dinner – unusual for Terry – and when I next see him on his way back from a phone call, he studiously avoids my gaze.

That night, I lie in my cell thinking, thinking, thinking, turning everything over in my mind. Every few minutes the thought of smack springs into my head like some irrepressible jack-in-the-box that screeches: 'Thought you'd forgotten me, did ya? Hello, here I am again! Hoped I'd gone away? Well hello me old friend.'

I start biting my fingernails off until I taste blood.

I can't believe I turned down Mackey's offer of a use-up. One last time before I packed it all in, that's all I needed. One last hit to forget.

What the fuck am I doing here anyway? I've always been a rebel. Hated do-gooders like Karen, trying to get people on the straight and boring narrow.

Karen with her funny gap-teeth. Christ, I'd like to fuck her, though. I'd have her ankles wrapped round my neck, giving her the ride of her fucking life. Can't even suggest it though... Fuck, I'm sick of being told what I can and can't do. I want to be free!

Deep inside, I know I can only be free if I get off the drugs. And I know I'm in the right place. All the rest of it is just blah blah blah. That's all it is, nonsense words trying to get to me.

At last, I tell that voice in my head to shut the fuck up and sink gratefully into sleep.

Everyone's excited. It's been four weeks since that natty-suited businessman came to talk to us and tonight there's going to be someone even better. Used to be a right hoodlum. A couple of cons, pals of this fella, have blagged themselves onto the wing to catch up with him.

On the way to the meeting, I notice Blake grab a new convict out of his cell and start shoving him along the

290

landing. He's got his face pressed so close to the curly-headed fella's ear that he doesn't notice me behind him.

'Move it, Harris, you sorry piece of shit,' I hear him growl. 'I've got my eye on you, you scummy blob of pond-life. You'd better toe the line or you'll find me coming down on top of you like a ton of bricks.' He's got one hand shoving the con in the back and the other in his pocket, and I swear he's rubbing his dick with it, turning himself on with his laughable clichés.

'You're a right ugly skinny little sicko. Junkies like you, I could snap you in two with my fingers; you wouldn't last one fuckin' minute if I 'ad my way with you, sonny boy.'

I fall behind, not wanting Blake to know what I've just witnessed. As Blake shoves the curly-headed con round the corner, the con turns and glances at me. His eyes gaze pleadingly out of a gaunt, pale face. I have a mad urge to fling Blake over the landing and grab the poor bastard to safety. I've never felt this chivalrous towards another con, especially one I don't even know.

'His name's Freddie,' the cleaner on the wing tells me when I poke around for information. 'Freddie Harris.'

I stare at him blankly. 'So?'

'Of the Harris family?'

The cleaners are always the first to get the low-down on new cons. This one gives me a look as if I should know what he's talking about; but I'm a stranger to Pentonville's usual catchment area.

'Everyone knows the Harrises,' he says leaning against his mop and looking at me as if I should also know the famous tagline: 'Don't nobody mess with Harris.'

'So how come Blake isn't worried about these Harrises, then?'

A smile creeps across the cleaner's face. 'Just takes one person to say something to them.'

Freddie's in pre-ads, but I get to have a close look at him in the meeting that night. He's sitting at the back with his hair hanging down over his face as if he's trying to be invisible. He looks as if he should be on a psychiatric ward, not a prison. For a brief moment, he glances up and our eyes lock onto each other. I can't help wincing.

Not so long ago I'd have avoided Freddie like the plague. But something's changed in me. It's as if I have a new energy coursing through my veins. Besides, I can't help it. Something about him reminds me of myself after Granny Guinness breathed her last.

I drag my mind off Freddie as a roar of enthusiasm breaks out. A fella with a cheeky-looking face strolls into the room as if it's his own gaff and he's invited a few mates round for a party.

Stories have been flying about him. Apparently his whole life everyone despaired of him – his teachers, his family, the governor, even his long-suffering girlfriend who, they say, topped herself over him. He's been in and out of the Ville like a boomerang.

I can see why everyone's been so eager to see him. They're wondering if he's still getting up to his legendary antics in his new, drug-free life. To look at the mischievous grin twitching around his lips, I'd say he probably does.

One of the cons who's managed to talk his way onto the wing starts to regale everyone with a story of how Dale once stuck a sign to Blake's back saying, 'Do us all a favour and kick the shit out of me.'

Dale laughs his head off, throwing a few mock punches and exchanging greetings with his old acquaintances. Gordon, the kind fella who got me on the programme, has organised this meeting. Eventually, he has to stand on a chair to get everyone to quieten down.

'Would you like to introduce yourself, Dale?' says Karen who's come in especially for this talk because she used to be his counsellor.

Dale whirls round to slip his arm round Karen's waist and give her a smacking kiss on the cheek, making her blush. 'I'm allowed to do that, not like you dirty-minded boys, 'cause I'm out at Downview,' he laughs.

'You lucky bastard,' someone comments. Downview is set to become a women's prison, but for now it's a cushy C-cat jail mostly for cons shortly due to be released.

Dale beams around the room. 'Hell-ohhh!'

I've never known anyone put so much warmth and welcome into two syllables.

'My name's Dale and I am an addict. I used to hate calling myself an addict. I used to say it like I was a racing driver,' he explains, speeding his words together, 'my-name's-Dale-n-I-m-an-add... blah blah blah blah.'

I glance round to see if Terry is laughing like everyone else but he's staring down at his knees. I glance back to Freddie, can't help it, just checking to make sure he's all right. He's twirling his hair around his fingers with a far away expression.

For the next half hour I'm mesmerised listening to Dale recount his life story. He could almost be telling mine. It starts off with the cheeky kid who wins friends by making everyone laugh, with horrible things going on at home and feeling like he was dying inside. Then he discovers the white stuff that brings him up. And the brown stuff that calms him down, and the pills and so on that help him forget all the bad things. Gradually, he's falling apart, physically, mentally, everything. He carries on kidding everyone, including himself, that all is ticketyfucking-boo, until one day he can't keep up the pretence any longer. That's when he comes face-to-face with the parts of himself that for years he's hidden under a fortress of jokes and pranks and shaggy dog tales.

Eventually, his jokes dried up along with his drug supply. For a week, he lay in his cell down the Block, contemplating his dark side, until he made himself so sick with it that he literally threw up whatever he ate.

'One day, I kept being sick and I was raking my fingers through my puke, round and round, saying 'This is the real me. Violent. Stupid. Uncaring. Unfunny. This is what I'm really like.' It was as if all the evil was coming out and I was seeing who I really was. And all the cheeky, funny, friendly stuff was just a sham I'd been making up.

'All this time, I'd had this never-ending urge for smack... Well, for any drugs that would take me away from knowing what a piece of shit I really was. But I was stuck down the Block. There was no escape from my cell and there was no escape from me. I didn't know which was worse. It was doing my head in.

'Anyway, that was my rock-bottom experience. And having reached rock bottom, I started to drill. I was rubbing my fingers in my own stinking sick and realising how fuckin' vile I was. I kept heaving and puking as if I was trying to puke my guts out. It was almost as if I was trying to puke myself to death. But then I realised something. You know, like one of those times when something just hits you and you think, fuck, where did that come from? I realised that it wasn't about getting out of my cell – the prison was in my own head. I mean, it didn't even matter that I was in prison because the prison I'd built around myself, with all the drugs and violence and crime and desperation, was a hundred times worse than any place that I was locked up in.

'Well, just before I got arrested that last time, my girlfriend had deliberately OD'd in my bath. She looked so beautiful, lying there with her hair floating in the water, even though she was a junkie and had wasted away almost to nothing. She'd stood by me through all my trips in and out of jail and all my mucking about with other birds. There was a letter crumpled up in her hand, all wet. I couldn't read most of it, except she told me she'd always love me, and at the end it said, 'Maybe this will make you wake up.'

All around the room feet shuffle and there's one or two mutters like 'Oh, mate, that's bad shit.'

'I'd always been fuckin' horrible to anyone who went on the RAPt programme,' says Dale. 'I took the piss out of them, when really I only hated them like a rat hates other rats for leaving the sinking ship.

'I'd even fallen out with Gary, who was my best mate. Eventually he went on the programme without telling me, and, good for him, he's sorted himself out and he's just got married on the out and his missus is expecting.'

'Good on you, Gazzer,' someone yells.

'He always wanted a couple of sprogs,' laughs someone else.

'Go on mate, what happened then?' a couple of cons shout out at the same time making everyone laugh.

'Yeah right, so I was kneeling there in my own puke, and I knew what I had to do was go and say sorry to Gary. Then I was going to have to make it up to everyone else I'd taken the piss out of. And just think that made me feel good.

'I wiped that puke off my hands and I didn't mind being down the Block another week. I started writing down my plans. Plans about making it up to everyone I'd ever hurt, especially my girlfriend's mum and step-dad, and getting clean and going straight. And, get this, don't let anyone tell you you're helpless in here.'

His gaze goes around the room, taking in our faces. His eyes burn into mine before moving onto the person next to me.

'Even though I'm still inside, all those plans I made started to happen. Like my girlfriend's mum and step-dad came to visit me a month ago; she'd OD'd in my bath, remember, and we were all hugging each other like family. And they used to hate my guts, I can tell ya. One time, her step-dad tried to run me over in his Jeep, and here he was giving me a fuckin' cuddle. If that ain't a miracle, I don't know what is!'

Every convict in here is staring at Dale, thinking the same thing. Yes, that would be a fucking miracle.

'I don't like to say the word 'God', right?' Dale grins bashfully. 'Even now, it's hard to get the word out, like: Uuuurrrggh... grrrrr... God! Fuck that hurts...'

A few nervous laughs break out.

'And a lot of you know that I used to be as anti-religious as they come. I was the fuckin' anti-Christ, for fuck's sake.'

'You were the devil, mate,' someone agrees.

'Devil, demon... that kid from the 'Exorcist', you name it. I'm the last person you'd expect to get on any do-gooding bandwagon. But look at me now. I'm here, talking to all you banged-up bum-bandits as if I actually give a shit about ya.'

'Oi! Watch it!'

'Ha ha. I mean talking to all you lovely people, about getting in touch with a Higher Power. Call it whatever you like. There ain't no long-bearded, sour-faced old codger up there judging us for being the way that we are. I'm telling you, ya gotta have faith in something other than your own puny selves or you'll walk a couple of steps and fall flat on your face.'

I've been all ears until now, but I don't like the way this talk is headed. Some of the other cons are frowning, and one or two downright scowling, as if he's started talking another language.

'Yeah, mate, that's all very well,' says one of Dale's old pals, 'but are you still the same bloke who hid that turd behind the radiator in the screws' office?'

A burst of laughter breaks out and Dale leaps to his feet. 'Too fucking right I am! And I'd do it again! I'll take my fuckin' trousers down right now and shit on that bullying bastard's spit-and-shined boots!'

The room erupts into laughter and Dale sits down pleased with himself.

'We all have to look for our own way out of our prison,' he shouts above the din. 'But there's help all around. That's all I'm saying.'

Dale sits back with a huge beam on his face. I glance around at the other cons. We've all got to be thinking he's the most unlikely convert we've ever seen.

When the meeting ends, the cons who've been on the programme for a while, say a prayer then hug each other. One of them comes up to me, with his arms held out making me squirm. Nevertheless, I grit my teeth and hold my arms out a bit and let him embrace me. It feels worse than being stabbed.

Then a voice in the back of my head starts laughing at me and I snap myself out of it and hug him back even though it makes me cringe. I'm willing to give anything a go if it will help me stay off drugs, even if it means having a cuddle with some hairy-arsed convict.

A couple of days later, I break off a chat with Roland to catch up with Freddie, who's on his way from his pre-ads group down to lunch. I want to see if he's as fucked as he looks or if there's hope for him yet.

'All right, Freddie? How's it going?'

He's lost in his own private world and jumps.

'Yeh... er... all right.' He gives me a slightly lopsided smile. 'I've got to get back to Freda,' he gabbles and hurries off.

Hmm. Well, the cat ain't nicked his tongue. I suppose that's a good sign. But Freda? Sounds like he might well be off his rocker.

I'm on his case, though.

On Wednesdays, the prison has its training day and I suppose they don't want to put off any new screw-recruits before they get toughened up to the mayhem, so they put us all on lockdown. Normally, I wouldn't mind because I enjoy lying in my cell letting my mind float away, when the bad thoughts aren't on me that is. But today it's hot because they have got the heating on full blast. I'm sweltering in nothing but my boxers, and every time my mind starts to drift, it gets dragged back to the conversation going on next door.

Tams is in the cell next to mine and Winston's in the one opposite. One look at Tams' shoes on his first day, and I could tell it wouldn't be long before he'd found a mate in Winston. They've been talking about shoes for a good fifteen minutes now, and I've already had a go at them for being a couple of clothes-obsessed faggots.

'I've got an excellent cobbler; been mending shoes for years,' Winston shouts. 'He's about eighty-five now. It's an art for him, returning shoes to their original glory. I wear my heels down on the outsides so I get 'im to re-heel them regularly.'

'Oh yeah?' Tams sounds like he's bloody fascinated. 'I wear my heels down on the insides. Usually I chuck 'em out and get new ones.'

'Nah, mate. That's a waste. A good pair of shoes is made to last a lifetime. They just need a bit of tender loving care. Like good wine, they mature with age. Build character.'

My hopes lift. Perhaps they'll change the subject to wine, never mind that booze is supposed to be an off-limits subject on the programme. They had a good chat about it yesterday and I learnt a couple of tips. Only buy French wine if it says: 'Mis en bouteille dans le chateau,' or some shit. 'Otherwise it's plonk,' Tams explained, and he should know 'cause his dad's a crime-lord who buys the best vino money can buy.

But no, Tams is thrilled with what Winston has just said and is going on about meeting up with this cobbler of his and salvaging a few of his old designer shoes.

'Would ya shut up you couple of old tarts?' I groan.

There's a couple of 'tuts', then I hear Winston mutter, 'That's what comes of a man who's worn trainers all his life.'

'Listen, you fucks,' I explode, 'I used to make a packet on the outside. I owned lots of pairs of expensive shoes myself. And I wear my heels straight down the middle so put that in your bloody pipe and smoke it.'

There's stillness for a while, then Tams says, 'Do us a favour, mate, and put your radio on.'

'Ever heard the one about silence being golden?' Christ, I sound just like my granddad. Hope I'm not turning into an old bollocks like him. I snap my radio on and hurl myself on my bed, wiping my face with a towel.

There's some DJ rattling on about his girlfriend's handbag fetish and I'm about to change stations when he announces the next song, 'I'm Going Down.' No one can make my frustrations float away like Mary J Blige.

'Time on my hands, since you been away, boy,' sings Mary J, soothing me, stroking my weary head, taking me down to that place with her.

'I ain't got no plans,
No, no no no,
And the sound of the rain,
Against my windowpane,
Is slowly, is slowly drivin' me insane, boy.'

I'm moving my head to the music, feeling free. Not free from this prison, but something far, far freer than that.

Confronting Demons

'Who'd like to start the group?' Karen flashes her gap-toothed smile around the room, making Jake's heart melt. He gazes at her soppy-eyed, too besotted to even think about sharing his own story.

'Yeah, I will.'

Everyone turns to Terry in surprise. He's hardly said a word in the last couple of groups, let alone cracked one of his jokes.

'Very good, Terry. Start with your name.'

Terry's laid-back grin is nowhere to be seen. 'My name's Terry and I'm... Oh fuck it. You're all a bunch of wankers. Might as well have a tea towel tied round your heads and a pinny on, getting things off your tits like a bunch of slags on your fuckin' monthlies.'

From the corner of my eye I can see Jake inching forward on his seat, face turning purple, and I'm expecting Karen to intervene when she says, 'Keep going, Terry.'

'That's what I was thinking, anyway. It's easier to think like that than to tell everyone what a cunt you are like Ugly Bollocks did last week.'

Ian throws him a look. There's less self-hatred going on this week, more of a forewarning of punching Terry in the snout.

'Don't take any notice, Ian, it's not about you.' Karen says softly.

'What's the point in all this fuckin' sharing, I kept asking myself.' Terry carries on. 'You don't talk about stuff. You keep it to yourself and don't even think about it. That's what I've always done. But when Bollocks-face, sorry mate, was talking about what he did to his mum last week, it was like I could see all this crap coming out of his mouth and I wanted to shove it all back in again, 'cause it was sort of like my own voice talking.'

For the first time, Ian looks at Terry with a glimmer of respect. Even Jake stops seething, although he's still poised to leap off his seat.

Terry takes a deep breath and spits out, 'I used to nick off my mum all the time.'

'Theeere, I knew ett!' yells Jake.

'But I had fuckin' good reason to.' The muscles in Terry's temples are working furiously. 'After Bollocks Face here shared his story, my own story flashed into my head. It wouldn't go away. Not when I was eating, sleeping, shitting or listening to you muggy bastards. There was no fuckin' way I was going to tell you in a million years what happened to me. But it won't leave me alone and now I'm willing to give anything a go.'

'Like a ghost that needs to be exorcised?' suggests a tall, foppish fella with a posh accent who's in for fraud.

'Bollocks to that!' Terry snaps. 'Well, all right. Maybe.'

'Whatever you say in this room stays in this room,' Karen reminds him. 'Why don't you begin at the beginning?' You're an excellent storyteller, Terry.'

Terry brightens a bit. 'All right then. When I was little, three or four, I went to a shop with my mum and when we came out I had a chocolate bar in my hand.

'Where did you get that?' she asked. 'You're not allowed to take stuff you haven't paid for.'

'I hadn't thought anything of it. I just liked its pretty wrapper because it was shiny and pink; a Turkish Delight it was, and I said, "I got it for you because it's pretty like you are." She used to wear a dress that was the same colour.' He throws a guilty glance at Tams as if he's half-expecting Tams to call him a poof for all the times he's accused him of being one.

Tams is listening intently along with everyone else.

'Well, this big smile came over her face and she said, "Terry, you clever boy. How did you know that was my favourite chocolate?" That made me feel good, so I told her about the dress I liked and she was flattered and didn't take the chocolate back into the shop; just gave me a wink which let me know that she liked getting gifts that way. My dad fucked off when I was about three and it was just me and my mum after that. We were really close.

'After that, I used to nick something for her whenever we went shopping. I always got away with it. I overheard her talking to a friend of hers once. She was saying, 'Tel's the best son in the world. He's got this really cute smile. One day he'll charm his way out of a shop with half their wares in his pockets.' When she said that my face glowed; it felt like she really loved me.

'After a while she started letting slip little hints about things she wanted. I'd get them for her after school. Then she dropped that and just stuck a list up on the fridge. She'd always make a big fuss of me, and once she admitted that she'd got caught nicking stuff a couple of times as if she'd got 'guilty' stamped all over her face. I never looked guilty because I never felt guilty. It made me feel good to nick stuff. I always made sure to buy something small and be friendly to the staff, so I never left a shop without paying for anything.

'So one day, just as I was leaving this shop with a bottle of wine and four cans of lager in my school satchel, 'cause Mum was having a party that night, the owner grabbed my arm and said, 'You're coming to the back of the shop with me right now, you little bugger.'

A wave of ill-feeling passes around the room. Most of us have been there.

'Well, I was sure I'd got away with it when I walked out that door. I've always had a sixth sense about it. A couple of times I'd put stuff back because I knew a customer was suspicious or something. Anyway, this bloke gave me the bollocking of me life, said I'd get arrested and thrown in jail with a bunch of bum-bandits who fancied little boys like me and I'd never see my mum again. He was glaring right in my face and I fuckin' shat myself. I was eight. I'd done a turd in my pants and I was... I was mortified. He started laughing at me and saying, 'That'll teach you!''

Terry's cheeks have gone crimson. He swallows hard before continuing. 'That night I threw my pants in the bin and didn't tell my mum nothing. It didn't put me off lifting stuff from shops, though, because that always gave me a good feeling. But I stayed low for a bit because I was scared shitless...' he hurriedly corrects himself, 'I mean, scared to death of those bum-bandits waiting for me in prison. Then one day, I was coming home from school and I saw my Mum sitting in the park with that bloke from the shop who'd terrified the shit out of me.'

Winston and Tyrees snigger but break it off hurriedly when Terry glares at them.

'They were laughing like old friends,' says Terry, shaking his head like he still can't believe it. 'My blood ran cold. How could she even be talking to him?'

'I went right up to them and told her what a horrible man he was and how he'd yelled at me. I was expecting her to give him a good bollocking and take me away from him. But she just laughed. And he laughed too. Then she said something like, 'Tel, darling, it was all getting a bit out of hand. You were robbing this poor bloke blind. You've gotta stop nicking stuff or you'll land us all in trouble.'

'I couldn't believe it. She was making out that none of it was her idea!' Terry glances up from his hands and seems surprised to see everyone listening, riveted.

'Gradually, it sank in that she'd set me up. My own mum had betrayed me! Never trust a woman that's what I learnt. Not if you can't trust your own fuckin' mother.'

His face is red and he looks a sorry sight without his defences up and that unconcerned grin of his. He looks like the heart-broken eight-year-old he must have been when he was grassed up by the person he most loved.

'My whole world fell apart right there. She didn't love me. She'd just been using me. And if I couldn't nick anything for her, then...' he trails off with a stricken look.

'Yes, then how could you make her love you?' Karen finishes gently.

Terry slumps in his seat, defeated.

'How do you feel about your mum now, Terry?'

'Fuckin' hate her!' Terry spits. 'I hate her just as much now as I did then. I buried it until now. Been pretending everything was OK for years.' His eyes gleam vengefully and a bitter smile makes its way across his face.

'From that day on, I got back at the deceitful slag. In little ways at first. A few coins from her purse here and there, nothing she could ever be sure of. Sometimes I'd hide something of hers in a different part of the house so she'd think she'd lost it and then it would turn up out of the blue. I was clever about it. Subtle.

'After a while, she started wondering if she was going out of her nut. Sometimes, I'd go a week or two without doing anything. I used to enjoy misplacing her house keys because that would really piss her off. She'd get all flustered and be late for wherever she was going, then I'd slip the keys back into her handbag or some other place she'd looked already. She never suspected me because I had this smile; I had this innocence about me.'

I find myself nodding along with some of the others. Terry has such a nice air about him that he can get away with things that would land anyone else in deep shit.

'Sometimes I'd be really helpful and help her find that stuff I'd hidden just to see this grateful look in her face. But underneath I was having a laugh.'

'You're a grown man now, Terry,' Karen murmurs, 'Do you think you would be able to forgive her?' Terry doesn't look like a grown man. He looks like a lost kid.

'That's when I started to eat... Sweets and crisps... anything to fill up this hole.' He pounds his fist into his gut. 'I was skinny at eight and fat at nine. The fatter I got the less she seemed to like me.'

He's not leaning back in his chair any more. He's hunched over on it, looking unguarded and exposed with his thick rolls of fat spilling over his thighs. 'My whole life,' he groans, 'every fuckin' thing that's gone wrong with it, goes back to that thing she did when I was eight years old. No, I can't fuckin' forgive her!'

'Terry,' says Karen, 'do you really, really believe your mum deliberately ruined your life when you were eight years old?'

Terry opens his mouth and closes it again. 'If I didn't blame her, who would I blame?' he says at last.

After lunch, I pace round my cell then go for a wander up and down the corridors before bang-up. I've got an assignment to write for the course tonight and Terry's got me thinking. Those shields we put up to protect ourselves from pain... What if they just keep the pain locked in? Something catches my eye. A glint of light flashes across my line of vision, then spreads in an arc across the floor and again into my eyes. I glance into the

306

cell I'm passing to see the reflection of a gaunt face regarding me in a mirror. There's the hint of a shy smile and then it disappears.

'What you up to, Freddie?' I ask, walking in. I count six mirrors positioned at odd angles around his cell, including one resting on his up-turned feet. 'I didn't take you as the vain sort. What ya doing with all these mirrors?'

Freddie tilts the mirror in his hands averting his gaze. Then again, I see it, his slightly lopsided smile, this time reflected from the mirror in his hands to another hung at a cunning angle on the wall. He tweaks on the string hanging from the mirror and his face disappears to be replaced by a reflection of the sun, dazzling me. I glance up to the window to see a patch of blue sky.

'Fuckin' 'ell Freddie, you're a funny sort,' I laugh, baffled. 'What's all these mirrors for then?'

Freddie shrugs, not looking at me. 'I like to see the stars in bed when I can't sleep.' The words sort of dribble out of the corner of his mouth.

I take another look and instead of seeing a chaotic arrangement of mirrors stuck to the walls with blue tack and chewing gum, I recognise a precise and intricate system of connecting reflections. An admiring whistle escapes me then suddenly I'm moving back startled. A large black spider is clambering along Freddie's arm.

'Fuck mine, Freddie. There's a fucking great spider on ya!'

'Sssh!' Freddie hisses, warning me back with his hand. 'It's ok,' he croons, cupping his other hand around the eight legged lump. 'Freda's very sensitive. It's ok Freda, Harry's a friend.'

I don't know whether to feel shocked or pleased. Pleased because Freddie's obviously not completely bonkers and knows my name, but a bit taken aback to hear him talking to a spider as if it were some frightened little old lady.

Freddie turns his arm upside down to let the spider walk back along the other side. He giggles with pleasure. 'She's tickling me.'

'You wouldn't catch me letting no hairy black thing crawl all over me,' I frown. 'That is one big fuckin' spider.'

'She's twice as big as when I found her out in the yard,' Freddie says with pride. 'I've been feeding her flies every day so she don't have to wait for them to fly into her web.' He raises his arm towards the ceiling. Slowly the spider climbs along his outstretched hand and onto a web in a corner of the cell.

I step closer and notice a movement in the web, where a struggling fly is making futile buzzing noises. Freddie's spider clambers delicately across her trap and starts tending to her meal. She wraps the fly with thread until it struggles no more, then sets about repairing a few strands that must have got broken when Freddie stuck the fly in her web.

I'm watching this fascinated, when I notice Freddie watching me, equally fascinated, like he's drawn me into his world. I realise I've forgotten all my usual problems and anxieties being in here with him. Then I feel a bit foolish, standing in his cell with all his mirrors and his pet spider and that shining look of enchantment on his face.

'Freddy and Freda. What a nutty couple,' I laugh strolling outside.

'Who wants to take some time?' asks Paul glancing encouragingly around the room. Paul told us last week the story of how he turned from raving coke-head to zoned out pin-cushion, Pentonville prisoner and finally,

RAPt counsellor with his own keys to come and go. We all respect him.

Owen flashes me a look. Yesterday he took a huge step and got over his crippling reticence to describe what happened to his little brother, Rory. A month ago, I would never have thought it possible for a bunch of hard-boiled cons to be choking back sobs and I'd have put money on it I wouldn't be one of them. That was before the vision of a bolt of electricity paralyzing a little kid to the rail indelibly etched itself into our minds. The meeting had to be finished early so that everyone could return to their cells to get over Owen's story in his own way.

Go on, Owen's gaze tells me. If I can do it so can you.

Suddenly I'm bloody terrified about opening up to my own shameful past. I can't help feeling a new respect for all the fellas who've managed to share their stories. By the time I summon up the bottle, Jake has started to shake and stutter and I reckon he's got something he needs to get off his chest a lot more urgently than me. He's never been able to talk about himself in Karen's groups because he's always so infatuated but all that pent-up rage has to be the result of something.

'I feckin' do,' he manages to splutter at last.

'Well done, Jake. Start with your name.'

'My name's Jake and ah'm an alcoholic and an addict tae every feckin' thing going.' He buries his head in his hands, overcome with shame. 'Mah Uncle,' he spits out, 'he held me done,' his shoulders heave up and down and his head goes back. 'He... held... me... done...'

'Oh great, here we go,' I groan to myself. I don't think I want to hear this, especially not after the emotional battering of Owen's story yesterday.

'Take your time,' Paul nods.

'Mah Uncle held me done an'… Raped me!' Jake manages to blurt out at last. A wave of relief travels through him, releasing a bit of that stored-up aggression. Then he slumps pathetically in his chair.

'Go on, Jake, tell us what happened,' Paul says softly.

Jake starts to rock back and forth in his seat. It's painful to watch. Part of me wants him to spit it out because I know that all the stuff he's been holding inside is poison. The other part of me wants to leap up and squeeze his neck until he can't say another fuckin' word.

'He held me done and stuck his cock up mah arse when ah came home fae school,' Jake gets it out all in one go then bursts into tears and starts slamming his fist down on his knees.

The atmosphere in the room has plummeted. I notice Terry angrily wipe his eye. My chest is hammering.

'How old were you?' Paul asks so calmly we barely hear him.

'Fae as young as ah can remember,' Jake sobs. 'Ah don't know. He used tae tell me it wouldn'ee hurt, but it always hurt! He tried tae be gentle but ah couldn'ee git aweey. He said ah'd enjoy it jist like he did, if ah jist relaxed. But ah was too wee, ah couldn'ee take it.'

In my mind's eye, I'm chaining Jake's uncle to a lump of concrete so that he can't move.

'He was sweet tae me, he gave me prezzies and cuddles, not like mah mam and da. Ah hated him but ah loved him too, 'cause he was mah uncle and he took me tae the races with 'im and he was the only person who listened tae me and called me a clever wee lad. But he hurt me… he hurt me so bad ah couldn't go to the toilet proper like… ah'd crap mahself and get teased for stinkin' like shit…

310

Oh fuck, I can't cope with these sorts of confessions. Now I'm smashing Jake's uncle over the head again and again with an iron bar.

'And ah stopped growing about then…'

So that's why poor Jake is a fuckin' midget; his uncle stunted his growth with his evil knob when Jake was just a defenceless kid. Now I'm grabbing the pervert's head by the hair and slamming it over and over against the pavement, until his blood and hair and brains mesh with the blackened splotches of chewing gum on the paving stones.

'Ah loved him and ah hated him,' Jake sobs. 'It would'nee been so bad if ah could'ae jist hated the feckin' bastard… but he was nice to me…'

Suddenly I'm on my feet with my fists clenched. 'Where is this fucker? Is he still alive? I'll fuckin' bury him! He was only being nice to ya because he was buying you, don't ya get it? He was an evil cunt and I'll fuckin' do him for you when I get out of here. I'll stick something so big up his fuckin' arse he'll never be able to shit again!'

I'm shaking. There's an arm round my shoulders and its Paul's and everyone's staring at me as if they're shocked, as if they're seeing me in a new light.

'I'll put a gun in his mouth,' I hear my voice go on, high-pitched and alien, 'and I'll pull the fuckin' trigger and watch his brains explode into tiny red bits and pieces…'

'Sit down, Harry,' says Paul, guiding me back into my seat. The others look from Jake to me a bit stunned.

'It's good this has come up for both of you. Jake, I'll come back to you in a minute. But first, if you don't mind, I need to ask Harry some questions.'

Jake nods, unable to speak.

'No one likes what rapists and paedophiles do.' Paul's choosing his words carefully. The others grunt agreement while someone, Tyrees I think, growls, 'Filthy cunts should have their bollocks chopped off.'

'But, if you don't mind my saying Harry, you have an aversion to them bordering on psychopathic vengeance. That sort of attitude, you know, it eats you alive. Do you have something you'd like to share with us?'

I'm glaring unseeingly at the floor, seething with rage. Paul's words only minutely register in my brain. Of course, I hate nonces. Everyone hates nonces! Not only should they have their balls ripped off but shoved down their evil throats too!

From somewhere at the back of my mind comes the story I'd been planning to share. About three years ago, when I was in prison, I'd been put on closed visits and was so desperate for drugs that I'd pretended to have acute appendicitis. I put on such a convincing act that I was taken to hospital. Not only had I been given plenty of morphine, as well as a visit from my good old brother, laden with a nice bit of the proper stuff, but I had my appendix taken out too. I let them take me down to the operating theatre because my brother hadn't been yet. I wanted to take a parcel back to prison with me and I'd put on such a good act of being in pain that the doctor said he would have to operate immediately. I'd been planning to pull up my top and show everyone the scar, satisfied that I'd got something profound off my chest.

Now the whole story seems meaningless. Instead, I'm thinking about my beautiful cousin Alice, lying under that paving slab, her pretty face smashed to bits. I'm holding my seat just like Jake was a minute ago and just like I promised myself I never would. And then it's all spilling out of me, even though I've held it in all these years, kept the lid on it, been a man about it.

I'm telling the group about my gorgeous, funny, lovely cousin, and how she went to a party and that was the last bit of fun she ever had before she set off for home on her own. Through bleary eyes, I register the sympathy in the faces of these criminals who are becoming my friends, fellas I never would have let an inch into my personal life until I came on this programme. Even in the midst of my fury, I can tell they're soaking up my words like buffers, as if they're somehow making the pain easier to bear.

When I stop talking for a moment, Jake comes over and gives me a fierce hug. I want to hold him in my arms like a kid and promise that no one will ever hurt him again, then go and hunt down his uncle like an animal. When Jake sits down again, I'm awash with guilt. It's so acute that I can't hold back talking about the innocent con that I kicked, and that awful squelching sound, that's been plaguing me at the back of my mind ever since.

'I was as sure that con raped his two-year old step daughter as if I'd seen 'im do it myself. But all I was thinking about was the nonce who killed my cousin.' I bury my head in my hands as a flood of self-hatred assails me. 'I shove it down all the time but I can't live with the thought that I fucked up some innocent bloke's life!'

Fuck I hate myself. Right now, I wish I had something to take away the pain of being such an evil bastard.

'It's ok, it's ok,' Paul's voice penetrates my thoughts, 'Nothing is entirely unforgivable. Not once we've learnt to forgive ourselves.'

I nod. Yes, I know it. I have to forgive myself or I'll just go back to the drugs and bury the guilt and the self-hatred again and again.

'And once we've learnt to forgive ourselves we have to learn to forgive everyone else too.'

My heart freezes. 'Bollocks! I'll never forgive that piece of shit who killed my cousin, or the uncle who destroyed Jake's life or any of those other cunts who prey on defenceless children!'

'I understand what you're saying,' nods Paul. 'But give this a chance. Once we've brought our secrets out into the open, they often have a way of resolving themselves. Have you ever tried praying about this, Harry?'

A wave of resentment hits me. What did God ever do for me? He took my grandma when I was six and I prayed and prayed for him to bring her back, and when he didn't, I prayed for him to take me too, only to wake up morning after morning disgusted to find myself still in my own bed.

'Religion's a load of bollocks!'

'I'm not talking about religion, I'm talking about spirituality,' Paul says while I seethe. I've heard all this kind of shit before. 'Religion is for people who don't want to go to hell. Spirituality is for people who have already been there.' He lets this sink in for a moment then turns quietly to Jake. 'How do you feel about your uncle now, Jake?'

Jake has stopped shaking and is rhythmically squishing his forehead between his fingers. 'Ma whole life I've been blaming ma uncle fae everything bad that ever happened tae me,' he says. 'But maybe... maybe not all those things were his fault.'

'Good work, Jake. Does realising that make you feel any better?'

Jake thinks for a moment, then nods. Then nods again.

That night I toss in my bed in a futile search for sleep while a thousand thoughts beset me. I wish I could see the stars from my bed like Freddie can. Maybe they would twinkle some clarity on this murky world.

My mind's a battleground of unpleasant visions. Everything that came up in the meeting... the paedophile that killed my cousin, the con I booted in the belly, that desolate look in Jake's face when he told us about his uncle... Round and round they go like scenes from some never-ending horror movie. Every so often, Paul's question bombards my tormented brain, *'Have you ever tried praying about this?'* I fight it away in disgust. If God didn't listen to me when I was a kid and believed in him, why would he listen to me now when I don't?

After several more hours of sweat-soaked anguish, I jump out of bed and hurl myself on my knees. 'All right, I give in, even though I fuckin' hate you and don't even think there is such a thing!' I whisper into the darkness. 'I'm beggin you now!' I don't know what words to say. I still don't know how to pray.

'Just help me to stay clean,' I say, but somehow it doesn't feel right. 'Help me stop hating.' That feels closer to the truth. 'Help me stop hating,' I say over and over again but every time I say it, I'm flooded with thoughts of hatred.

I don't just hate the nonce that killed my cousin; I hate all people elsewhere who kill and rape and torture children. And not just them but teachers who make little kids feel like they're worthless wastes of space. And not just them, but... but *everyone.*

I hate. That's all there is to it. I don't know who they are or what they've done, but right now there's not one person on the entire fuckin' planet that's exempt from my hatred. There's no particular target; my fists are clenched and my face is twisted in a malevolent grimace and all I can feel is pure, evil loathing.

'Fuck you, God,' I mutter out loud, tossing myself back into bed. 'Fat lot of fuckin' good you've ever been.'

315

After that, I consign all notions of a higher power to the big recycle bin in my brain and just try to keep up with the programme as best I can. I'm putting everything I can into it and lapping up its promises, because it's all I've got to keep me sane.

Live and let live

Time always seems to rush by in meetings. Before I got to the RAPt wing, it's as if the hours used to drag by, unless I had some drugs in me that is or if I'd managed to calm my mind down and stop my brain from working overtime. Time would go by so quickly when I was out of it that it was like I was the living dead. I wasn't participating in life and wanted nothing to do with it. I didn't want to be a normal member of society and responsibility terrified me. I also couldn't see the point in it all and used to wonder what it was all about. I suppose I rebelled against it all.

I feel like I'm changing with every story that's shared, like I can see things differently and that life really does have meaning. So many years I wasted using crack and heroin then working out ways to get money so I could buy it, that life just passed me by. Now I want to grab hold of it with both hands and climb back into it.

Terry gets the next meeting off to a start with his re-found good spirits. 'A few months ago, I was a bit down on my luck with the ladies, know what I mean?'

'Were ya Terry?' asks Roland, ever eager to chat about birds.

'Yeah, I was, Roly, so anyway, I tried using some date rape drugs to improve my chances. They were fuckin' useless,' Terry shrugs. 'I just ended up passing out and couldn't remember a thing the next day.'

The rest of us don't know whether to laugh at Terry's joke or at Roland for falling into Terry's easy-mannered trap once again.

Yesterday, Roland told everyone about his rock bottom experience while suffering the worst cluck of his life. There was the cellmate who wouldn't shut up for a minute, the large lump of heroin stuck in his bowels and

317

the owner of the lump threatening to cut him open to find it. By the end of the session half of us were weeping with laughter, which wasn't quite the result Roland had been hoping for, but today he looks like he's got a huge burden off his chest.

When an older con who's hardly said a word until now starts telling us about his life, I notice I'm listening to him. Really listening, like I could never be arsed to listen to anyone. You wouldn't know it to look at him now, but as a child he'd been a gifted chess player. The Prodigy of the Slums had been his nickname, because he came from a part of the East End that had remained derelict long since the war.

At fourteen, he'd fallen head over heels for a budding chess player, some precocious thirteen-year-old from a wealthy part of London. Their romance had caused a bit of a sensation in the junior chess world. He loved her so much he taught her everything he had painstakingly taught himself. One day, she passed off his unique opening sequence as her own, beating him to win a major junior championship. She hadn't been interested in him after that and life had gone steadily downhill for Eddie until... well, until he wound up in here with the rest of us.

'I've something I'd like to share,' says the fella with the plumy voice. He said something the other day and Terry was quick to praise him; 'Hoorah Henry! What-what! Which had us all cracking up except this bloke of course, who didn't appreciate the impersonation. Since then, the name has stuck although the counsellors use his real name of course.

'Well done, Guy,' Karen says warmly. 'We don't have a great deal of time left but go ahead if that's ok with you.'

'My name's Guy,' and I am an alcoholic and a drug addict. To cocaine, that is,' says Hoorah Henry.

'Well, as you may or may not know,' he begins nervously, 'I used to go to Harrow long before I ended up in the Ville.'

Terry breaks wind so loudly that it vibrates around the room.

'That's enough, Terry,' Karen warns as everyone sniggers.

'I didn't mean it. It's the food we get fed in here,' says Terry blushing. And I believe him, as he seems to have taken the group more seriously since he opened up. I still laugh though along with the others.

'Food shit in here,' agrees Winston, 'don't know how anyone eats it.'

'Ha ha,' Hoorah Henry says gamely, going a bit red in the face. 'You're right about the food being rubbish but, if you think Pentonville is bad, you should try a few years in a boys' boarding school. I assure you, the board and lodging's ten times better in here.'

I'd like to laugh along with him, but there's something I don't like about this bloke. The only thing we know about him is that he's in for tax evasion and some scam involving hedge funds to pay for his daughter's school fees. The judge must have taken a right dislike to him the day he sent him down with us lot.

'Anyway,' says Hoorah with a gruff cough, 'there's something that has been playing on my conscience for many, many years, which pains me whenever I think of it.'

Everyone stares at the bloke as he rubs his forehead, eyes cast down. He's a geeky sort, in his early forties with a shifty look in his eye. I can well imagine that shifty eye darting about over his tax forms, spotting opportunities to defraud the tax man. I've got no beef with that but there'e something about him that makes my skin crawl. Next to me, Roland's stomach rumbles expectantly. It's almost time for lunch.

'Well, one night, I... I...' Hoorah scrunches his cheeks in his hands hunting for words. Minutes seem to tick by while he gathers his thoughts. 'Well, er... to cut a long story short, as they say, I a-hem... I know this is going to sound odd – very odd, ha.. ha... had. I found myself having sex with my sister.'

Everyone stares at him disgusted.

'I was twenty-three at the time and she was seventeen, so above the age of consent,' he splutters, 'but er... the fact is, she was very sweet to me and gave me a lovely kiss and a cuddle and I er... thought she really wanted to but turns out, wouldn't you know, that she didn't, only it was a bit late by then, you see, because I was er... rather drunk.'

Glances are exchanged around the group. *High up on the list of things you do not admit to in prison: shagging your relatives.* Hoorah hasn't been here very long but surely he knows that? Even on the RAPt wing where we are trying to be much more accepting. He should have left it to talk with his counsellor on a one-to-one basis.

'So,' says Winston. 'You nonced your sister?' Outside, footsteps head along the landing and down the stairs towards the servery.

'Er... not quite,' says Guy, flustered. 'You see, gosh... I thought she really wanted me to and...'

'But she didn't want you to,' Roland insists with a sneer. There's a hard look in his eyes.

'Roland, it's my job to ask the questions,' Karen interrupts. 'I think you're very brave to tell us this, Guy,' she says, 'and I want you to finish your story next time we meet. It's a shame we have to finish now but it's lunch time and we have to be going. However, I do have to say this.' She looks around at us with a warning expression. 'Guy hasn't finished sharing, so I trust you *not to pass judgement on him.* I'm suspecting there's more to this than what you've told us, Guy?'

Guy looks up, slightly bewildered. 'Oh absolutely. It's all rather complicated...' he trails off.

'Seems pretty clear-cut to me,' I hear Winston mutter as we get to our feet and head for lunch.

Winston is on the phone. I'm waiting for him to get off so I can call my sister, but Winston's conversations are so entertaining that I don't mind hanging around. Hoorah Henry is waiting for the phone to call his lawyer. He doesn't look like he's enjoying Winston's conversation.

'You're missing me, aintcha babe?' Winston schmoozes down the phone, 'I miss you too. I'm missing those gorgeous, honey-tasting juicy lips of yours.'

Winston is tall, suave and black. That what-do-you-do-for-a-living? – I'm-an-armed-robber line of his, is obviously a winner. Photos of his many conquests – black, blonde, Taiwanese, you name it – are stuck to the walls of his cell. He's been away for quite a few years already but the birds are still waiting for him. He's on the phone at every opportunity, keeping them sweet.

Hunching over the phone, he says in a sleazy half-whisper, 'No, not *those* lips, those *other* ones.' I hear a delighted shriek on the other end of the line.

Winston doesn't mind who overhears him; it's these telephone-sex chats that seem to keep him nourished in the clink with all its mechanically-recovered items on the menu. 'Yeah, dontcha worry, pretty babe, I'll be out soon and I'll be right round to sort you out.'

"Out soon," the madman! He's got five to go and he's talking to her like he'll be stuffing her this afternoon.

'Excuse me, do you mind?' Hoorah smiles desperately, 'I have a rather urgent call to make to my solicitor.'

Winston turns round, his smile switching to a frown. 'Shut up, you slag.' He returns to his conversation the tender, romantic look flooding back into his face like the sun coming out after a flash storm.

'Look, I'm really sorry about this,' wheedles Hoorah, 'but it is absolutely imperative that I speak to my solicitor. He's actually waiting for my call as we speak. It will only take a moment.'

Any other con I'd feel sorry for but there's something so off-putting about this bloke, even before his jaw-dropping admission today, that I'm half-hoping Winston will turn round and give him a clump.

'Hold on a sec, babe,' says Winston covering the receiver with one hand. Again, his face turns to business mode and this time he says in a resounding clipped voice, 'If you don't shut your mouth, I will wrap this telephone cord around your fuckin' neck.'

Hoorah steps back, running his fingers through his hair in agitation. When Winston starts blowing tender kisses down the phone, Hoorah can't bear any more. 'For crying out loud!' he exclaims in his cut-glass voice.

'You keep doing that, babe, I'm listening,' Winston croons to his lover then turns round and grabs Hoorah by the hair. With gritted teeth and no hint of the sweet-talking Lothario he was a moment ago, he yanks Hoorah's head towards the phone, winds the cord around his neck and, as promised, starts tugging furiously.

Hoorah's face goes red and bloated, his mouth coughing out words. 'Help!' I think he's trying to say throwing me a look of desperation.

'Drop it out Winston, you'll be kicked off the wing,' I say sharply.

Winston releases the fella and shoves him away in disgust. Violence isn't tolerated on the RAPt programme and Winston's come too far to risk his place.

'Thanks, mate,' he says. At the same time, Hoorah, rubbing his throat in the background mouths, 'Thank you,' and I almost laugh because they're both so grateful to me when I haven't done a thing. Then again it doesn't feel all that funny.

Winston cradles the phone and breaks into a loving smile. 'Oh nothing, nothing, sweetheart. Just getting rid of some nonce who shagged his sister.'

At this point Hoorah gives up on his solicitor. A plaintive howl escapes his throat and he hurries away down the landing.

'Hey, Harry. You ok, mate?'

Winston's holding out the phone to me. I've been lost in my thoughts for a while and hadn't noticed he'd finished his call.

'I'm surprised you didn't give that creep a dose of the old ultra violence,' he grins. Winston's been picking up a few expressions from *A Clockwork Orange* lately. 'You're the one who hates nonces.'

His words hit me with their truthfulness. A week ago, I would have used any excuse to vent my hatred of them and I would have been the one winding the telephone cord round Hoorah's neck.

'I think there's more to it than that, mate,' I say a bit lamely, before walking away, no longer wanting to make my phone call.

Hoorah Henry is crying in his cell when I pass. He's trying to keep it down, but even the way he sobs makes him sound like a toff and part of me wants to shout at him to put a sock in it. The other part, some new part that keeps surprising the fuck out of me walks back and says, 'What's wrong, mate?'

He glances up, wet eyes regarding me warily. Something in my expression seems to convince him he can trust me.

'The cleaner just paid me a visit. Called me a dirty bacon and told me to watch my back because I'm "in for it". But I'm not a bacon.' He stares at the floor, looking like a forlorn kid.

'Well, mate, shagging your own sister doesn't go down too well in these places.'

'I'm not a complete fool. It's more complicated than that. And it was hard enough telling everyone in group without going into all the frightful details.'

The old part of me is urging me to bugger off at top speed. The new part is keen to hear this bloke's story. I find myself sitting a bit uncomfortably in Hoorah's cell while he fills me in on his bizarre, upper-class background.

'I didn't know Clarissa was my sister. She knew that I was her brother, though, which was why she was being so sweet to me that night,' he explains. 'She'd been sworn to secrecy never to divulge our true relationship. I didn't know anything about it because I'd been packed off to boarding school at a very young age. My mother had had an affair with the gardener, very 'Lady Chatterley's Lover,' and the result was a pregnancy she was ashamed of.'

'Oh, *right*, so Clarissa is your half sister,' I say, wondering if perhaps that makes shagging her not quite so bad.

'Er, not exactly,' Hoorah says unhappily. 'My mother did actually ahem… maintain sexual relations with my father during her affair with the gardener, and many years later, when Popsy… Father decided that Clarissa looked more like him than Jones, the gardener, he insisted that Clarissa have a blood test and it turned out that she was actually his.'

I shake my head, baffled by this unfolding soap opera. 'So when your mum gave birth, why didn't she just tell you it was ya sister?'

Hoorah shakes his head horrified. 'It just wasn't *done* to have the gardener's love child and she had four children already and with father's consent, she passed this fifth one onto her older sister, who had been barren for years, as they say.'

'Didn't you notice your mum getting a big belly at the time?' I frown.

'Mother didn't visit me all that often. Besides, I was quite naïve about such matters,' he groans.

I can't help feeling sorry for him. For some reason he's not looking like so much of a creep. He looks like just another fucked-up bloke that needs help. I think his posh accent got my hackles up, what with me having had a life-long suspicion of upper-class twats.

My face brightens. 'In that case, you must have thought you were shagging your cousin!'

'Oh, gosh no. I was told that my aunt had adopted Clarissa at birth,' he says, staring broodily at the floor.

Bloody hell, this is more complicated than an Agatha Christie plot. I hold my head in my hands, having a good long think. Finally, I say, 'So Clarissa was just being friendly to you because she knew you were her brother and you took that as a come-on.'

He looks relieved. 'Yes, exactly so. And, of course, once she said: 'Stop it, there's something I have to tell you,' even though I was very drunk, I did of course, stop er... shagging her at once.'

'Give the fella a break,' I tell the cleaner on my way back to my cell. 'He didn't know it was his sister.'

The cleaner leans against his mop with an incredulous frown. 'He didn't know he was screwing his sister?'

It strikes me that everyone on the wing has made up their minds and condemned the bloke. I've done it myself many times. It's the law of the jungle. We are the judge and the jury. Fuck any grey areas; in our minds everything is black or white. So much easier that way.

'No, mate. He had *no idea*. So drop him out, OK?'

'Yeah, yeah, of course. I'll pass the word around.'

I lie down in my cell exhausted. My mind flits back to the prayer I said to the God who never listens and how I'd been consumed with vile, seething, venomous hatred.

There's no hatred in me at this moment. Just like Paul said, once we open ourselves up our problems seem to have a peculiar way of resolving themselves.

'Doctor, doctor, I can't seem to stop stealing things,' beams Terry. 'Take these pills, says the doc, and if they don't work, I want a new laptop and a diamond necklace for the wife.'

Terry's back on top form. Must be because Roland's nearly pissing himself and a few of the others are chuckling gamely.

'Nurse says, Doctor, there's an invisible man in the waiting room.'

We're waiting for the group to start and Terry's got a sitting audience.

'Doctor snaps at her, I'm busy right now. Tell him I can't see him.'

Hoorah Henry lets out his ridiculous baying laugh. He told the rest of his story a couple of days ago and, because I started laughing and said it was the funniest tale I'd ever heard a few other cons joined in, then Hoorah saw the funny side and started off that horrendous baying, making everyone laugh at him even more and well, most of us seem to like him a bit better now. At the end of the session, Terry amazed everyone by apologising for farting *even though he didn't mean to let one go,* and Roland and Winston said sorry for getting the wrong end of the stick.

Almost everyone in the group has shared except Tams.

None of us knows much about the con with the neat clothes and the slick haircut, except maybe Winston, 'cause he and Tams are always having their discussions about the finer things in life. Tams knows he's got to open up soon to keep with the programme. Some of us suspect he's got something he's not telling us because he often looks uncomfortable when the rest of us are talking honestly about ourselves. Anyway, Tams looks as if he's ready to bite the bullet.

'My name's Tams and I'm an addict,' he starts. 'Crack, pills and booze, in that order.'

'When I was younger,' Terry interrupts in a canny imitation of Tams' voice, 'I had an unlimited supply of drugs and alcohol. That was before they cut the umbilical cord.'

'Terry, this is supposed to be serious,' giggles Karen.

Tams smiles and continues, 'I never wanted to be a criminal. My dad's Bob Tamsworth.' There are a few impressed whistles and Tams doesn't need to elaborate. 'Dad always expected me to follow in his footsteps. I did try but it just wasn't me. My sisters are better at the dodgy stuff than me; they were born criminal-minded. I had a couple of well-paid jobs. Could never make my dad proud of me though, no matter how successful I was. Only time he ever praised me, apart from when I was a kid and I was a really cool dancer...'

He trails off then hurries on self-consciously, 'was when I went on an errand for him, smuggling a couple of hundred grand of drug money through Calais. Thing was, though, the way it had been set up – this friend of Dad's knew I'd be shitting myself if he'd told me the car was loaded like he was s'posed to – I didn't know. So I drove through customs totally innocent and only got the phone call on the other side. I was fuckin' furious that my dad had put me at risk like that. I vowed I'd never do what he did.

'Trouble was I got addicted. First coke, then crack, then just about anything to bring me down. One night I was down to my last score and I had to get a hit and there was only one way I could get the money. I'd tried to rob a petrol station the day before but I hadn't got a gun and well, I fucked it right up and got caught on camera.'

'It makes me feel really really shit telling you this,' he continues, cringing. 'The only way I could get money and it had worked a couple of times before… and it wasn't strictly robbery… was… I, er… chatted up this guy in a gay nightclub.'

'Told ya he was queer,' beams Terry as if he's been biding his time, waiting for just this moment.

'I am not fuckin' queer!' Tams shouts, then hurriedly composes himself. 'Anyway, the poof took me back to this cool pad of his in Hampstead, worth about four mill it was and I knew I'd struck it lucky.'

'Had a nice tight arsehole, did he? Sorry! Sorry!' Terry grins with his hands up. 'Couldn't resist. Carry on.'

Tams tries not to look flustered. 'Tel, this is hard enough as it is, mate,' he says through gritted teeth. 'Anyway, I ended up kidnapping this geezer for five days and fleecing his bank accounts and nicking his clothes, paintings, vintage port, you name it. Trouble is that's why I feel so gutted about it now – he was a really nice guy and

I treated him like shit. I tied him up and gave him a bit of crack now and again to keep him happy.'

'Tied him to his four poster bed, did ya?' Terry asks, glancing around at the rest of us to draw us in on his joke. There's a few laughs and Tams turns red.

'Yeah, as it 'appens,' he admits. 'I at least wanted him to be comfortable while, I mean.' He grits his teeth steeling himself to carry on.

'But the thing is, when the old bill broke into his gaff and arrested me, because to be honest I'd made a pig's arse of the whole kidnapping – didn't take care of the details, you know what it's like – they asked him to press charges. I was expecting him to say, 'Arrest this young man at once, officer,' because he spoke like that,' he says, glancing at Hoorah Henry who's listening intently, 'but he didn't say anything like that. He told them I was a decent young man and needed help, that's all. It really fucked with my head.'

Owen frowns thoughtfully. 'Maybe he was embarrassed about the story getting into the papers. Especially if he was a well-known businessman.' I throw Owen an admiring wink. He's nothing like the deaf and dumb zombie I met a couple of months ago.

'Or maybe he was just a very genuine and kind man who could see you needed help.' Says Karen, looking at Owen then smiling and shaking her head.

'Duh! Tied him up… fucked him royally… plied him with drugs?' Terry says incredulously. 'Sounds like you gave the poof the thrill of his life. No wonder he didn't want to press charges!'

'I didn't fuck him!' retorts Tams, looking fraught. 'Anyway, he got a lot of the money back and most of his clothes and his oil paintings and he never even mentioned the crate of Château Baron Rothschild which was worth…'

'I didn't say anything about you fucking him Tams. Come on, just admit you're a homo,' says Terry, looking him directly in the eye like he knows something none of us knows and he's known it a while.

Tams glares at him. 'As I was saying, I only got nicked for the attempted robbery on the petrol…'

'You're a shirt-lifter,' Terry says as if he were explaining something to a five-year-old. 'You're a bum-bandit. A backdoor boy.' He shrugs. 'You know, a Brighton Pier…'

Some of us are looking at Karen, wondering why she isn't trying to stop this. If Tams is gay he's always done a bloody good job of hiding it, right down to the photos he's got of some gorgeous bird in his cell. Unless, maybe it's his sister.

Tams looks away, grinding his teeth.

Terry beams around at everyone. 'He's a fudge packer,' he tells us, tapping his nose. 'A fairy. Friend of Dorothy.'

We're all watching Tams, wondering what he's going to do.

'You're a bottle of scent,' Terry says cheerfully. 'Just face it, Tams. People like you are sometimes better known as shit stabbers and… what's that other one…? Oh yeah, turd burglars.'

Something in Tams snaps. 'All right!' he explodes. 'Fuck it! I'm gay. I'm *gay*, ok? Drop me out now.'

Something snaps in me too and I find myself saying, 'Well done, my son!' as if he'd won the Grand National or something. And I now know why Karen didn't stop Terry from winding Tams up. She must have known Tams was gay and that it would free him if he got it out there.

There's a surprised silence, then Terry says, 'Good on ya, mate.'

The whole atmosphere in the room has changed. Winston starts clapping and then we're all praising Tams for his honesty even though most of us are almost as bad as Terry when it comes to taking the piss out of other bloke's sexuality.

'I'm er... gay, too,' says a new fella to the group, a gruff-looking bloke with a scarred face who doesn't seem the sort to tickle your fancy.

Maybe he was expecting everyone to congratulate him too. I doubt he was expecting Terry to say, 'There ya go Tams. Thanks to me you've pulled!'

Tams starts shaking, and for a moment we're all thinking he's reached the end of his rope but then he looks up and he's laughing hysterically. 'Sorry, mate, I'm not laughing at you,' he tells the gruff-looking bloke who's gone red in the face. 'I'm just wondering why the fuck I didn't say something before.' He turns to Terry, 'I don't even care if you take the piss out of me now.'

Terry gives a theatrical sigh. 'Nothing to take the piss out of any more, is there?' You've taken me joke away, you slag. Talking of jokes,' he adds, breaking into a cheeky grin, 'Did ya hear the one about the gay burglars?' They broke into a house and rearranged the furniture.'

I walk with Tams down the steps to get lunch. He's looking pensive again. 'What am I going to tell my dad?'

'Tell him the truth, mate, like you did just now. Tell him the truth and let him deal with it. Look what happened when you told us.'

'Yeah, the fear was worse than the reality,' he shrugs. 'But you don't know my dad. He's always asking me when I'm going to get a proper girlfriend. Must see through all the ones that I've blagged to act like my bird. He'll fuckin' kill me. Not with his own bare hands, though. You know what I mean.'

I think maybe he's being a bit overdramatic.

'He'll get someone else to do it. That's how he operates.'

I keep my mouth shut as he breaks away from the lunch queue. Bob Tamsworth has an evil reputation. The last person I would want to be come to think of it would be his homosexual only son.

'All right, Harry?'

I don't recognise the voice. It sounds like someone's really glad to see me. Not too many people fit that bill. I glance round to see Owen following me with a grin.

'Owen!' I gasp. We often meet up on the corner and go to group together, but usually he's as caught up in his thoughts as I am in mine. I've noticed that he doesn't stare out the window in meetings any more. He listens as if his life depends on it. Just like I do.

'Fuckin' 'ell, you've got that look in your eyes.'

'What d'ya mean?' I ask, stepping back.

'They're clear,' he says, looking a bit embarrassed. 'I mean, I can look into them instead of getting shut out. It's like they're coming alive.'

Owen thought I was shutting *him* out? We stare into each other's eyes and, for a moment, I'm afraid Terry's going to come past and call us a couple of salivating bum-bandits but then I laugh, 'So are yours, mate. They're like winders to your soul.'

'Steady on,' he says.

'The cunts!' Winston's voice screams from our landing. 'They've ripped all my girlfriends off the fuckin' walls!'

332

I hurry upstairs with my lunch try as an animalistic howl rings out. Passing Winston's cell I notice photos of his beautiful birds strewn amidst the rubble of his belongings. I know it will leave a bad taste in Winston's mouth as he hates mess.

I dump my lunch tray on my upturned bed and hurry on down the landing. That agonised wailing sound is drawing me relentlessly toward it.

At the end of the landing, I spot Blake coming out of a cell with his toffee-nosed screw pal, whacking the bars with their sticks. They love the racket they're making 'cause they know it disturbs the fuckin' daylights out of us convicts.

'What's the matter, Freddie?'

Freddie's plastic mirrors once so carefully aligned, are strewn round the floor, several of them broken. I don't know why it bothers me so much that Freddie's kneeling on the ground letting out gut-wrenching sobs, but I do know that if I could take his pain away by giving it to myself, I would do it right now. He glances up and stares right through me. He looks as if he wants to die.

'Freddie, talk to me. What's the matter, mate?' I glance around at the chaos the screws have made of his cell, his mattress flung into a corner and letters strewn over the floor.

'She's dead!' He points blindly to the web in the corner, 'They've killed her!'

Over the past week, whenever I've passed Freddie on the wing or in the yard, I've asked, 'How's Freda?' and he's glanced round conspiratorially and filled me in on some pressing spider-news bulletin. Glancing up to the web, I don't see a spider. I see a motionless black blob in the centre of the broken strands. Moving closer, I notice several tiny splinters hanging from the threads. A bitter hatred passes through me. Someone has carefully ripped

333

off the spider's legs and stuck its lifeless body back in its web. This is the work of a sadist and I'm damn sure I know who.

Freddie's crouching on the floor beside himself with anguish. The realisation that I can't make him feel better fills me with a crushing sorrow. There's only one way I know how to handle this situation and there's nothing spiritual about it.

'It'll get that cunt for you, Freddie. I'll fuck him up good. It might take a couple of weeks but I'll find a way.' I angrily say, as I storm out of Freddie's cell.

Getting honest

My sister is frowning at me over a visiting table. It's the first time I've seen her since she visited me in Bristol. She's got a heart of gold, my sister, till you cross her, then she cuts you out of her life and forgets you ever existed. Typical bloody Scorpio; I wasn't expecting to see her again. I'm remembering the last time she looked at me, full of pity and contempt, stuffing the photos of her grinning children back in her bag. There's a sickening feeling in my belly because I'm worried that she's here to tell me about a death in the family.

'You look like a different person,' she says at last.

My heart lifts, but I'm still half-expecting her to remind me of the animal I really am deep inside, even though she's never done anything like that before.

'It's amazing,' she says, reaching across the table. 'You *are* a different person!'

'What d'ya mean, Eva?' I'm staring at my hand in hers as if it doesn't deserve to be there.

'I dunno. I just feel like I've got my brother back.'

I remember how I promised to look after her when Dad was sent down and how she'd looked up to me for years and years, even after I became a useless junkie and how that look of respect dwindled until that day in Bristol.

Suddenly I've got this great stupid grin on my face and I can't hide it. 'I haven't used in nine weeks, Eva. I'm telling ya. I'm not sure where 'there' is yet, but I'm getting there.'

'I know Harry, I can see it in your eyes,' she smiles.

I know what she means. I've seen my eyes in the mirror. Like Owen said, it almost scares me how open they are.

She starts telling me about my brother-in-law and my niece and nephews. It's as if I'm hearing about them for the first time. I'm not shut down; I'm not on guard and my eyes aren't roving past her looking for odd lumps in visitor's cheeks.

A commotion across the room interrupts us. We glance over to see a boy of about five, hands on hips, glaring up at one of the screws. 'My dad says you lock him up and don't let him out and don't feed him properly!' he hollers. His cheeky face reminds me of someone.

'Get back 'ere, you little sod!' snaps a woman and I look across to see an attractive blonde. Opposite her sits Terry. Red-faced, he mouths 'sorry' to the screw on duty. I'm about to tell my sister about Terry and his jokes when I notice the screw bend down and pat the kid on the head. I can't hear what he says but, whatever it is, the kid breaks into a grin, runs back to Terry and jumps on his lap to give him a fierce hug.

Terry's latest joke flies out of my head. I'd labelled that particular screw a total prick. I make a mental note not to be so fucking rude to him next time he pats me down.

'It's all right, Dad, it's sorted,' the kid yells, making everyone turn to stare at Terry. 'The guards are gonna take much better care of you from now on!'

A dozen or so cons and visitors chuckle and Terry squeezes his son in his arms, not caring who's looking at him. Next to him is a young girl, so skinny she's been hidden behind Terry until now. She's clutching onto his arm as if she's never going to let go. Terry told the group a few days ago that sometimes he misses his kids so much that he could almost gnaw his way through the bars with his teeth and that's even though the little girl ain't strictly his. About four years back his wife dumped him for some local philandering Don Juan, then hot-tailed it back to

336

Terry when it all went tits up, six months pregnant, she begged him to forgive her and he'd taken the girl on as his own. We can't help admiring him for that, not many of us would do the same. Looking at them now, I'm glad he feels that way. Terry's the only dad she knows. Lucky for her he'll be getting out soon.

'I'm starting to care about the people in here,' I say, hearing my voice go hoarse. 'When you're on drugs, you don't give a shit about no one but yourself.'

'I understand.' Eva smiles at me, then directs her eyes sideways and shrugs her shoulders with a giggle. I glance aside to see Winston with one of his many devotees. Annika from Sweden maybe, his tongue down her throat and hands wandering towards her forbidden areas as if they're starring their own soft porn film.

'Any news from Dawn?' asks Eva, wiping the smile off my face.

'Last I heard she'd cleaned up and didn't want me coming anywhere near her.'

Eva squeezes my hand. 'So you're both clean,' she says urgently. 'Maybe you could write to her about seeing Tom...'

'She said I'd ruined her life,' I interrupt. 'She said I'd never see Tom again if I didn't change my ways.'

'But you have changed your ways!'

My happy mood has crumbled thinking about Tom. He must be nearly four now, brought up without his daddy, probably doesn't even know about me. Maybe he's got some other bloke to call 'Daddy.' I'm feeling bereft all of a sudden needing something to bring me up again...

I glance across to see Tams sitting at the next table, staring moodily at his fingers. Christ, I'm glad I'm not him. I know he's shitting himself waiting for his dad to arrive. And I know he's sat next to me for moral support but I don't care anymore.

'Harry, I have to ask you something.' Eva's clutching my hands again. I resist an urge to shove her away. 'Since you're being so honest with me, there's something I want to know that will make me trust you even more, ok?'

'Yeah, carry on.' I try not to frown.

'Was it you who took that bag of coke on top of the fridge when we had that party round at ours?'

'I look her in the eye, feeling sick. 'No, Eva, it wasn't me.'

I'm not on Step Nine of the bloody Twelve Steps yet. I can't suddenly tell the truth about everything.

'OK Harry, thanks,' she says. 'I'm just going to get some coffee.'

I watch her walk over to the drinks machine. This fucking honesty lark is killing me. I feel ill, fighting with a conscience I didn't have to bother with before. Who needs a conscience? So much easier to make things up to fit the occasion.

I'm grateful to be distracted by the arrival of a shortish fella with silvery hair strolling across the room towards Tams' table. He's wearing a purple silk shirt, white linen trousers and espadrilles. Behind him stride two dark-suited minders looking right at home as if they've been around prison visiting rooms all their lives. They stand behind their boss in such a way that it seems like every con and visitor in the room resolves to remain on their best behaviour.

So this is the infamous Bob Tamsworth I think, remembering a few hair-raising stories I've heard about him. He's smiling and giving his son a friendly slap on the shoulder but there's an icy look in his pale blue eyes.

My sister returns with two cups of coffee and I lean towards her. 'That bloke next to us is one of the biggest coke smugglers in London. His son's just about to tell him he's gay.'

Eva raises her eyebrows and we both listen. Tams takes a deep breath and says something, making Bob frown at the bodyguards towering over him. 'Bugger off and get yourselves a cuppa.' A moment later he explodes.

'You're a fuckin' *what?*'

Everyone, including the two muscle-bound hoods making their way to the drinks machine turn to stare at Tams who cringes in his seat.

Across the room, Terry gives Tams the thumbs up and starts talking loudly to his wife, encouraging the people around him to more or less remember their manners, which allows Bob Tamsworth to come to terms in private with the fact that he's probably never going to have a daughter-in-law or grandchild to call his own.

In her thoughtful way, Eva starts talking quietly about nothing in particular allowing me to listen in on the events unfolding beside us.

'I just don't believe it,' Bob Tamworth is shaking his head. 'I can't believe my son bats for the other side. What about that lovely bird you was seeing, the posh one... Sadie... Sasha...?'

'Saskia. Just a friend, Dad.'

'I don't understand why you never fucking told me before,' says Bob regarding his son with those cold blue eyes.

Tams says something I don't catch and Bob leans back in his chair looking perplexed. 'You was scared I'd have you taken out? What d'you think I am, some sick bastard who'd snuff out his own kid? Son, one of me best workers is gay.'

'Who do you mean? Graham?' asks Tams biting his lip.

'Yeh, Graham. How did you know?'

Tams shrugs. 'Well, it takes one to know one, I suppose.'

Then it's his turn to look bewildered because Bob Tamsworth has broken into a hearty guffaw.

'But he always acts so straight,' frowns Tams. 'I assumed you didn't know.'

Bob Tamsworth laughs even louder and rubs his hands together. Terry exchanges a wink with me.

'I didn't know till I caught him kissing some bloody sailor when we was out on a job in Morocco,' Bob Tamsworth growls. 'I know everything about the blokes who work for me. Not me own son, though. Not what's going on right under me nose. Ha ha. No wonder you was such a good dancer when you was a nipper!'

Tams glances over at me with an amazed look as if to say, 'You were right – how the fuck did you know?'

I find myself turning to Eva. 'Never mind all the bollocks. Eva. It was me that took that Charlie.'

She starts to well up. 'Harry, I love you. Now I really know I've got my brother back.'

I start to well up too. From the corner of my eye I notice Bob Tamsworth stand up and give his son an affectionate pat on the back. Then the notorious smuggler is coming over to me. Hurriedly I wipe my eyes wondering out of habit what the fuck I might have done wrong. His gruff voice mutters in my ear. 'Thanks for helping my son come off the drugs, mate. He says you've been an inspiration to him.'

Before I have a chance to reply, he's turned to a screw walking past and says in a completely different tone, 'You make sure my son gets well looked after in 'ere. Know what I mean? Otherwise I've got a present for you in my glove box.' He gives the screw a wink. 'And it goes bang.'

340

Then Bob Tamsworth is off, strolling across the visiting room, his two enormous hoods following like docile rottweillers. The unfortunate screw turns pale in their wake.

Visitng time almost over, I feel compelled to tell Eva about the new me that's emerging. 'I've been reading all these books lately about spirituality and all sorts of stuff. There's a whole world out there I had no idea existed.'

She draws back looking wry. 'Steady on Harry, you'll be sitting around a bonfire growing a beard and chanting soon if you ain't careful.'

'Not a fuckin' chance,' I say, a vision of Blake's vicious mug popping into my head. I stand up and take my sister into my arms for a cuddle just like I used to after Dad told me I was the man of the house and had to take care of my family. 'Listen, Eva, I got a small favour I want you to do me.'

I mutter a few details in her ear then step back and watch her break into a knowing smile.

On the way out of the visiting room, I spot a familiar pair of hands with the *love, hate* tattoos on them. If it ain't my old mate Gavin. He's sitting opposite some suspicious-looking geezer with an enormously thick neck; might be the fella that poor Roland had to snog to get Gavin's package.

'Got your visits back, then Gav?' All right, mate?' I nod to his visitor who makes a strangled noise in reply. Must have a nice big package in his mouth and now with everyone leaving it's the perfect time to take the package and put it where the sun don't shine. Nice and safe.

Gavin glances up at me and does such a classic doubt-take I can't help laughing.

'Fuck me that ain't you is it 'arry? You look 'ealfy! Whatever they're doing to you on your crackhead wing looks like it's working.'

'Why don't ya give it a go yourself, mate?'

'Not a chance.' He gives me a wink to show me he's about to have a night in the fluffy clouds. But I can see in his eyes. They're dead.

When we're not in groups and meetings, we have assignments to do in our cells that help us route out our deep, dark histories. We get it all down on paper and reading books about lawn-mowing, granny-torturing psychopaths isn't forbidden, but hasn't really been on my agenda.

I've read a couple of books on Buddhism. It's all quite interesting but I doubt I'd have a panic attack if I stepped on an ant by mistake, although I wouldn't intentionally step on one like I may have done before. And as for turning the other cheek if someone has a pop at me, well that's not very likely either. I've been told that just 'cause I'm in recovery now it doesn't mean that I have to be a doormat. And, after all, it's life on life's terms as the saying goes.

Still, I'm discovering a part of myself I'd forgotten about and the more my heart opens up with all this questioning and honesty, the more I want to see my son. His fourth Christmas is coming up. I've missed the others, been too wrapped up in my own problems to so much as send him a card. When I think about Tom I think about his mum and all the old feelings come flooding back. This time there's no smack to blot them out and I just have to feel all the pain I went through with Dawn like it happened yesterday.

I never did go to church after that chat with the vicar and now I don't need to. There's someone here we can tell all our problems to. Maggie wears jeans and colourful scarves, a different one every week and she's a nun.

There's a light that seems to dance in her eyes when she listens to us and it doesn't fade even when someone talks about smashing some con over the canister with a bed leg or beating someone senseless in a pub. It's like she can see so deeply into us that she can forgive us anything. It blows me away that she doesn't judge us. We're our own worst judges she explains, we don't need everyone else jumping on the bandwagon.

She's got this happiness that surrounds her, making us feel good just to be in the room with her. That's because God has forgiven her everything, she explains, which really means that she's forgiven herself too.

'Oh, leave it out Maggie, what did you ever do that was bad, luv?' asks Tyrees. 'Nick a packet of sugar out of a café?'

She laughs the tinkling laugh of a woman at least half her sixty-odd years. 'Nick a couple of packets of sugar out the supermarket more like,' she smiles giving us all a shock. 'I used to be a shoplifter. Well, to be more honest, a kleptomaniac. Not sugar, of course,' she explains, serious now. 'We're the ones who've been there, done that, ticked all the wrong boxes, gone through hell and come out here to the other side. Just as you will if you keep a little faith.'

We're all staring at her stumped, trying to imagine this lovely lady sliding a couple of bottles of booze into her coat lining.

'Aaah, Maggie, you're the girl after me own heart,' sighs Terry.

Maggie beams. 'I don't need to do that sort of thing anymore. One day it hit me that I was just robbing myself. You see, I had this voice in my head going, 'You can't afford this and you can't afford that so I was walking around thinking I was poor, even though my flat was crammed with expensive items. Anyway,' she shrugs meekly, 'I got my come-uppance and ended up doing a little time myself.'

'Maggie!' we yell.

'That's why I'm here. I've been where you are and I found the way out.'

'Blimey, I think, any minute now she'll be telling us she had a little heroin habit on the side.

'I had a drink problem for many years,' she continues, 'but we'll save that for another time. Enough about me darlings, let's talk about you.'

'That's what I love about this woman. She's got no interest in herself which leaves tons of interest for other people.

Over the next couple of hours she gives us her attention, making notes for us on the blackboard in her lovely flowing handwriting, which is a sort of art form for her. Why do something any-old-how she explains, when you can make it special, even something as ordinary as writing on a board? Afterwards we bombard her with questions. She always gives us such reassuring answers. It's as if she plucks each one out of the air, an individual solution for each of us.

'Maggie, could I have a word with you, please,' I ask when everyone heads down to dinner. She brings out the best in us and I can really let my guard down around her.

'Of course, Harry,' She smiles. 'I could see you had a question you didn't want to ask in front of the others. Sit down.' She pats the chair beside her.

I sit down feeling like a kid; I can almost see my skinny knees poking out from under a pair of school shorts. I can feel the warmth and kindness radiating out from her. It reminds me of climbing onto my grandma's lap and feeling a peace and acceptance I haven't felt since.

'Well, er... my grandma died when I was six,' I manage to get out.

'Yes,' she nods and puts her arms around me.

Whatever question I was planning to ask floats away. For about five minutes neither of us says a word.

When I go down to dinner I know there's something different. I can't put my finger on it until I'm eating today's dessert: strawberry sponge with custard. It brings back a memory of my grandma carrying a wobbling bowl of jelly to the table with its chequered yellow and white tablecloth, where me and a tiny Eva wait giggling. It's a happy memory.

Maybe, after all these years I can finally get over the pain of when my Granny Guinness died.

Late that afternoon when we're all banged up for a few hours, I'm working on an assignment when my heart starts pounding. Something terrible is happening downstairs. There's a vicious yell followed by pounding footsteps. I leap off my bed and peer down through the hatch in my door to see screws hurrying along the landing below where the cons on detox are.

'Don't you fuckin' die on my turf!' screams a voice. 'I'm not having any of you junkies overdosing on my wing! Wake up, you pathetic piece of shit!'

I can't see him but I can clearly imagine Blake down there, his face screwed up with venomous hatred.

'That's enough! Do you wanna get done for assault?' yells another voice. 'Leave him alone.'

There are three or four screws down there wondering what to do by the sounds of it. One of them gets on the bell for a doctor then I hear someone shout incredulously, 'what the fuck are you doing? He's dying!'

'He ain't fuckin' dying, not if I can help it,' comes Blake's voice. Tight with exertion. There's a few sharp,

345

slapping noises then his voice again screaming out with fury: 'Don't you die on me, you've got five years to do, you dirty bastard!'

I pound my hand against the bars as I realise what must be happening. My blood begins to boil. Some unfortunate con must have consciously, or unconsciously, chosen this moment to end it all, and he's got a sadistic screw screaming at him like a madman. Other cons start shouting through their doors and Winston and Tams start kicking and banging. 'Leave him the fuck alone,' shouts Winston, so loudly that his voice crackles and echoes along the landing.

It's tough trying to calm down after that. I'd love to be like Sister Maggie. I really would. But the only way I can forgive something like this is to imagine myself punching Blake's face to a pulp over and over again.

That evening, word from the cleaner is that one of the cons overdosed and anything else that might have happened has been hushed up. Poor bastard. The last thing I'd want to see as I took my dying breath would be Blake's mug leering down at mine.

Terry's great fun these days. He's opened up about his addiction to booze and come to terms with some of the issues that led him to get shit-faced, tanked, pickled, blotto-ed, blitzed, cockeyed, three sheets to the wind... in the first place. Terry's the resident expert on getting pissed. Sometimes he even has something serious to contribute to the discussion. Like when Paul was telling us that we're only as sick as our secrets and if we keep them locked inside how they will maybe get us using again.

'That's right, alcohol is never the answer,' Terry nods sagely. Except when the question is: what is C_2H_5OH.'

'Oh right, ha ha, excellent!' bays Hoorah while the rest of us catch up.

Hoorah Henry has become quite popular lately. A few of us on the wing have had a sort of running competition making up ever more bizarre plot twists for the story of 'The Nonce Who Shagged his Sister.' Eddie, the chess player, came up with the latest one this morning, something about Hoorah not knowing that his sister is his sister and his sister not knowing that Hoorah is her brother and them hitting it right off 'cause they're so similar and having the shag of a lifetime none the wiser. I'm working on a much better one than that.

Winston is the only member of our original group not to have shared. He insists he's an open book, the handsome-as-a-devil black boy from the East End enjoys a bit of culture; used to enjoy a bit of crack; knocked it on the head; now he's right as rain. Just needs his retinue of besotted birds coming to visit till he's paid for his armed robbery and he'll never look back. Simple.

I've seen him get angry a couple of times but never emotional. Even the counsellors seem taken in by his no-flies-on-me persona. Then one day something triggers off a bit of fuse somewhere deep inside him and, lo and behold, it turns out he's just as fucked up as the rest of us.

We'd been taking it in turns to discuss how we felt the moment when we were last arrested; that feeling of despair or guilt or regret or in my case, a sort of sickening relief, only Winston says, 'I just thought: Thank fuck I'm not wearing odd socks.'

Everyone laughs and Winston beams back dapper sod that he is.

'Why's that, Winston?' asks Paul with his interested expression. 'Were you feeling self-conscious?'

Winston's smile freezes a bit round the edges.

347

'Cause he's a snazzy dresser, that's all,' Tams comes to his rescue.

'Yeah, I was wearing an Yves Saint Laurent and a Kenzo tie and I was being filmed by a Channel Four documentary, so I wanted to look cool,' says Winston. 'No big deal.' Blimey, he sounds like he set up the whole thing just to look cool on camera.

'No big deal,' nods Paul. He's picked up on some thread and has started gently pulling. 'How would you feel if you were wearing odd socks right now, Winston?'

Some of us look at Paul as if he's out of his nut. What sort of stupid question is that? Winston, however, is looking as uncomfortable as if he's being interrogated.

'I'd feel OK.'

'Are you sure? I can see your socks right now. Supposing one of them was blue and the other was green with stripes and we were all looking at them. How would you feel?'

Winston's foot twitches with annoyance. 'I'd tell you to mind your own fuckin' business. Can we move on?'

Paul's onto something and he's not letting go. 'I'd say it would make you feel embarrassed. How does that word suit you?'

Winston glares at the floor, hands clenched. Personally, I wouldn't risk asking him another question. Paul presses on regardless.

'When was the first time you felt embarrassed like that, Winston?'

'Don't know.' Winston's lower lip has started to stick out a bit. The rest of the group stare from him to Paul wondering where this is going.

'I'd say you were very young. Maybe five or six? Your face might have felt like it was burning. Maybe everyone was looking at you... laughing at you?'

What is he, some kind of mind-reader?'

'... Pointing at you because you looked silly...?'

'All right, that's enough!' Winston says in a high-pitched tone. 'One morning before school, I couldn't find my.. any trousers to put on, my mum was skint so I didn't have many clothes... I used to wear old football boots as trainers. He trails off; staring at Paul in an agony of humiliation... I would cut the studs off with a knife because I wanted to be like the other kids who all had decent clothes...

It's almost magical, watching him draw something out of one of us. I've never seen Winston look anything other than a tough, smart geezer who's got everything pretty much under control. Right now, he looks like a helpless kid wishing he could disappear through the floor. He tries to say something but the words keep getting stuck in his throat.

'These things that you've been holding onto all these years,' says Paul, 'they're like little cancer cells, harmless in the beginning. The more you tried to ignore them and make them go away, the bigger they got, until they grew into great big tumours that are constantly draining the life out of you. Winston, how would you feel if you were sitting here wearing a scruffy old dressing gown and slippers with holes in them...?'

'I wouldn't,' Winston cries out. 'I'd never let anyone see me like that!'

'What happened that day before school when you couldn't find any trousers?' asks Paul.

'I... I had to wear a pair of my sister's trousers. She was roughly the same size as me but they were too small in the legs... When I got to school, my teacher asked me to go along to another class, to give the teacher there a note... I ran out as fast as I could to the other class with the note. My sister went to the same school as me and was in the classroom when I walked in... The kids there started pointing and sniggering, and my sister who had gone to school before me and didn't know I had worn something of hers, stood up and shouted, 'you've got my trousers on...' They were corduroys... bright orange corduroys that came up to my ankles.'

'Good, carry on. How did that make you feel?'

Winston's lips are quivering. 'I thought they were my friends and even though my sister didn't mean it, I was hurt and embarrassed. They were all laughing at me like they'd laughed at this clown who'd come to visit a few weeks before.'

'Yes, Winston, and what did you make this experience mean?'

Winston stares uncomprehendingly at Paul.

'I mean, how did you change your behaviour after that to make sure you would never get laughed at again?'

'I made sure I always looked cool,' Winston says sombrely.

'Did it work? Did you feel cool?'

Winston's shoulders slump and I can sense his despair. We're all starting to understand where this has been heading.

'No, I never felt cool. No matter how many suits and ties and designer clothes I bought or nicked, I... well, I always felt I looked like an idiot.'

He looks up at us like a vulnerable kid without his mask on, as if he's expecting us to point at him and burst into laughter. He seems relieved that we're not laughing. We're not even smiling. We're looking at him as though we've never really known him before. Looking back, I can see that most of us were put off by his pristine clothes and all his talk about designer gear which made him seem a bit superior. Now, we understand what an act that was we're amazed. Winston's got to be one of the coolest dudes in prison and yet he feels like an idiot.

At the end of group I grit my teeth for the hugs which get a bit easier every time and go up to Winston to congratulate him on his breakthrough. I'm not the only one. Now that his barricade has come down, Terry, Tams, Jake, Roland and a couple of the others are crowding round to give him a slap on the back as they would never have done before. Even Hoorah, who almost got throttled by him a couple of weeks ago, is hanging round to give him one of his nerdy high-fives.

'That reminds me of a joke,' says Terry, arousing a groan. 'What do you call a scouser in a tastefully decorated house?'

'A burglar!' shouts Winston, nicking the joke and all the laughter, Terry doesn't seem to mind.

Winston's trying to look cool but he's holding back the emotion and when we all go down to lunch he heads for his cell and stays there the rest of the day. Next morning, he comes down to breakfast looking all chipper again.

I can't be certain but I'm fairly sure that his shirt isn't tucked into his trousers quite as neatly as it was the day before.

I'm in my cell skipping without a rope. One-two, one-two, my knees are coming up so fast I'm in danger of chinning myself. I've been determined to get fit ever since I watched Deano running around the yard, his muscles rippling as if he'd never been a scrawny smackhead.

It's working. A sheen of sweat lends definition to muscles that have lain dormant for years. Three minutes skipping then a one-minute break strolling up and down my cell filling up my lungs for another round.

First time I did this, I only managed a couple of rounds before collapsing with a stitch but now I'm up to twelve. I feel as if I'm going in for the fight of my life. It's

Blake's face that's embedded deep in my mind and whenever I start to flag that's what keeps me going.

One-two, one-two. I was a pathetic nine stone smackhead when I got here. Now I'm over eleven and down the gym at every opportunity building more muscle. Got my appetite back, even for mechanically-recovered chicken nuggets and mash. Never mind what Winston says, they taste fuckin' delicious after years of hungering only for drugs.

Unfinished Sympathy is blasting into my ears. I love this song. In fact, I'm loving it so much that I suspect there's probably some other good things to come out of Bristol after all. Even Jazz I can almost forgive, because anyone who comes from the same place as Massive Attack can't be a complete wanker.

> *...How can you have a day without a night,*
> *You're the book that I have opened,*
> *And now I've got to know much more,*
> *Like a soul without a mind,*
> *In a body without a heart,*
> *I'm missing every part...*

After another three rounds, I head down the landing for a shower. I'm feeling good about the feedback the counsellors are giving me on my essays, just like that crazy Trevor with all his classes and hobbies back at The Mount. Trev would be chuffed if he could see me now. I notice lightness in my step and an unfamiliar feeling, something very natural but which I haven't felt for a long, long time.

Suddenly I realise what this feeling is. I feel normal. Normal! I'd got so used to waking up feeling like shit every day I'd thought *that* was normal. And I thought everyone felt the same. Ha ha ha. This isn't just normal, it's also-fucking-lutely fantastic.

I've stopped running away from my problems. I've confronted those fuckin' demons that keep us chained up. There are no chains holding me now. I feel so free that I'm outta here already. This programme is so deep in my heart that I know I won't be scoring the minute I hit the street. I will be going to a meeting instead.

The chains are off, my head is high and my eyes are glowing, because right now I'm feeling better than I've felt on any drug that's ever been invented.

Flying High

Karen is giving us a lecture on addiction and obsession. She's looking lovely today even in a shapeless top that comes down to her knees. Jake's staring up at her with soppy eyes totally smitten. God knows what would happen if Karen were to wear something more flattering to the curvy little figure she's got hidden under there. There'd be a whole bunch of fanatical desperadoes trying to get clean just to get close to her.

Patiently, Karen explains how we need a break between putting the drugs down and taking up a relationship, in order to give ourselves a chance at living without any compulsions holding us back. Jake's hanging on to her every word. I can tell her words are going in one ear and straight out the other.

'Not much chance of having a relationship in here,' chuckles Terry, 'unless you're Tams that is.'

Tams laughs and gives Terry the once over. 'You're too fat for me though, Tel. And your breath smells like something sicked up by a dead sewer rat.

'Watch what you're saying,' says Terry throwing a wink at Karen. 'There's young ladies about and no one's ever complained about my snogging technique.'

There's a couple of laughs, and Hoorah Henry's letting out his usual baying hoots, when there's the sound of a chair flying into the door. Jake's charging across the room with a ferocious grimace and leaping onto Terry to do him an injury. It's like some crazy déjà vu. Terry's holding the flailing Jake at arm's length while Jake screams in his face trying to reach him with his fists.

'Ye feckin' bastard! I'll feckin kill yee! I'll kill yee, ya cunt!'

Terry manages to throw him off and he bounces against the wall only to come zooming back again, fists pummelling the air and spittle flying.

'Come on, have it with me Terry yee fat feck! 'Ave it out with me like a man!'

Karen does her best to calm him down but she's in danger of getting caught in the flurry and, seeing this, Terry picks up the irate Scotsman, dumps him outside and closes the door in his face.

Jake head-butts the door a couple of times shouting: 'You're all cunts! Feck the lot of ya!' There's a sound of retreating footsteps; then footsteps stampeding towards us. Blood sprays against the glass window of the door when Jake brains it for the third time and then he's led away by the screws.

Karen sits down looking shaken.

'What did you say to piss Jake off, Terry?' Tyrees demands accusingly.

Terry shrugs bewildered. 'Fuck knows.'

Karen takes a deep breath. 'I think Jake got the wrong end of the stick that's all. Let's carry on with the subject of obsessions, shall we?' She says brightly.

That's appropriate I think to myself, wondering why no one but Karen seems to have realised the cause of Jake's crazed attack.

I think about what she said earlier. We've all got this longing that we used to fill with drugs, so we're vulnerable to anything that comes along to take our minds off the longing. We'd probably all fall in love with a bag of crisps if we were left alone with them for long enough. If I'm honest, I'm becoming obsessed with exercise. But if Karen didn't have that funny gap between her teeth, that reminds me of an old school-teacher, it could be me falling in love – with no possibility of a shag or even a kiss, nothing but the same old hand shandies that have to keep us going for years. And how sad that would be.

'Get your lunch!' a screw yells out just as Freddie approaches along the landing. I haven't seen him for what seems like ages.

'All right, Freddie?' I smile, slowing down so that we go down the iron steps together. He mumbles something out the side of his mouth not looking at me. He's still in the preliminary group more unreachable than ever.

At the bottom of the stairs Blake is holding cons back allowing two past at a time. He says nothing to Owen and Tyrees, who are in front of us, but he has some snide comment for Hoorah Henry; I see the back of Hoorah's neck turn pink.

Blake greets Freddie as we draw level. 'All right, Goldilocks? Now don't go nicking everyone's porridge you greedy little thief.'

Freddie and me ignore his lame insult as we stand in line. Blake can't bear to be ignored.

'Not talking to me you germ-infested addict?' he asks, his lip curling comically with disgust. Blake regards me with a challenging stare, decides not to say anything and draws closer to Freddie.

'Cat gotcha tongue? How's your spider?'

His words hit Freddie like a blow. I find myself reaching a protective arm around his shoulders.

Blake studies his fingernails, one eyebrow raised in the patronising manner that makes me want to rip his head off his shoulders. 'Couple of queers aintcha? Bet you RAPt boys are all at it after your lovey-dovey group cuddles banging away at every chance. I'll catch you at it one day,' he says, tapping his nose.

There's no one in the queue behind us. If I wasn't here, Freddie would be defenceless against this barrage.

'Leave him alone,' I say, warningly.

'Oh, so you're the 'ard one are ya?' says Blake, delighted. 'You've been nicked for assaulting screws, 'aven't you, Shaw?'

'That's right. Been looking at my record, 'ave ya?'

He looks me over with his snake eyes. I have a vision of poking them out with a spoon.

'Come on then, you gonna 'ave it with me?'

'Do you ever wonder,' I reply, 'what it would be like if you'd had enough oxygen at birth?'

His eyes narrow. 'Think you're a bit of a lad, dontcha Shaw, you and your clever dick mouth. Don't matter how smart you are, you got no parole, 'ave ya you naughty boy? Come at me and I'll make sure you get a couple of years extra 'oliday time, right here on my lovely wing.' His eyes gleam maliciously.

'All right I will. Sooner than you fuckin' think,' I growl as I shove his leg down and usher Freddie past.

'Looking forward to it, you plastic gangster.'

I let him have the last word; he'll pay for it later.

I follow Freddie to the servery, taking several deep breaths and praying for the strength to resist going back and doing him right now.

I glance behind with a big grin to show him I've got it all under control and notice Gordon, the kind, fat fella who got me onto the programme, marches up to Blake and starts having a go at him. 'Don't talk to any of my clients like that again!'

I can't help smiling, hearing Gordon call us his 'clients.'

Blake makes some retort that I don't hear causing Gordon to yell in his face: 'I'll report you to the governor for that, you cretin!' Then he marches furiously towards his office.

Blake's left standing in the corridor wearing a soppy been-put-in-my-place expression. For a moment our eyes meet. Hurriedly, he switches on his customary leer but it's too late. I burst into laughter and give him the wanker sign, as my tray gets loaded up with food.

Time seems to be flying faster than ever. I'm busy writing an essay listing five occasions when I committed a crime in order to buy drugs. It's hard to keep it down to five but I'm really getting into it, describing some of the dire circumstances I landed up in. I'm really getting into this writing lark, I think, when my door opens and a screw comes in.

Not all the screws are as vile as Blake and his toffee-nosed side-kick. A couple of them have been hand-picked for this wing, both decent fellas who support the programme. It's one of these that now ushers Jake into my cell.

'Someone wants to talk to you, Shaw.'

Jake has a massive white bandage wrapped round his head.

'No probs. Thanks mate.' I call out to the screw as he closes the door behind us for privacy. Jake plonks himself on my bed.

'Don't yee feckin' laugh, 'arry,' he says with a serious face that looks even more comical under all those bandages.

I start guffawing helplessly and notice the return of the infuriated grimace he used on Terry, which tickles me even more. 'I'm sorry, mate, but you remind me of that kiddie character, Mr Ouch or someone... oh yeah, Mr Bump,' I say, trying to stop my lips twitching.

Suddenly he's on his feet with his fists up yelling, 'Ah told yee! Didn't ah fecking' tell yee not to laugh.

'Slow down, Jake, I'm not in the mood for a tear-up,' I yell, holding my hands up for protection.

'Well stop feckin' laughing at me then, yer bastarrrd!'

I manage to stop laughing for a few seconds, but then I'm off again.

'Ah'll 'ave yee for that yer cunt!' he screams and this time I know he means it, and I force my face into a serious expression to ask him what's up.

'Ah'm in love with Karen,' he says, calming down. 'But yee can't tell no one.'

That love-sick teddy bear look has come onto his face again. 'I know you are. But why are you telling me?' I ask, curious.

He looks at me as if I'm mad. 'Because you're like thaim. The counsellors. Yee understand people.'

I'm touched by his words, but I'm at a loss as to how he thinks I can help him. Then the thought occurs that maybe it doesn't matter what I say; maybe all he wants is for someone to take him seriously.

'Have you told Karen you love her?' I ask

'Nah. Not yet ah ain't but ah will,' he tells me earnestly.

'Why d'ya have a pop at Terry then?'

'Cause the cunt was eyein' her up!'

'Mate, everyone eyes Karen up. We're in prison and she's the only bird around.'

Better not let *me* see 'em doing it,' frowns Jake, swinging his arms, limbering up.

'You've gotta get real here. Karen's a counsellor. What you gonna do?'

'When ah get outta here,' he tells me, perfectly serious, 'ah'm going' tae take her out.' He's got another

359

four on his sentence and I'm about to tell him that he might be being a tad unrealistic, when again it dawns on me that it might be better to prolong his fantasy, rather than let him lose the plot just now.

'Now you're talking sense,' I smile at him. 'Wait for your release date and ask her then.'

Slowly his face brightens. 'Yeah. Yeah! Ah'm glad ah spoke tae yee 'arry, thanks.' He walks out the cell happily shadow boxing with the bandage slowly starting to unravel around his head.

Yeah, I think, surprised at how easy that was. I pick up my essay and carry on writing. Fuck it. I'll write about *six* incidents of committing crimes to feed my habit. Another one won't hurt.

Tyrees is off. He's a Londoner, born and bred, but he's been paroled to a seaside resort and can't wait to sit on the beach, never mind that it's the middle of November. He tells us he's going to be watching the waves and the birds, the sort with thick red lips and big tits.

'Thick blue tits with red lips?' frowns Roland.

'No, you muppet, fit birds with red lips and big tits,' Terry helps him out.

'Yeah whatever; I don't care how fit they are, as long as they've got the tits and the lips' Tyrees shrugs.

Later on he goes round everyone's cells, excitedly saying his goodbyes. Ever since we nearly had that tear-up in the lunch queue and Tyrees introduced me to a whole new world of feelings, we've respected one another but never been what you might call friends.

He puts his bag down and sticks his hand out to shake mine, because he knows I'm not into all the hugging stuff. I push his hand away.

'Gi's a kiss then,'' I laugh and put my arms around him. 'I'll miss ya but I'm pleased you're off.'

'Me too, mate.' He gives me a slap on the back. 'Don't forget me. I'll send you all a Christmas card letting you know how many birds I've shagged.'

The visiting room is packed. It's Christmas Eve and I'm watching Terry's wife and kids come in. The kids are wearing little Santa outfits, 'cause cards and presents can't be brought in. Terry grabs his whole family in his big arms and does his best Santa impression, 'Ho ho ho, Merry Christmas me darlin's!' making them squeal with pleasure.

My sister's on her way. She's visited twice since that time I admitted nicking her fella's Charlie all those years ago. Now that there's nothing to come between us, we can have a cuddle and I can kiss the top of her head, and feel like a human being again.

My mum and dad aren't going to be coming. Eva's told them I've changed but they're going to wait and see before they believe it. I can't blame them really; I'd have given up on me too. They'll understand soon enough.

Looks like it's gonna be just me and Eva again.

At a distant table I spot bulldog-face Ian sitting with some dumpy, incredibly ugly woman, wearing a tracksuit three sizes too small in salmon pink. Must be his mother. I'd like to say that the two of them are having a touching reunion, to make up for that time he cleaned out her purse, and packed her off to the chippie so he could swipe her brand new TV. But no. She's having a right go at him and he's sitting there nodding and looking hounded.

Winston's got a girlfriend; I know the poor bird won't have long with him 'cause he's got another one coming in halfway through, but he's working fast, got his hand halfway down her sweater already. Hoorah's wife and daughters have just arrived. They're looking awkward. One of the girls is glancing around with an air of disgust,

making her dad wince, and the other one just looks scared.
I throw him a sympathetic look.

My face lights up when Eva arrives with a little
boy in tow. Must be Jamie or Rowan. I'm pleased to
remember their names, though I'm a bit surprised because
she never usually brings her kids. Doesn't want them to
have the experience that me and her had as children, sitting
in some stifling visiting room, while our Dad goes on
about how much we've grown since the last time. What a
miserable way to raise your kids, I think, glad at least that
Tom hasn't had to go through the same thing.

'Happy Christmas, Harry.' Eva kisses me on the
cheek and gives a little nudge to the kid, who stares at me
not saying a word. Eva bends down and whispers in his
ear.

He's got a shock of blonde hair and wide, liquid
eyes that lend him a really winning look, which I hadn't
picked up from the photos Eva showed me. I'm wracking
my brain, trying to work out whether he's Jamie or
Rowan. One's about five and has started school the other's
three, still a baby really, but this kid has just started to get
that independent look about him, though he still looks a bit
too young for school...

'Happy Christmas, Daddy,' he says shyly.

My heart lurches. Now, I'm looking at him with
completely new eyes.

Eva smiles encouragingly. 'Thought we'd surprise
you, Harry.'

My first instinct is to scoop him up in my arms
and give him a huge hug. But I don't want to scare him,
seeing as I must seem like a complete stranger. So I bend
down, take his little hands and gaze into his sombre eyes
to say, 'Happy Christmas, son.'

He looks down at the rough hands enveloping his
and I'm hit by a fear that he doesn't really know who I am;

that word 'Daddy' means nothing to him. In the silence that follows, I wonder if Dawn's told him anything about me being a lying, thieving, worthless junkie.

Suddenly his little face sparkles. Glancing this way and that, as if he's got some big secret to tell me, he whispers, 'I've got a card for you.'

I glance warily at Eva, hoping she hasn't been crazy enough to smuggle in a Christmas card. She could be kicked out and my son dragged away with her, ruining my happiest moment in years. She slides an envelope out of her coat and passes it to me under the table. Her eyes flicker towards one of the screws on duty. Fuck knows how she's managed it, but she's persuaded him to turn a blind eye.

'Open it, open it!' my son whispers, so eager for me to open his card that he reaches under the table to scrabble at the envelope tearing it apart. I glance round to make sure no one's watching, and then look down to see a handmade card with bits of tinsel glued to a cut-out Christmas tree.

'Do you like it?'

'I love it, son.'

'Mum hid something inside it,' Tom whispers. 'She said it would make you really happy.'

A frown flickers across my face as I remember three years ago how Dawn got caught doing our drugs-hidden-in-the-jeans trick.

'Did she now?'

Surely Dawn wouldn't send me some smack as a Christmas present when she knows I'm in rehab? I glance at Eva who shrugs back wonderingly.

Under the table, I open the card and immediately spot the wrap hidden in the fold. I glance up, out of habit to make sure no screws are about.

My heart has started to pulse with anticipation just like old times. I'm remembering that irresistible feeling of being wrapped up in downy blankets, watching my problems float away like so many wisps of nothingness...

'What is it? What did mummy hide in there?'

...That wonderful peaceful glow, a sensation of oneness, of wholeness... and on top of all that an unsurpassed sensation of relaxation and well-being...

'Show me!' Tom pleads in a whisper.

I look down at his little face, unblemished as yet by the scars of life, and suddenly I'm bubbling up with happiness. Life – normal life – has many joys to offer and one of them is staring up at me right now. I've forgotten, for the most part what the others are but as Liam would say, *'ar'll in good toime.'*

With trembling fingers I undo the folds ready to tip any contraband on the floor. Instead of a line of powder I see several tiny, hand-written sentences.

Tom's face falls. 'Is that all? Mum said she'd hidden something that would make you really happy!'

'Wait a minute,' I smile, 'let's see what it says Come up here and I'll read it to you.' He jumps on my lap and peers intently at the handwriting. 'Can you read yet, son?'

'I know the whole alphabet and I can write my own name!'

'Always knew any kid of mine would be smart,' I say, feeling an almost painful blast of pride. 'Now let's see what your mum wrote to cheer me up:

Did I get you going there for a minute? Did you just prove to yourself that you're free from drugs? Really free?

I shake my head smiling, remembering some of the old tricks Dawn used to play when we were a young couple, getting me at it and then bursting into giggles before I blew my top.

Well done for getting clean, she continues, *I knew you could do it. You will always be Tom's Daddy. As long as you're clean I want you to be a big part of his life.*

Tears come to my eyes, and seeing them Tom says scornfully. 'Mum said you'd be happy, so why are you crying?'

'Because I'm so happy I could cry,' I laugh.

He frowns at me suspiciously.

I glance up and notice that the short dumpy woman bulging out of her salmon pink tracksuit has her feet dangling above the floor. She's in her son's arms and they're laughing.

'Listen, Tom,' I smile, sliding the card under my waist of my jeans. 'I know this doesn't look like much, but actually it's the best Christmas present your mum could have given me.'

His little face perks up. 'Oh! That's what she said too!'

'I love you, son.'

'I love you too Dad,' he says, giving me a cuddle, arms round my neck and squeezing. He might be small but he's bloody strong. I squeeze him back. With all the feelings of love that I've learnt to feel on the RAPt programme.

Breaking Free

We've just had our Christmas lunch. Dry chicken breast with soggy roast spuds, sprouts and gravy followed by a dollop of Christmas pud, eased down with vivid yellow custard. 'Bloody lovely', as they'd say down Wales; compared to our usual fare anyway.

There's going to be a party for everyone on the RAPt wing this afternoon. The counsellors are giving up half their day to make it special.

Liam, Paul, Gordon and Karen are all coming and Maggie's got a surprise for us.

Last night was the first night I didn't have a using dream. Using dreams are a bit like wet dreams, where you're dreaming that you're guzzling down booze, or hitting the pipe or whatever, and it's ten... twenty... fifty times better than it ever is in real life, until you wake up and undergo a massive disappointment. Or it feels so real, that you worry you've lost your clean-time. This morning, I woke up and, after a long, peaceful moment, realised I wasn't missing anything. I felt like the best Christmas present I could have after Dawn's promise yesterday.

I should be happy now too but I'm angry. I've just heard that the government is going to close down the RAPt wing in Pentonville 'cause it's too expensive to run or something. No one asked us. *We're* the drug addicts; *we* know that most of the crimes we committed were to feed our habits. This programme must have stopped thousands of crimes taking place! Besides, RAPt saves lives. I'm certain it saved mine.

I'm so outraged that I'm in my cell, ranting down the whole lot on paper to send to my MP. Yeah my MP. Didn't even know I had one.

'Got a joke for you, 'arry,' Terry grins from the door.

'Fuck off, Tel. Sorry, mate, but I'm not in the mood.'

'Nah, it's a really good one!' Roland yells out from his cell.

'That's what you always say,' I mutter, scribbling furiously.

'How can you tell a bloke from the Isle of Wight?'

'I dunno, Tel,' I say, not really listening.

'Well, when he goes Christmas shopping for his mum, his sister and his girlfriend, he only has to buy one gift.'

It tickles me but if I laugh I've had it. He'll go on cracking jokes till the cows come home.

'Tell 'im that other Christmas joke,' yells Roland.

'All right.' Terry is ever amenable to sharing his humour. 'One convict says to another convict, what you in for, mate?

'Doing my Christmas shopping early', says the other convict. So? That ain't no offence,' frowns the first convict. The second convict says, 'It is if you do it before the shops open.'

I'm trying to keep a straight face, so that I can make a convincing case in my letter but Terry's pulling on my funny bone and he knows it.

'Listen 'arry, I got one just for you, mate.' He comes in and leans towards my ear. 'Tailor-made this one, 'cause I know you hate paedophiles.

I feel my hackles go up but carry on writing regardless.

'But at least they slow down when they drive past schools.'

Hmm, much as I hate paedos, he's got me with that one. I snort back a laugh.

'Listen, Tel, thanks for trying to cheer me up but you'll have to do better than that. Only not right now. So would you please fuck off 'cause I am trying to write a fucking letter!' There I go saying 'please' and 'thank you' again; my politeness knows no bounds, thanks to Maggie. I'll be giving up the swearing soon if she has anything to do with it.

Terry gets the message and ambles off breaking into a cheerful rendition of Jingle Bells. I can hear him chugging up and down the landing, persuading other cons to join in. I tune it all out and get on with my letter. A few minutes must have passed by the next time I look up 'cause I see about five or six cons, some with tinsel wrapped round their necks, trooping along behind Terry.

'Jingle Bells, Jingle Bells, Jingle all the way... Come on, 'arry, you miserable sod,' yells Terry. Roland, Jake and Bulldog-faced Ian are trotting along behind him, as well as the two nice screws, who actually volunteered to work Christmas day.

They're off down the end of the landing and back again all too soon, this time with Tams, Hoorah and a few other cons to make up the rear, and now they're raising alternate legs, as they prance along like a band of monkeys.

'Come on 'arry, you gloomy old spoilsport,' Terry's voice rings out as they hop, skip and jump past my cell again.

'Yeah, come on 'arry!' half a dozen voices yell.

'It's *Harry* with an aitch!' I scream at them. 'Fuck off and jingle your bells somewhere else.' I'm even more pissed off now, noticing that the king of good taste himself has joined in.

'All together, now, just for that grumpy old git in there,' Winston laughs. 'Oh what fun it is to ride on a one horse open sleigh...'

At some point, I give in. I'm not exactly sure how it happens. When the whole lot of them come back, for the sixth or seventh time and Hoorah yells out, 'We love you Harry with an aitch! And then the whole lot of them, are making their biggest effort ever, to pronounce their aitches and going, 'Happy Christmas, Harry with a *haitch!* Happy Christmas, happy Harry!' I can't seem to keep up my pissy mood any longer.

Anyway, who knows what will happen in the future? The RAPt programme was there to help us just when we needed it, and it's in other prisons too, so who knows? Who blooming well knows!

'Happy Christmas, my darlings!' Maggie beams. She's standing in the doorway of the meeting room, wearing a red, gold and green scarf and a Christmas party hat, hugging us as we come in. Armed robbers, burglars (turd burglars included,) plain old thugs and con artists of every description. She doesn't care; we all get an equal dose of her overflowing affection. Today, if possible, she's radiating even more warmth than usual and we're all unconsciously basking in the glow.

Paul and Liam are unwrapping several mounds of sandwiches and sausage rolls, and Karen is slicing up a gigantic Christmas cake, her every move watched by her obsessive stalker… I mean her adoring Jake.

When we're sitting in a rowdy, but compliant, circle wearing our paper Christmas hats, Maggie puts on some music. Bing Crosby's *White Christmas* blasts its festive cheer into the slammer and Maggie brings out an enormous gift. She hands it to Bulldog-face Ian who stares at it blankly.

Terry laughs. 'Great idea, Maggie. Pass it on you muppet!'

The gaily-wrapped parcel begins its way around the ring as it is passed, snatched, and bounced between our hands. When the music stops, Roland rips open the paper in excitement and is dismayed to find a different sort of wrapping paper underneath, making a few cons burst into scornful hysterics.

'Poor Roly,' smiles Maggie, starting the music again. 'Look what he missed out on in his childhood.'

The parcel's off again and every time the music stops, a con tears open the paper and tries not to look disappointed when he meets another layer. The next song is Jingle Bells. Terry starts accompanying it in his jolly baritone, as if we hadn't heard enough of it already, encouraging a few more would-be singers to join in.

I glance around at all the grinning faces. This has got to be one of the maddest things I've seen, watching a bunch of crooks playing Pass the Parcel. The only face that isn't grinning is Freddie's. Whenever the parcel comes his way, he holds it in a sort of dull disbelief, until the con next to him snatches it out of his hands.

I wish I could snap him out of this. The other day I found a lovely big spider out in the yard; it only had seven legs and I thought it would be perfect for him, to nurse back to health or whatever he does with them. He cast one sorrowful glance at the spider, trying to climb out of my cup and trudged back to his cell. I couldn't blame him, I wouldn't want to get attached to a pet, only to have it snuffed out when I wasn't around to protect it.

The parcel is so slim by now that, when the music stops halfway between Terry and Winston, Terry snatches the parcel back from Winston's waiting fingers, certain he's won. That pisses Winston right off, so he makes a crafty grab for the parcel and raises it above his head. Terry's the master shoplifter though. He leaps in the air, all sixteen or seventeen stone of him and swipes it back making everyone laugh. Winston gets the last laugh though when Terry encounters another layer of wrapping.

The parcel sets off once again and this time everyone's lingering over it a bit too long, while staring intently at Maggie's finger on the CD player. We're certain there's only one layer left and there's an atmosphere of increasing avarice. When the parcel passes through my hands I feel a stab of greed too. Then one of the cons snatches the parcel from the fella two seats away from him, without letting his neighbour so much as touch it, and my sixth sense tells me we're heading for a tear up.

'Calm down, it's only a game,' I shout over the music. 'Can you imagine the headlines: Pass-the-Parcel Riot at Pentonville?'

'Nor feckin' weeey!' Jake shrieks with laughter.

'We'd never her the fuckin' end of it,' shouts someone.

'Convicts killing each other over a mystery gift,' laughs Terry. 'That reminds me of a joke.'

'Quick, put the music on again, Maggie,' someone yells. Terry saves his joke as the music starts up and, when it stops at Freddie, we good-naturedly let him keep it.

Freddie frowns at the package half-lost in his world. His fingers scrape uselessly at the sellotape. Then something clicks and he starts ripping into the paper.

'Well done, Freddie, you've won!' I laugh, hoping to fuck that he really *has* got the last layer, 'cause I couldn't bear for this to add to all his other disappointments in life. A glance at Maggie and I know she's planned it this way.

Freddie looks up from his box of chocolates and smiles at me. He takes one of the chocolates out of the box, unwraps it and starts munching. He unwraps a second and a third, cramming them in together. Melting chocolate begins to dribble out the side of his mouth. He starts laughing, teeth brown and sticky, and everyone seems to forget how envious they'd been a few minutes ago, because Freddie's happiness is infectious. At any rate, there's a ton of party food to take our minds off his chocolates. Maggie starts the music again and a few cons start dancing.

'How about a game of musical chairs? Yells Roland.

'Er... perhaps musical statues would be better,' laughs Maggie, probably envisaging a riot started by two cons trying to sit on the same chair.

'Listen up,' shouts Paul, waving a Christmas card in the air. 'Got a card from Tyrees here.'

The room breaks into cheers and whistles. 'How many birds has he shagged?' someone shouts and the cry goes up:

'How many birds? Come on, how many birds?'

Paul opens the card and reads it out. 'Happy Christmas to all you poor bastards rotting away in the Ville... I mean recovering from your addictions in the Ville. Life is rosy out here in sunny Eastbourne. Got my own room with a T.V., shower, tea and coffee making facil...'

'Get on with it!'

Paul scans the rest of the card and says finally, 'Seventeen.'

The room erupts into scornful laughter. 'Yeah, right. Seventeen. He only left three weeks ago.'

Only Winston seems to believe Tyrees's declaration. 'I could have done better than that,' he says with a shrug.

I help myself to a mince pie, and glance around at all the cons and counsellors who have become my friends. This will be the last Christmas I spend in here. I wish I had a camera. In the absence of a happy snapshot, I shut my eyes for a second burning this image into my memory.

It's the last day of the year. In a few days' time I'll be graduating. I've been clean three months. I've worked my way through the first five Steps. I've cleaned up some of my relationships and written letters to Dawn, my Mum and Dad and a few other people whose lives I've messed up, and I've even come clean to the vicar about my imaginary vision, the day before I came on this wing. He patted me on the back and told me that he's had a good laugh with his wife about it that evening.

Tomorrow I'll be starting on Step Six – letting my higher power handle my defects of character. I doubt it'll stop me making a dodgy couple of grand when the opportunities arise. That's a genetic trait, not a character defect. Anyway, tomorrow I'll be turning over the new leaf. Today, I have business to attend to.

I've chosen my moment carefully. The other cons have gone to their groups and Blake and his Toffee-nosed screw pal are doing their cell searches. There's a cleaner about but he's been tipped off.

Peering out from behind my door, I spot Toffee-nose tap the bars and enter a cell at the end of the landing to have a sniff round. My muscles stiffen. Here comes Blake marching out of a cell with that revolting look on his mug. I steal back behind in my cell waiting.

Closing my eyes, I remember what some unfortunate con once said about Blake finding phoney contraband in his cell and losing him some remission.

Slag.

Taking a deep breath, I remember Blake screaming obscenities at the luckless con who overdosed.

My fists clench expectantly.

Finally, I think about Blake pulling Freddie's spider apart. The thought fuels my anger, until I'm ready to wrench his limbs off and toss him into the net slung between the landings, which stops cons tormented by screws like Blake from jumping to their deaths.

Perhaps that would make Freddie smile.

Blake doesn't see me coming. I'm as quick as fuck and fit from all that skipping. Before he knows what's happening, I've forced his arm up and behind his back, the same way the screws have been trained, only a lot harder. Then I'm shoving his head into the bars that he's always whacking with his baton. He doesn't let out so much as a yelp, until I twist him round and sink my knee hard into his balls.

'That's for Freddie and everyone else in here you've fucked over,' I spit in his face. 'Now, you listen to me you piece of shit.'

He doesn't say a word, just stares at me with his sinister, low-life eyes, trying not to reveal the agony in his nuts.

Grasping him by the throat with one hand, I reach round and grab a piece of paper out of my back pocket. 'You are a bully and a cunt,' I growl into his face. 'I know where you live, and I know where you drink, and I know where your poor bastard of a son goes to school. Understand?'

His eyes swivel round, snatching a glance at the addresses written on the piece of paper that my sister smuggled in for me. He tries to nod, but his head doesn't move because my hand is gripping tightly and he can barely breathe. All the strength I've been building up over the last few months has paid off. Calmly, I crack my nut on his head and watch with satisfaction, as he sinks to the floor like the dog that he is, sniffing concrete. I don't let him know that I got a letter out addressed to Freddie's mum, explaining what Blake's been doing and where

Freddie's brothers can find him. I want that to be a surprise. He deserves it.

Later that day I pass Blake, limping along the landing with a sore head and a scowl. His baton dangles uselessly from his hand.

'Happy New Year, scumbag,' I tell him, knowing that he won't forget the old year in a hurry.

He gives me a vicious look, but I know he won't say a word. Screws like him, Northern Bollocks and Buckteeth might be evil, but they're not stupid. They don't want to be looking over their shoulders in their own neighbourhoods, feeling that same terror and dread, that they instigate every day in their own workplace.

'And a Happy New Year to you too, Harry,' I laugh to myself; because, for now, I feel completely at peace.

Two days into the New Year I'm graduating from the programme. Owen's graduating with me. I'm almost as proud of him for getting through this as I'm proud of me. I can hardly remember what a self-hating shadow of himself he was, when we first met, or for that matter how depressed, volatile and self-torturing I was.

We're sitting in a circle, with me on one side of Karen, Owen on the other and everyone else spread out in between. Karen holds up Owen's ninety-day key ring and showers him with praise, making him smile bashfully. She passes the key around and, as each con receives it, he's obliged to say something positive about Owen, starting with Jake naturally, 'cause he's sitting as close to his would-be lover as possible.

'What ah like aboott yeeee, lad,' Jake says with his earnest expression, 'is the way yee didn' condemn that kid who took yer little brother over the embankment. Yee

375

understood that it wasn'ee all his fault. Ah can respect that. But it took me a long taime tae git there.'

Owen is touched by Jake's words; then it's Eddie, the chess-player's turn.

'Have ya ever thought about workin' with delinquent kids?'

Owen frowns as if such a thing hasn't occurred to him in his life.

'You've got this patience about you,' says Eddie, who has a patience about him that I've often admired, 'and you're a good listener.'

A light goes on in Owen's eyes, as if he's seen a way forward when he gets out of here, together with a way he might be able to make use of what happened to his brother. By the time everyone in the circle has said their bit, Owen is close to tears.

But if Owen was moved by what the group said about him, I'm completely overwhelmed. I wasn't expecting Jake, Roland, Hoorah, Owen, Tams and even Freddie, who's finally made it out of pre-ads, to thank me personally for helping them through their problems.

I'm blushing like an idiot and it gets even more difficult when Tams says, 'I reckon you'd make a good peer-supporter or even a counsellor,' and all the others nod their agreement.

A warm glow spreads over me. It feels good to help people. Don't know why, but helping seems to be a reward in itself. Still, I can't see myself sitting in a room trying to help people sort out their lives. It's too much like hard work, listening to people's problems all day would be too emotionally draining.

Then Winston says out of the blue, 'Nah, fuck that, 'arry, what I like about you is your observations. You notice stuff other people never notice and you've got a way with words.'

'Absolutely, and you're often the first to work out what's actually going on,' Hoorah says appreciatively, no guesses why.

One by one, the other cons find something to praise about me and I cringe in my seat, waiting for my key ring to make it back to Karen. I've watched other cons go through this before, but I'm still not prepared to take in these kind words. It's easier to hear that I'm a bad person and no good, because I've told myself that for years. Kind words I have to try to accept.

Then a thought comes from nowhere.

'That's it! That's fuckin' it!' I say, surprising myself as much as anyone else. 'I'll write a book about what we used to be like and how this programme helped us. Then people, like we were a few months ago, can read it and maybe get inspired to do what we did.'

Karen's nodding at me and so is everyone else. A spirit of warmth is in the room.

'You can put my story in your book,' says Roland. 'It's a pretty fuckin' funny. Just ask Mackey about the vanload of empty boxes we nicked.'

'You're welcome to mine. It's not very funny though,' says Winston.

'Oh, yeah?' says Terry. 'What about when you was arrested and all you could think about was what fuckin' socks you were wearing?

'Oh, right,' Winston smiles sheepishly as everyone laughs. 'S'pose that was quite funny.'

I'm starting to buzz. This feels great; it's like we're all coming together with a common purpose.

'You'd better put me in, you bollocks,' says Terry. 'You can tell the story of the night it all went tits up for me... '

'Yeah, you and your wife's fluffy white dressing gown,' I laugh, a few details flooding back from a share he did a couple of weeks ago.

'Tell us aboot tha' taime again, Tel,' begs Jake, who loves the idea of Terry getting a shit-soaked dressing gown tossed over his head. Terry doesn't want to go into it again though.

'My story's interesting,' offers Tams, making me grimace.

'Er… maybe.' I wonder, for a moment, if writing about stuff like what Tams did to that poor rich bloke in Hampstead is really such a good idea.

'I'd be happy for you to include my story, Harry,' says Hoorah as soon as he can get a word in.

'Hmm, The Toff Who Shagged his Sister – it does have a kind of a ring to it.' I give him a wink. 'By the way Hoorah… I mean, Guy,' I hadn't been planning to say this and, suddenly my voice is cracking up, '… you er… you really helped me come to terms with, you know… that problem I had.'

Everyone stares at me expectantly. Now I'm really in the shit.

'I still hate nonces,' I manage to carry on, 'but at least now I haven't got the desire to go around obliterating every one of them off the face of the planet.'

'Put that in yer book, Harry,' laughs Eddie the chessman.

'Put me in yer book. Yee can write about me days of boxing glory, please 'arry!' begs Jake, demonstrating a few left hooks in the air.'

I'm grateful for his idea. I'm thinking I'll be able to write about my own days of boxing glory. I turn to Freddie, he's smiling at me in his sideways fashion.

'What about you, Freddie? Will you be in me book?'

His head comes round and he looks me straight in the eye. 'Only if you write about my spider.'

The room goes quiet.

'Of course I'll write about your spider,' I tell him sombrely. I notice Owen staring at me, and I know he wants me to write about his brother. Ah well, the book is going to have to be sad as well as uplifting.

As I walk down the landing to my cell, feeling miles better than when I was out on a self-destruction mission, a screw calls me down to his office.

'Shaw, you're off to Downview in two weeks.'

Wow, Downview! It'll shortly become a woman's jail but, for now, it's a cushy men's prison. Used to be called Brownview because of the amount of gear floating around in it. Or maybe it's cause the screws are extra nice to the cons there. But I doubt it. I'm particularly excited because Dale's banged up there, and he helped turn my life round with that talk he gave us, about having faith in something other than our puny selves.

That's it, I think, breaking into a smile when I'm back in my cell. I'll spend the next couple of weeks getting everyone's stories down on paper, then I'll start writing about my own experiences when I get to Downview. It's amazing how everything looks different when your life suddenly has purpose.

Hmm. Where will I start? I find myself thinking back to all that time ago when I hurt a man with boiling water and a small knife, in order to hold onto a bit of gear. The next thing I remember is the dismay in my cellmate's face as I got hauled down the block. I smile at the blank wall, as if he were there in front of me now.

'Sorted, Stinky,' I tell him.

Publisher's Note:

Look out for more books by Harry Shaw…

Reviewer's comment

This is a soul-searing and penetrating book. Has the world yet seen how desperate is life in prison these days? Not since 'The Ballad of Reading Gaol' has an author shown the ghastly and hopeless state facing long-term prisoners and the true meaning of escape to that 'little patch of sky' can only be glimpsed until one reads this powerful book and truly understands the agony!